Wii
FITNESS

VOLUME ONE

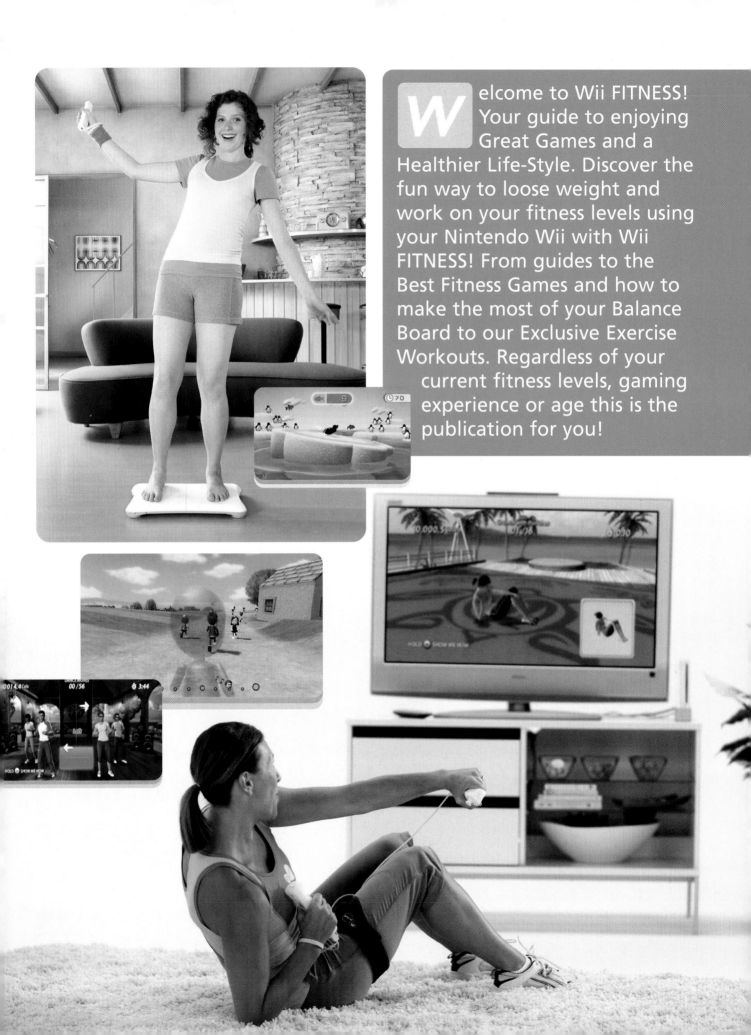

Welcome to Wii FITNESS! Your guide to enjoying Great Games and a Healthier Life-Style. Discover the fun way to loose weight and work on your fitness levels using your Nintendo Wii with Wii FITNESS! From guides to the Best Fitness Games and how to make the most of your Balance Board to our Exclusive Exercise Workouts. Regardless of your current fitness levels, gaming experience or age this is the publication for you!

CONTENTS

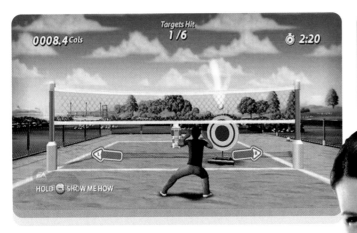

There are so many Wii games that are so good that you can't help jumping to your feet and leaping around the room with your Wii-mote spinning cartwheels and as you know any exercise is good exercise! With this in mind we have put together our exclusive A-Z of cheats for those addictive active games, so there is nothing stopping you!

The amazing Electronic Arts know their sporting games, from the makers of the FIFA and Madden series comes a whole new way to work out. With intensive exercise routines, EA Active can become your very own personal trainer and with our help we are positive that you will shed those pounds and have a blast doing it!

Looking for a more intensive exercise program to aid you in your goal to drop a dress size or deflate those spare tires, then why not try our work out for EA Active? We have put together what we think is a great way to help you get a few steps closer toward your goal of loosing weight and getting healthier.

The long awaited follow up to one of the most beloved and popular Wii games of all time is finally here and we have compiled this Player's Guide for you to bring you all the much know info on the new features that await!

There are many more ways to enjoy your Wii Fit Balance Board once you have finished your fitness training for the day. From walking the fashion catwalks to stepping into the boxing ring. What follows is our break down of the best balance board compatible games around.

Wii FITNESS

VOLUME ONE
ISBN 978 0 9558090 9 5

PAPERCUT

Published by Papercut Limited
www.papercutpublishing.co.uk

James Gale *Managing Editor*
Mark Ayshford
Design & Production
Josh Hearn *Games Editor and Exercise Workouts*
Cliff Smith *Photography*
www.cliffsmith.co.uk
Larry Brunt *Staff Writer*
B. Snell *Contributor*
S. Christmas *Contributor*
Many thanks to our workout models Lois Jervis & Josh Hearn

Printed and bound in Great Britain by Wyndeham Press Group *Distributed in the EEU by* Computer Bookshops Limited

Wii Fit
fun guide!
>>>

Wii Fit is the perfect way to get yourself in shape, without having to go to the gym. And with this complete Master's Guide on all the Best Hints and Tips for completing each individual exercise routine to the best of your ability, you'll be fighting-fit in no time!

Wii Fit aerobics

Wii Fit Aerobics are exercises and routines that focus predominantly on the Fitness side of things, rather than the Fun side!

Hula Hoop & Super Hula Hoop

YOUR OBJECTIVE: Spin the Hula Hoop around your waist as fast as you can, and successfully catch the Hoops that are thrown your way as you progress!

■ Hints and Tips on How to Play:

To begin spinning the Hula Hoop, simply start rotating your hips and waist around in any direction, but make sure that you perform perfect circular movements as you do this. The faster you rotate your hips and waist, the faster the Hoop will spin, and ultimately the more Points you will earn come the end. Not just that, but the harder you try, the fitter you'll become!

Every now and then, another Mii character will start throwing more Hoops your way from either the left or right, in

which you must move and catch, in order build up the number of Hoops that you're currently spinning. To do this, simply lean in the direction of the oncoming Hoop. If the Hoop is thrown in from the left, then lean left, and vice versa for right. This is where things can get tricky however, as just leaning to the side isn't enough - The Balance Board picks up on Movement and Weight, but for this exercise, it's predominately your Weight which is the main factor; therefore in order for the Board to sense which

direction you're leaning in, you must deliberately place more Weight on the side in which the Hoop is coming from, so that your Mii character on screen will lean in that direction. This is what most people don't understand. The most effective way to do this is to put your arms up in the air, and forcefully lean to the side, but make sure you put pressure on either the right or left foot depending on the direction of the Hoop! The Timing and direction however is up to you.

Super Hula Hoop is exactly the same as Hula Hoop, however much more challenging! More Hoops will be thrown your way in quick succession and your skills will be put to the test. Master the Hula Hoop, then try and crack this.

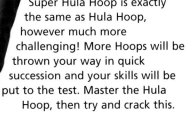

Rhythm Boxing >>>

> **YOUR OBJECTIVE: Use the Balance Board and Wii Remote and Nunchuck for this exercise. Step off the Balance Board and Punch forwards using either the Wii Remote or Nunchuck (left or right hand), in time and Rhythm with the beat.**

■ Hints and Tips on How to Play:

For this exercise, you'll be required to use the Balance Board, and both the Wii Remote and Nunchuck to Punch. In order to Punch however, you'll need to step forwards off the Board first as if you're stepping towards the Punch Bag, and then Punch forwards using either the Wii Remote or Nunchuck gripped in your left and right hand, depending on which hand you're told to Punch with.

This entire exercise is all about your Timing and Rhythm when Punching, so the most effective way to succeed in this routine is to wait until the Target appears on the Punch Bag before you actually step off and throw the punch. As soon as the Target appears, immediately throw the punch in time with the beat, using the required Hand to perfect your punch-timing. In order to score high, you'll have to memorise and mimic your Trainer's punch-pattern. Keep a close eye on his actions, and do your best to

memorise it perfectly, then step off and throw the exact Punch-combination with timing and precision to score big! Afterwards, your Trainer will perform the same routine, but in reverse. Remembering that it's in reverse will make life easier! If you can master the first combination of punches, then you can master the second - simply alter it so that the last Punch is now the first, and the first Punch is now the last.

Once you've completed this exercise, your Trainer will offer you the chance to increase your score, by attempting to knock the Punch Bag down by repeatedly throwing big punches at it. Don't worry about timing or rhythm here, or stepping on and off of the Board, instead just throw as many punches as you can within the 10 Second Time Limit, and try to bring the Punch Bag down off its hinges, and earn yourself some easy Points

Basic Step & Advance Step

> **YOUR OBJECTIVE: Step on and off the Balance Board when told to do so, in perfect Timing and Rhythm, and follow the Actions shown on screen.**

■ Hints and Tips on How to Play:

The Basic Step exercise is all about Timing as well. When the Moves and Actions appear on screen, you must step off the Balance Board at the correct time to the rhythm of the beat. We keep mentioning the word 'Beat', and this is because if you get into the routine of listening to the Beat of the music, then you can time perfectly when to step on and off the Board. Like we said, timing is everything here, so you need to master this in order to score big. Pay close attention to what appears on screen, but make sure that you listen to the beat of the song also in order to judge the timing of your Step. If you successfully complete the Step-action, then you'll earn yourself an 'OK' rating, however if you

can successfully master the timing of the Step as well, then you'll receive a 'Perfect' score, and this exercise will be made easy!

Advance Step is pretty much the same as Basic Step, however this time round; you'll have a few more Moves to take into account. The overall objective of the exercise is still the same – i.e. follow the actions on screen with perfect timing to the beat to score Points. However you'll also have the Green

and Purple Arrow actions to master this time; when the Green Arrow appears on screen, then you must kick out your required-Leg in the direction of the Arrow; and when the Purple Arrow appears on screen, then you must Step back on the Board from the Side, depending on which direction the Arrow is pointing. Master Basic Step, and you'll do fine on Advance!

Free Step >>>

YOUR OBJECTIVE: Step on and off the Balance Board when told to do so, in perfect Timing and Rhythm for 10 Minutes. Simple.

■ Hints and Tips on How to Play:

This a great Training exercise, and can get you toned and in shape in no time. Free Step is dull and extremely tedious, however for the Fitness side of things, it does work well! All you have to do here is Step on and off the Board for a straight 10 Minute period. Make sure that you're in perfect time and rhythm to the Sound coming from the Wii Remote, and if you want, then you can alter the Pace and Speed of the exercise also by pressing either the (A) Button, or D-Pad; increase your Step-speed or slow it down if needs be. That's pretty much it for this routine.

>> >> >

Basic Run & 2-P Run

YOUR OBJECTIVE: On Basic Run, Jog on the spot at a steady Pace to keep up with your Trainer; and on 2-P Run, Jog on the spot to keep up with a Friend.

■ Hints and Tips on How to Play:

For this exercise, you're not actually required to use the Balance Board at all, instead, you can simply hold the Wii Remote in your hand, or place it carefully and securely in your Pocket. Once in place, simply Jog or light Run on the spot. The motion sensor from the Wii Remote will pick up on your movement, so the only thing that you have to worry about here, is maintaining a steady pace! If you can successfully maintain the same speed throughout the entire routine, then you can easily earn yourself a 100% rating every time! The most effective way to succeed in this exercise is to begin at a slow pace so that you can continue at this speed throughout, and then perfect your Jog-timing and your breathing as you do so.

There is in fact a clever trick in which you can speed up the exercise and increase your Score even more. Further into the Run, a Dog may appear on screen, and sprint off ahead. When you notice this speedy creature, start to increase your speed, and try to catch it. This will ultimately lead you down a quicker route, usually a timesaving Shortcut, if you can keep up of course!

2-P Run is exactly the same as Basic Run, only this time round; you're competing against a Friend, who's Jogging on the spot next to you, at the exact same time. Again, both players must maintain a steady pace throughout. Remember to keep an eye out for the Dog, as chasing after it can usually determine the Winner!

Free Run >>>

YOUR OBJECTIVE: Jog on the spot at a steady Pace for 10, 20 or 30 Minutes.

■ Hints and Tips on How to Play:

Again, this exercise is like the Free Steps; it's dull and tedious, but ideal for your health. A continuous 10-30 Minute Free Run is perfect for your Fitness, thus making this one of the most effective exercise-routines in the Game! Just like Basic and 2-P Run, simply maintain a steady pace throughout – this is absolutely vital when

Jogging for long periods of time – and stick to a continuous Jog or light Run on the spot for the required amount of time. Keep it slow, control your breathing, and make sure that you have a bottle of water with you also to prevent yourself from dehydrating. Again, keep a close eye out for the Dog, and speed up considerably when you see it. That's about it - keep a steady pace going, and see out the 10, 20 or 30 Minutes to complete the regime.

Wii Fit balance games

Wii Fit Balance Games are entertaining exercises and routines that focus predominantly on the Fun side of things, rather than the Fitness side!

Soccer Heading

YOUR OBJECTIVE: Head back the Balls that are kicked your way; but make sure that you avoid the Cleats and Panda Heads that also appear!

■ Hints and Tips on How to Play:

On screen, the other Mii characters will start kicking Balls your way, and the idea of the game, is to manoeuvre yourself either left or right on the Balance Board, towards the Ball, and Head it back to score Points. Every now and then however, Cleats and Panda Heads will also be kicked at you, and these must be avoided at all times if you want to succeed and score big! If you Head a Cleat or Panda by mistake, then you'll lose a Point.

For this Game-exercise, you'll be required to put pressure on the Balance Board depending on which direction the Balls or Cleats / Pandas are coming from. For example, if the Ball is coming at you from the Left, then place added pressure on your Left Foot, in order to lean in that direction, and vice versa for if the Ball is being kicked from the Right. If you're lined up perfectly with the oncoming Ball, then your Mii character will automatically Head it for you. This also works in reverse for Cleats or Panda Heads however – if one of these hazards are coming at you from the Left, then you must put pressure on your opposite Right Foot, in order to move out of the way and avoid the object!

As you advance through this exercise, you may find find yourself veering off to either side. If this starts to occur, then try edging back to the centre slowly, as being in the centre of the screen, and the Balance Board, will make life easier when

attempting to Head the Ball. The more you play, the harder it will become, and eventually, you'll have more than one object coming at you simultaneously; for example, you'll have to focus on the oncoming Ball, and a Cleat or Panda! For these parts, try your very best to move towards the Ball, and avoid the Cleat or Panda, but if you're struggling to do this, then it may prove easier and more effective, to simply avoid them both altogether. Remember, place deliberate force on the Balance Board to move your Mii in that direction, and Head as many Balls as you can, whilst avoiding the hazards as you do so, to increase your score dramatically. But ultimately, have fun!

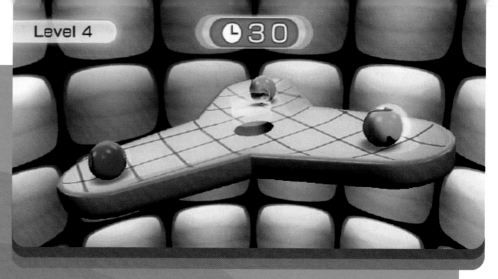

Table Tilt >>>

> **YOUR OBJECTIVE: Use the Balance Board to Tilt the Table on screen, and Roll and guide the Marbles into the Holes. No real point of exercise here however.**

■ Hints and Tips on How to Play:

For this Game, you need to use the Balance Board to manoeuvre the Table around on screen, and ultimately control and guide the Marbles into the Holes. This can be as difficult or as easy as you want it to be, depending on how forceful you are with your footing. If you put too much pressure on the Board, then this challenge will be extremely difficult, however, if you're light with your feet, then there

is no way in which you can fail!

The trick is, to be light with the pressure; this is because, if you look carefully, you'll notice a small Lip on each side of the Table. Therefore if you're not too forceful with your footing, then the Marbles should never actually fall off. This is absolutely vital when controlling multiple Marbles at

the same time. Doing this will enable you to control and guide a single Marble into a Hole with precision, whilst being able to completely forget about the others, if you use the Lip correctly. Tilting the Table too much will cause the Marbles to drop off, so refrain from doing this, and you'll master this challenge in no time!

Penguin Slide

> **YOUR OBJECTIVE: Use the Balance Board to Tilt the Iceberg on screen, and manoeuvre it around so that the Penguin can Catch the Fish.**

■ Hints and Tips on How to Play:

If you can master Table Tilt, then you should be fine at this, as it ultimately requires the same sort of tactics and control. On screen you'll see a Penguin stranded on an Iceberg, and every now and then, Fish will leap out of the water and land on the Iceberg itself. The idea is to put pressure on the Balance Board in order to manoeuvre the Iceberg around, and do your best to catch the Fish with

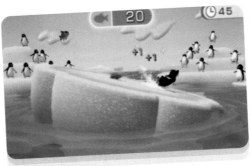

the Penguin. You'll have to judge correctly where the Fish are going to land, and then shift your body weight around to line the Penguin up with the oncoming Fish. That's not the tricky part however! You also have to be careful that the Penguin doesn't slip off the Iceberg, so when putting pressure on the Board, try not to be too forceful, as slipping off the Iceberg will waste valuable seconds when climbing back on.

The most effective way to succeed in this event, is to try and remain as central as possible. The closer you are to the centre of the Iceberg, the easier it is to catch the Fish, as you'll only have a minimal distance on both sides to cover. If you're

too far to the right, and the Fish jumps from the left for example, then you won't reach it! Plus, being close to the edge, makes it far too easy to fall off!

There are a few different types of Fish that you need to watch out for, and each one will earn you a different amount of Points. The Blue Fish are worth 1 Point; the Green Fish are worth 2 Points; and the Rare Red Fish are worth a whopping 10 Points, however these only appear once or twice during the game! The Blue and Green Fish are the most common, however in order to catch the Red Fish, you'll have to continue with the challenge for a period of time, and eventually you may notice it appear beneath the Iceberg. Keep a close eye on its movement, and wait until it submerges deeper – this indicates that it's about to leap! Now listen carefully; you'll be unable to catch the Red Fish by simply moving around on the Balance Board, instead you'll have to put pressure on one side of the Board – the opposite side from where the Fish is leaping from – and then quickly shift all of your body weight onto the other side of the Board, thus causing the Penguin to flip up and jump to reach the higher-unreachable Fish! Master this for 10 Points and you'll dominate the challenge!

Ski Slalom

YOUR OBJECTIVE: Use the Balance Board to Ski down the Mountain, and manoeuvre yourself through the Slalom Flag Posts as you do so.

■ Hints and Tips on How to Play:

For this challenge, you'll need to shift your weight around on the Balance Board to manoeuvre yourself around on screen, and ski down the Mountain as fast as you can at top speed! Along the way however, you'll have to guide yourself through the numerous Slalom Posts by putting more pressure on either the left or right side of the Board. Each time you successfully pass through a Flag Post, you'll receive 1 Point. The most effective way to manoeuvre yourself through each Post, is to remember that they appear from left to right, the entire way down the Mountain. Therefore, if the first Post is found on your left, then the next will appear on your right. This will continue in a left, right, left, right motion the entire way. To master this, you'll need to pass through a Flag Post, and then immediately put pressure on the opposite side, so that you quickly veer off in that direction, enabling you to easily make the next Post!

One more thing; the Blue Bar found at the top of the screen, shows the Speed Zone. The more central you are on the Balance Board, the faster you'll travel; and the faster you speed down the Mountain, the more Points you'll earn come the end. Maintain a central position and power down the Mountain at top speed to earn Big Points!

Tightrope Walk

YOUR OBJECTIVE: Use the Balance Board to carefully Cross the Tightrope on screen, but avoid the Traps that appear as you do so.

■ Hints and Tips on How to Play:

The idea here is to put a little pressure on either side of the Balance Board in order to carefully walk across the Tightrope. If you're too forceful with your footing, then you'll fall off, so remember to be as light-footed as possible, but not too light so that the Board can't pick up on your movement. In order to walk forwards across the Tightrope, you'll need to imitate your Mii's Walk, by almost hobbling left and right on the spot. This will cause your Mii character to walk forwards, but be on the ready at all times to put more pressure on one side if you're starting to fall off the other!

As you advance across the Tightrope, hazard Traps will appear in the form of Metal Jaws. You need to avoid these at all costs! To avoid the Jaws, you must Jump over them, but there's a way in which you must do this without actually jumping. When the Jaw appears in front of you, blocking your path, simply crouch down, and then stand up quickly in a 'ready-to-jump' motion – this will cause your Mii to Jump over the hazards! This should only be done however, if your Mii character is completely centered on the Tightrope! If you're wobbling on either the left or right side of the Rope, then you'll need to shift your weight and get more central before Jumping, otherwise you may accidentally jump off to the side! Keep a steady walk going throughout by walking left and right on the Balance Board, keep your footing light, be on the ready to jump at all times, and you'll master this event in no time.

Ski Jump >>>

YOUR OBJECTIVE: Use the Balance Board to Ski down the Mountain, and then perform a Jump at the end.

■ Hints and Tips on How to Play:

To Ski down the Mountain, simply Crouch down on the Balance Board in a Downhill Ski stance, so that you're leaning forwards. This will put the correct amount of pressure and weight on the front of the Board, whilst putting you in the correct Jump-position also. Make sure that you're as central as possible within the Blue Speed Zone as well, as this will maximise your top speed, and ultimately earn you more Points come the end.

Squat with your knees bent.

That's pretty much it for the downhill Ski; however, once you reach the Red Jump Zone at the end of the slope, you'll need to Stand upright from the Crouched position, to cause your Mii character to Jump off at the end! Again, you don't actually have to jump, instead time it right, and simply stand up in the 'ready-to-jump' motion as quickly as you can, and get some serious Air!

The more you crouch and the more weight you put onto the front of the Board, the faster and ultimately better your run will be; and the faster you stand up at the end, the more successful your Jump will be. Perfect the two, and you're laughing!

Balance Bubble

> **YOUR OBJECTIVE: Carefully manoeuvre and guide the Bubble throughout the Course, and avoid the Sides and Walls as you go.**

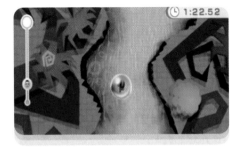

⏱ 1:22.52

■ Hints and Tips on How to Play:

The idea here is to shift your body weight around on the Balance Board to in turn manoeuvre the Bubble on screen around, and guide it carefully throughout the course. Sounds easy enough right? Wrong – you also need to avoid the Sides and Walls as you do so, which can get extremely tricky at times. The course is pretty narrow, and some sections are narrower than others. You must be gentle and light-footed at all times for this game, as the more pressure you use, the faster the Bubble will travel. This can make things difficult, but as long as you take your time, and are careful with your footing and movement, you should be fine.

As you advance through the course, hazards will start to appear! You must avoid these as you go. Now there are two ways in which you can do this; either take it nice and slow and try to manoeuvre yourself slowly and carefully around them at the correct moment, or simply speed past them by putting more force on the Board. The first method can be safer, but if you misjudge it, then starting the Bubble rolling at speed again to avoid the oncoming hazards, can take time. Whereas the second method is more dangerous, as it's easier to accidentally hit the walls, however speeding past the hazards immediately when you see them proves effective also. The choice is yours; just remember to take it nice and slow, and steady throughout, and avoid speeding when there's no need, as this is when silly mistakes occur!

Zazen

> **YOUR OBJECTIVE: Sit perfectly still on the Balance Board to avoid blowing the Candle out.**

■ Hints and Tips on How to Play:

...Do you really need an explanation for this one?! OK then, just for you. On screen is a Lit Candle – the idea is to sit as motionless as possible, and avoid extinguishing the Flame with any movement. Simply sit cross-legged on the Balance Board and DO NOT move, or even twitch! The slightest movement can make the Candle flicker – too greater movement will put it out! This is a test of your patience, endurance, steadiness, and muscle control. This one is completely down to you I'm afraid, so good luck!

unlockable boots items

Yoga >>>

■ Deep Breathing
How to Unlock: Already Unlocked
Number of Minutes: 2

■ Half Moon
How to Unlock: Already Unlocked
Number of Minutes: 2

■ Warrior
How to Unlock: Already Unlocked
Number of Minutes: 2

■ Tree
How to Unlock: Already Unlocked
Number of Minutes: 2

■ Sun Salutation
How to Unlock: Complete 15 Minutes of Game-play
Number of Minutes: 2

■ Standing Knee
How to Unlock: Complete 45 Minutes of Game-play
Number of Minutes: 2

■ Palm Tree
How to Unlock: Complete 1 Hour and 20 Minutes of Game-play
Number of Minutes: 2

■ Chair
How to Unlock: Complete 2 Hours and 15 Minutes of Game-play
Number of Minutes: 2

■ Triangle
How to Unlock: Complete 2 Hours and 50 Minutes of Game-play
Number of Minutes: 2

■ Downward-Facing Dog
How to Unlock: Complete 3 Hours and 10 Minutes of Game-play
Number of Minutes: 2

■ King of the Dance
How to Unlock: Complete 3 Hours and 20 Minutes of Game-play
Number of Minutes: 2

■ Cobra
How to Unlock: Complete 3 Hours and 20 Minutes of Game-play
Number of Minutes: 2

■ Bridge
How to Unlock: Complete 3 Hours and 40 Minutes of Game-play
Number of Minutes: 2

■ Crocodile Twist
How to Unlock: Complete 4 Hours of Game-play
Number of Minutes: 2

Strength >>>

■ Single Leg Extension 6 Reps
How to Unlock: Already Unlocked
Number of Minutes: 2

■ Single Leg Extension 10 Reps
How to Unlock: Complete 'Single Leg Extension' Three Times
Number of Minutes: 2

■ Single Leg Extensions

20 Times
How to Unlock: Complete 'Single Leg Extension' Six Times
Number of Minutes: 3

■ Press-Up & Side Stand 6 Reps
How to Unlock: Already Unlocked
Number of Minutes: 2

■ Press-Up & Side Stand 10 Reps
How to Unlock: Complete 'Press-Up & Side Stand 6 Reps' Three Times
Number of Minutes: 2

■ Press-Up & Side Stand 20 Reps
How to Unlock: Complete 'Press-Up & Side Stand 6 or 10 Reps' Six Times
Number of Minutes: 3

■ Torso & Waist Twist 3 Reps
How to Unlock: Already Unlocked
Number of Minutes: 2

■ Torso & Waist Twist 6 Reps
How to Unlock: Complete 'Torso & Waist Twist 3 Reps' Three Times
Number of Minutes: 3

■ Jacknife 10 Reps
How to Unlock: Already Unlocked
Number of Minutes: 2

■ Jacknife 20 Reps
How to Unlock: Complete 'Jacknife 10 Reps' Three Times
Number of Minutes: 3

■ Jacknife 30 Reps
How to Unlock: Complete 'Jacknife 10 or 20 Reps' Six Times
Number of Minutes: 4

■ Lunge 10 Reps
How to Unlock: Already Unlocked
Number of Minutes: 2

■ Lunge 15 Reps
How to Unlock: Complete 'Lunge 10 Reps' Three Times
Number of Minutes: 3

■ Lunge 20 Reps
How to Unlock: Complete 'Lunge 10 or 15 Reps' Six Times
Number of Minutes: 4

■ Rowing Squat 15 Reps
How to Unlock: Complete 20 Minutes of Game-play
Number of Minutes: 2

■ Rowing Squat 30 Reps
How to Unlock: Complete 'Rowing Squat 15 Reps' Three Times
Number of Minutes: 3

■ Rowing Squat 45 Reps
How to Unlock: Complete 'Rowing Squat 15 or 30' Reps Six Times
Number of Minutes: 4

■ Single Leg Twists 10 Reps
How to Unlock: Complete

30 Minutes of Game-play
Number of Minutes: 2

■ Single Leg Twists 20 Reps
How to Unlock: Complete 'Single Leg Twists 10 Reps' Three Times
Number of Minutes: 3

■ Single Leg-Lift 10 Reps
How to Unlock: Complete 1 Hour and 10 Minutes of Game-play
Number of Minutes: 2

■ Single Leg-Lift 20 Reps
How to Unlock: Complete 'Single Leg-Lift 10 Reps' Three Times
Number of Minutes: 3

■ Parallel Stretch 30 Sec
How to Unlock: Complete 1 Hour and 50 Minutes of Game-play
Number of Minutes: 1

■ Parallel Stretch 60 Sec
How to Unlock: Complete 'Parallel Stretch 30 Sec' Three Times
Number of Minutes: 1

■ Parallel Stretch 90 Sec
How to Unlock: Complete 'Parallel Stretch 30 or 60 Sec' Six Times
Number of Minutes: 2

■ Tricep Extension 10 Reps
How to Unlock:

Complete 2 Hours and 30 Minutes of Game-play
Number of Minutes: 2

■ Tricep Extension 20 Reps
How to Unlock: Complete 'Tricep Extension 10 Reps' Three Times
Number of Minutes: 3

■ Arm and Left Lift 10 Reps
How to Unlock: Complete 2 Hours and 40 Minutes of Game-play
Number of Minutes: 2

■ Arm and Left Lift 20 Reps
How to Unlock: Complete 'Arm and Left Lift 10 Reps' Three Times
Number of Minutes: 3

■ Single Arm Stand 6 Reps
How to Unlock: Complete 3 Hours and 50 Minutes of Game-play
Number of Minutes: 2

■ Single Arm Stand 10 Reps
How to Unlock: Complete 'Single Arm Stand 6 Reps' Three Times
Number of Minutes: 3

■ Press Up Challenge
How to Unlock: Complete 'Press-Up & Side Stand 6, 10 or 20 Reps' Five Times
Number of Minutes: Depends how many Press-Ups and Side Stands you complete

>>> Aerobics

■ Hula Hoop
How to Unlock: Already Unlocked
Number of Minutes: 2

■ Basic Step
How to Unlock: Already Unlocked
Number of Minutes: 3

■ Jogging – Short Distance
How to Unlock: Already Unlocked
Number of Minutes: 4

■ Jogging – Long Distance

How to Unlock: Complete 'Jogging-Short Distance' Three Times
Number of Minutes: 5

■ **Jogging – Island Lap**
How to Unlock: Complete 'Jogging – Long Distance' Two Times
Number of Minutes: 6 - 10

■ **Super Hula Hoops 3 Min**
How to Unlock: Complete 'Hula Hoop' Three Times
Number of Minutes: 3

■ **Super Hula Hoops 6 Min**
How to Unlock: Complete 'Super Hula Hoop 3 Min' Four Times
Number of Minutes: 6

■ **Super Hula Hoops 10 Min**
How to Unlock: Complete 'Super Hula Hoop 6 Min' Two Times
Number of Minutes: 10

■ **Step Plus**
How to Unlock: Complete 'Basic Step' Five Times
Number of Minutes: 5

■ **2-P Jogging – Short Distance**
How to Unlock: Already Unlocked
Number of Minutes: 3

■ **2-P Jogging – Long Distance**
How to Unlock: Unlocked with '1-P Jogging'
Number of Minutes: 5

■ **2-P Jogging – Island Lap**
How to Unlock: Unlocked with '1-P Jogging – Island Lap'
Number of Minutes: 6 - 10

■ **Rhythmic Boxing 3 Min**
How to Unlock: Complete 1 Hour and 40 Minutes of Game-play
Number of Minutes: 4

■ **Rhythmic Boxing 6 Min**
How to Unlock: Complete 'Rhythmic Boxing 3 Min' Five Times
Number of Minutes: 8

■ **Rhythmic Boxing 10 Min**
How to Unlock: Complete 'Rhythmic Boxing 3 or 6 Min' Six Times
Number of Minutes: 13

■ **Free Step**
How to Unlock: Complete 'Step Plus' Three Times
Number of Minutes: 10, 20 or 30 (your choice)

■ **Free Run**
How to Unlock: Complete 'Jogging' Six Times
Number of Minutes: 10, 20 or 30 (your choice)

Balance Games >>>

■ **Soccer Heading – Beginner**
How to Unlock: Already Unlocked
Number of Minutes: 1

■ **Soccer Heading – Advance**
How to Unlock: Complete 'Soccer Heading – Beginner' Five Times
Number of Minutes: 2

■ **Ski Slalom – Beginner**
How to Unlock: Already Unlocked
Number of Minutes: 1

■ **Ski Slalom – Advance**
How to Unlock: Complete 'Ski Slalom – Beginner' Six Times
Number of Minutes: 1

■ **Ski Jump**
How to Unlock: Already Unlocked
Number of Minutes: 1

■ **Table Tilt – Beginner**
How to Unlock: Already Unlocked
Number of Minutes: 3

■ **Table Tilt – Advance**
How to Unlock: Complete 'Table Tilt – Beginner'
Number of Minutes: 5

■ **Tightrope – Beginner**
How to Unlock: Complete 10 Minutes of Game-play
Number of Minutes: 1

■ **Tightrope – Advance**
How to Unlock: Complete 'Tightrope – Beginner'
Number of Minutes: 1

■ **Tightrope – Expert**
How to Unlock: Complete 'Tightrope – Advance'
Number of Minutes: 1

■ **Balance Bubble – Beginner**
How to Unlock: Complete 1 Hour of Game-play
Number of Minutes: 1

■ **Balance Bubble – Advance**
How to Unlock: Complete 'Balance Bubble – Beginner'
Number of Minutes: 1

■ **Penguin Slide**
How to Unlock: Complete 1 Hour and 30 Minutes of Game-play
Number of Minutes: 1

■ **Snowboard Slalom – Beginner**
How to Unlock: Complete 2 Hours of Game-play
Number of Minutes: 1

■ **Snowboard Slalom – Advance**
How to Unlock: Complete 'Snowboard Slalom – Beginner' Five Times
Number of Minutes: 1

■ **Lotus Focus**
How to Unlock: Complete 3 Hours of Game-play
Number of Minutes: Depends on your overall Time

mario & sonic >>>
at the olympic games

Two gaming titans battle it out in the World's ultimate sporting event, what better a place and what better company to help fight fat by working up a serious sweat!

Olympic Games >>>

O lympic Games are all the different Events that you can play and take part in! When you first start the game you'll only be able to select a few Events until you unlock the rest. To unlock all Events, you must first complete all the Circuits in Circuit Mode including Beginner's Class, Advanced, and Master's Class! Complete each Circuit in each Class and unlock every Event in the game!! The following are the most effective tactics and ways to complete and come first in every Olympic Game event!

athletics

100m:

Best Type: Speed
Controls: Wiimote & Nunchuck

100m is a straightforward 100m sprint! The most effective way to get an advantage and a head start at the beginning of the race is to get a Boost start with perfect timing! When the word "Ready" appears on screen at the beginning of the race, press and hold down the [B] button to build up your Energy bar! Shortly after, the word "Go!" will appear; when this appears, immediately release the [B] button and flick the Wiimote down to sprint off!! If you leave the start immediately when "Go!" appears, then you'll get a perfect Boost start! To sprint along the Track, repeatedly shake the Wiimote and Nunchuck up and down, one after the other, in the same way as your legs would run! The faster you alternate the Wiimote and Nunchuck, the faster you'll run! Maintain this method and pace until you reach the finish line!

400m:

Best Type: Speed & Stamina
Controls: Wiimote & Nunchuck

400m is a straightforward sprint just like the 100m event, only longer! Begin this event in the same way as the 100m; press and hold the [B] button to build up Energy and release it and flick the Wiimote down when "Go!" appears to receive a Boost! Shake both the Wiimote and Nunchuck to sprint! Now there is one slight difference that you'll have to take into account; as this is a 400m sprint, your Stamina bar will decrease; the Heart shaped icon above your character indicates your Stamina. When this fully depletes, your character will slow down briefly until it fills up again, losing you valuable seconds! The idea is to find a steady pace in order to maintain your Stamina so that it is never completely empty! Alternate the Wiimote and Nunchuck, but at a slower pace than the 100m event so that your Stamina is round about the half way mark within the Heart for the majority of the race! This will enable you to complete the event without losing breath; once you reach the end 20m, hold the (A) button to sprint to the end at top speed!

Fitness / Exercise Workout:

Athletics Sports, such as the 100m, 400m, 4 x 100m Relay, 110m Hurdles, and 400m Hurdles, are all great Intense Cardio and muscle-building workouts! These five Sport Events will get your Cardiovascular System working significantly, as you'll be continuously shaking both Arms up and down to run, thus increasing your heart-rate greatly! For the longer Events such as 400m, 4 x 100m Relay, and 400m Hurdles, the muscles in your Arms and Shoulders, will be worked also, thus increasing muscle size in your Forearms, Biceps, Triceps, and Deltoid! The faster you alternate your Arm movements, the more your Cardiovascular System will be worked, and the faster your muscles will grow over time! These Events are ideal for quick Intense workouts Before or After the more Intense Training sessions.

4 x 100m Relay:

Best Type: Speed & Stamina
Controls: Wiimote & Nunchuck

4 x 100m Relay is a four person Relay race with each character running a 100m stretch with a Baton; after the 100m, the Baton is passed to the next character! Again, hold [B] to power your Energy and release and flick the Wiimote at "Go!" Shake the Wiimote and Nunchuck to sprint! Once you get roughly 3/4 of the way along your 100m stretch, 'Speed Lock" will kick in; when this appears, you can stop alternating the Controls, as you'll now run automatically! When you're near your next character – about 10m away – press the [B] button to encourage them to start jogging! Timing is everything; if you press [B] too soon, then your following runner will stop before you pass the baton, losing valuable seconds; and if you press too late, then they won't have time to adjust! As your next runner is jogging, you'll begin to get closer; once you're pretty much touching each other, flick the Wiimote up to pass the baton! Again timing is everything; aim for a 'Great' pass to smoothly pass the baton! Repeat this same procedure for the following characters and sprint to finish line!

110m Hurdles:

Best Type: Speed
Controls: Wiimote & Nunchuck

110m Hurdles is a race across a distance of 110m with Hurdles to jump and clear along the way! You know what to do; press and hold [B] to power up and release and flick to Boost off! Sprint by shaking the Controls and proceed to the first Hurdle! Now again, timing is everything! As you approach the first Hurdle, press the [B] button quickly just before you reach it; if your timing is correct then you'll successfully jump over and clear it, giving you an added bit of speed as you land whilst maintaining pace! If you fail to clear the Hurdle then you'll connect with it, thus slowing you down and losing pace and seconds on the clock! You want to jump just a split second before you're touching the Hurdle; the closer the better! Sprint to the next Hurdle and do the same again; repeat this procedure for all 10 Hurdles and cross the finish line!

400m Hurdles:

Best Type: Speed & Stamina
Controls: Wiimote & Nunchuck

400m Hurdles is exactly the same as the 110m Hurdles, only longer; whilst incorporating the same technique as the 400m sprint, you'll now have to take into account your Stamina meter! Hold [B] at the line-up and release and flick to Boost

start! Sprint to the first Hurdle and time your jump correctly by pressing the [B] button to successfully clear it (Read 110m Hurdles Above)! Once you've cleared the first Hurdle, slow down by lightly alternating the Wiimote and Nunchuck at a slower speed to maintain a steady pace in order to keep your Stamina meter around halfway within the Heart! Like we mentioned before, if your Stamina completely decreases, then you'll lose speed! Maintain this steady pace whilst successfully jumping the Hurdles at the correct time, and once you reach the end 20m stretch, hold (A) to sprint to the finish!

Long Jump:

Best Type: Speed
Controls: Wiimote & Nunchuck

Long Jump is a short run, followed up by a jump once you reach the white line! The winner is determined by the furthest landing! At the very beginning of the event at your character's introduction, move the Wiimote and Nunchuck together and away from one another in a clapping motion to encourage the applause of the crowd; this will give your character added confidence when jumping! Begin by sprinting forwards along the straight until Speed Lock is activated! Once you reach the white line, immediately flick the Wiimote up to jump! The idea is to get as close to the white line as possible, touching it if you can; however if you overrun the small green line, then it's a Foul and your following jump won't be accepted! You need to flick the Wiimote up at the perfect speed and force to receive a "Great" jump! If you're too light with the Wiimote then your jump will fall short, however if you're too heavy handed and forceful with it, then you'll overpower the jump and receive a "Bad" rating! Find the power and force that best suits you and perfect the timing and power!

Triple Jump:

Best Type: **Speed**
Controls: **Wiimote & Nunchuck**

Triple Jump is pretty much the same as Long Jump and requires the same tactics and methods! Again, clap the Wiimote and Nunchuck together to applaud the crowd, and then begin your sprint down the straight! The idea is to perform three perfect jumps in a hop, skip and jump motion using both the Wiimote and Nunchuck! Once you reach the first white line, immediately flick the Wiimote up to hop! Remember not too hard, but not too light; timing and power is everything (Read Long Jump Above). As you're about to land from your first hop, quickly flick the Nunchuck up in the same way as the Wiimote to skip on your next foot! You want to raise the Nunchuck just before your character's foot touches the surface again! And finally, just before you land for a second time, flick the Wiimote up once again to perform your final Jump!! So It's Wiimote, Nunchuck, Wiimote! Practice timing and power and aim for three "Greats" for a perfect Jump!

Hammer Throw:

Best Type: **Power**
Controls: **Wiimote**

The Hammer Throw is all about power and timing and how far you can throw the Hammer after spinning on the spot! Unhook the Nunchuck for this event and hold the Wiimote vertically so that the front of the Wiimote is pointing at the ceiling. When "Go!" appears on screen, press (A) to begin spinning! To build up power and speed, rotate the Wiimote around in a circular motion as fast as you can! Your power is indicated by the

different colours surrounding the Hammer as you swing; Orange is poor power and Blue is the top! Aim for the Blue coloured arc! Rotate the Wiimote around for a few spins until 3, 2, 1 appears on screen; when 1 occurs, keep spinning until your character is facing through the small opening at the front of the cage, and then press the [B] immediately to release the Hammer up field! To receive an extra Power Boost, press both the (A) and [B] button simultaneously when releasing the Hammer!

Fitness / Exercise Workout: >>>

The Hammer Throw is great for increasing muscle size in your Shoulders and Arms! This Event doesn't focus on Cardio at all, however when you repeatedly rotate your Arm around above your head to build up power for the Throw, your Shoulder (Deltoid muscles) are worked greatly. Your Bicep and Triceps muscles are worked slightly also. The faster you rotate your Arm around and the more movement and force you exert, the harder your muscles will work, and the faster they will grow over time! Switch your Wii Remote holding Hand in between sessions, and rotate with your weaker Arm, to increase muscle size in both the Right and Left hand side of your body, as well as increase equal balance in both sides too! This Event is ideal for a quick Intense muscle-building workout.

Javelin Throw:

Best Type: **Power**
Controls: **Wiimote & Nunchuck**

The Javelin Throw is all about power and timing and how far you can throw the Javelin after the short run! Alternate the Wiimote and Nunchuck to begin running; once 'Speed Lock' has been activated, stop running and wait until you near the white line. If you look carefully at the side of the stretch, you'll notice small red cones; just as you reach the final cone along the straight, press and hold (A) and [B] and then flick the Wiimote down at the correct speed and force to throw the Javelin! If you lower the Wiimote too hard then you'll receive a Failed throw, which will fall short of the mark; the same applies for if you put too little power into the throw also! Perfect the power to perfect your throw! If you overstep the white line then it'll be classified as a Foul! Remember that your character will perform a little hop and run before they throw the Javelin so you'll need to take this distance into account beforehand; run towards the end cone and flick the Wiimote down lightly to perform a 'Great' Throw every time!!

High Jump:

Best Type: **Speed & Skill**
Controls: **Wiimote & Nunchuck**

High Jump requires perfect timing in successfully jumping over and clearing the bar! At the very beginning of the event you can alter the height of the bar using the D-Pad! At your characters intro, clap the Wiimote and Nunchuck together to get the crowd going! Once ready, shake the Controls to start running; the more Blue area you have in the meter on the left hand side of the screen, the easier it will be for you to successfully clear the bar! As you raise the bar higher, the amount of blue in the meter will be less, making things more difficult! Run towards the bar and wait until 'Speed Lock' kicks in; once this occurs, stop running and wait until you near the coloured section of floor directly in front of the mat! The idea is to flick the Wiimote up to jump, just as you stand on the Blue-coloured ground,

WR 86.74
OR 85.985

which represents the colours in the left hand meter! Flick the Wiimote up at the perfect power, not too hard but not too light, to jump! The idea is to keep the jump within the Blue area of the meter; if you fail to do this and the meter drops below the blue area then you'll fail the jump and clip the bar! Once you've successfully jumped and have kept in the blue section, flick the Nunchuck up to realign your characters body and legs to successfully clear the bar!

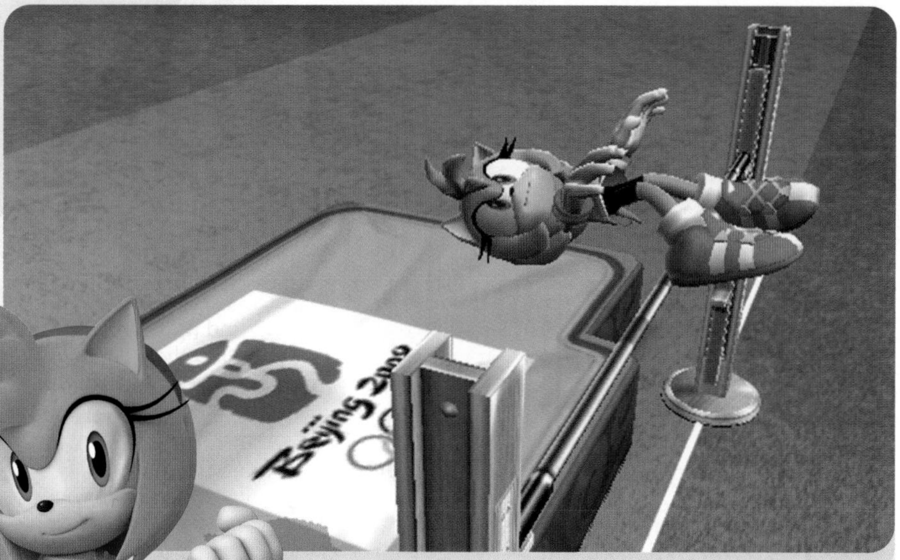

Pole Vault:

Best Type: Speed & Skill
Controls: Wiimote & Nunchuck

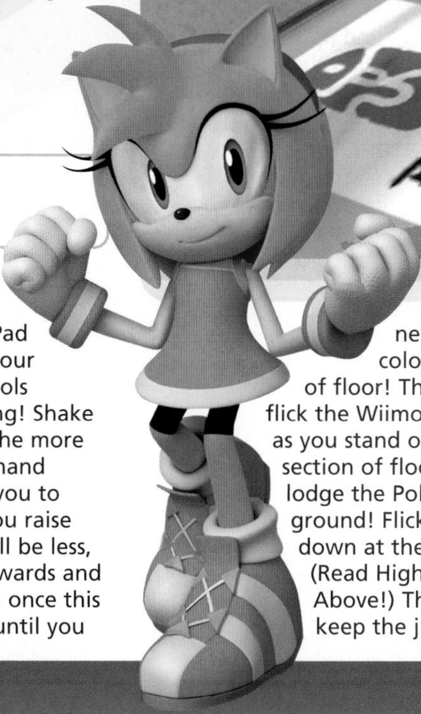

Pole Vault is pretty much just like the High Jump! Alter the height of the bar using the D-Pad at the start of each event! At your characters intro, clap the Controls together to get the crowd going! Shake the Controls to start running; the more Blue area you have in the left hand meter, the easier it will be for you to successfully clear the bar! As you raise the bar, the amount of blue will be less, making things harder! Run forwards and wait until 'Speed Lock' kicks in; once this occurs, stop running and wait until you

near the coloured section of floor! The idea is to flick the Wiimote down just as you stand on the Blue section of flooring, to lodge the Pole in the ground! Flick the Wiimote down at the perfect time! (Read High Jump Above!) The idea is to keep the jump within

the Blue area of the meter; if you fail to do this then you'll have great difficulty in levelling yourself out in the next part! Aim for a 'Great' jump and once you're in mid air, alternate shaking the Wiimote and Nunchuck to get more height and maintain the bar within the blue area! If you don't do this fast enough, then the left hand bar will drop! Finally, just as you're characters body is tuning at the highest point, flick the Nunchuck up to realign your body and legs!

gymnastics

Trampoline:

Best Type: Skill
Controls: Wiimote

Trampoline is all about how fast and accurately you can follow the commands that appear on screen! At the start of the event, flick the Wiimote up in the air to begin jumping! Just before you land, flick the Wiimote up again to get a higher jump! Repeat this procedure and aim for 7m until the commands appear to the right of the screen! There will be three different commands to look out for; (A) button, [B] button and twisting the Wiimote! The idea is to quickly press the commands in the order that they appear from top to bottom before you land on the Trampoline again! Once you land after completing the sequence, a new and longer sequence will appear at which you'll have to do the same again before landing! Be quick and finish the button combos before you land, and then flick

the Wiimote up again just before landing to get a higher jump in between combos to make the next sequence easier! Continue following the button commands to the end of the event! Be careful; you lose points and height when pressing the wrong buttons!

Vault:

Best Type: Skill & Speed
Controls: Wiimote & Nunchuck

Vault is a short run and a flip onto a springboard and over the apparatus whilst performing spins and twirls in mid air to score points! Shake the Controls to sprint to the springboard and just before you reach the board, stop running. You'll then automatically jump onto the board; just before your character lands and touches the board, flick the Wiimote down to perform the high jump into the air! Aim for a 'Great' jump to get maximum height! As you're in mid air,

you can perform one of three moves using both the Wiimote and Nuchuck! They are as follows:

Flex Spin: Flick Wiimote Down!
Stretch Spin:
Flick Nunchuck Down!
Twist Spin: Flick Wiimote and Nunchuck Down simultaneously!

Execute a variety of mixed Spins one after the other with perfect timing to score big points! Variety is key here! If you land perfectly on both feet then press (A) to finish your routine! If you land unsteady, then rapidly shake the Wiimote and Nunchuck to regain stability!

shooting

Skeet:

> **Best Type: Skill**
> **Controls: Wiimote**

Skeet is a test of your own skills and accuracy at a Shooting Range consisting of 8 parts! Each part is different and the Skeet targets will appear from different areas depending on which part of the range you're on; remember where they

appear for later use! At the beginning of the event you'll be shown a Heart icon containing a moving dot; when the dot is in the centre of the Heart, press [B] to set your accuracy! The closer you are to the centre, the more accurate your shots will be! Take your time and perfect this! You'll now arrive at your first Range; aim your Wiimote cursor at the screen and wait for the Skeet's to appear! The most effective way to hit the targets is to aim the cursor directly in the centre of the screen, giving you a clear view of the entire area and maximising your time in spotting the targets! When the targets appear, aim for them and press [B] to shoot! You only have as many bullets as Skeet's so accuracy is everything; DO NOT waste any if possible! Once done, move onto the next part of the course and repeat the same procedure!

rowing >>>

Fitness / Exercise Workout: >>>

Single Skulls Rowing is a great combination for a Cardio and muscle-building workout! Continuously Rowing back and forth will help keep your heart-rate going throughout, thus increasing your Cardiovascular System greatly, plus with increased movement, your entire Upper Body will be worked also, increasing muscle size in your Arms (Biceps and Triceps), your Shoulders (Deltoids) and Upper Back muscles (Trapezius and Latissimus Dorsi muscles)! This is by far one of the best workouts in the game, as it incorporates an Intense Cardio workout, whilst simultaneously increasing muscle size where it matters most. This Event is ideal for an Intense workout Before or After Intense Training sessions, to either Warm-Up or Cool-Down. Do this regularly and feel the difference.

Single Skulls:

> **Best Type: Speed & Stamina**
> **Controls: Wiimote & Nunchuck**

Single Skulls is a straight-line Rowing event from one point to another using the Wiimote, Nunchuck and button combinations! At the beginning of the race, a button combo will appear on screen; quickly press the required button or buttons and pull both the Wiimote and Nunchuck back simultaneously in a rowing motion to start rowing! Repeatedly push and pull the

Controls back and forth at speed to row faster! When the buttons appear on screen such as (A) and [B], (A) and [Z] or [Z] and [B], press them as quick as you can whilst simultaneously rowing with the Controls to maintain speed and lead the race! The faster you row and the faster you press the button combos when they appear, the easier it will be to win! If you accidentally press the wrong buttons then you'll lose speed and slow down significantly, so pay attention throughout this event and maintain your rowing speed and button-bashing at all times!

dream events

Dream Race:

Best Type: Speed
Controls: Wiimote & Nunchuck

Dream Race isn't an Olympic event; instead it's a fun sprint over a few short laps consisting of Mario Kart rules! Avoid your enemies' attacks and smash them with your own to take the lead! At the start of the Race, build up energy by holding [B]. Release [B] and flick the Wiimote down to start running! Shake the Controls to speed up and once your speed bar in the top left hand corner is full, you'll run automatically so you can stop alternating the Controls! If you hit an obstacle and slow down, then shake the Controls again to speed back up! Use the Analog Stick on the Nunchuck to move left and right along the track to avoid obstacles such as sand, fences, and other obstructions. Press the [B] button whilst running to jump over obstructions also! Use the Analog to move towards flashing Item Boxes, which contain useful attacks to use against your rivals! They are as follows:

> **Boot: Speed boost for 5 seconds and gets rid of Boo status!**
> **Star: Invincibility for 5 seconds; nothing can slow you down, except Boo!**
> **Bomb: Drop Bombs to attack rivals behind you!**
> **Boo: Automatically slows down the leader briefly!**
> **Green Shell: Fire Shell backwards or forwards to attack opponents!**
> **Red Shell: Locks on, follows, and attacks opponents ahead!**
> **Lightning: Attacks all opponents ahead and stops them briefly!**
> **Green Gem: 'Use for major comeback' – Very Rare!**

Once you run into a Box and collect your Item, press the (A) button to use it! The idea is to simply avoid obstacles and attacks by using the Analog Stick or jumping with [B]; and to collect as many Item Boxes as you can to attack your rivals with, or to use to your advantage! Use the Speed-Up arrows on the ground to add boost and sprint through each lap to win the Race!

Dream Platform:

Best Type: N/A
Controls: Wiimote & Nunchuck

Dream Platform again, isn't an Olympic event; instead it's another fun game incorporating the rules from Trampoline and Dream Race! You'll jump from 10,000m into the water below; along the way you'll have to avoid obstacles and Blocks; collect Item Boxes to hinder your opponents or give you the upper hand, and perform Trampoline-like button combos using the (A) and [B] buttons and twisting the Wiimote! (Read Trampoline Above). As you jump and start to descend, tilt the Wiimote down to pick up speed or tilt the Wiimote up to slow down! Remember, it's not a race to the finish line; it all depends on points, so speed isn't everything! Use the Analog Stick to move left, right, up and down through the sky and dash towards the different coloured Rings to enter the button combos, thus earning you BIG points! The smaller Rings require more buttons to be pressed within a quicker time limit, therefore earning you more points! If you hit the Blocks then points will be deducted! Enter the water first and hit all checkpoints, and you'll receive Bonuses! Be quick with the button combos and hit everything that you can to win the event!!

Dream Fencing:

Best Type: Skill & Speed
Controls: Wiimote & Nunchuck

Dream Fencing is basically exactly the same as Fencing, Individual Epee, just with a few added Dream special features! The idea is to attack your opponents by thrusting the Wiimote forwards in order to reduce their Health to nothing, thus winning the event! Move backwards and forwards using the Analog Stick and Attack using the Wiimote! Dodge using either the (A) and [B] buttons when your opponents attacks to evade their blows and counter! (Read Individual Epee Below). In this event, you'll have a Special Moves Meter below your character, which when full, can be used for devastating attacks! Once the bar is full, press both the (A) and [B] buttons simultaneously and

swing the Wiimote forwards to perform your Special Move! If you push your opponent far enough back, then you can thrust them off the wooden decking into the water, taking away a large amount of their health; be careful though, as this can also happen to you! Keep attacking and evading blows until you've defeated your rival and then move onto the next round and do the same again!

Dream Table Tennis:

Best Type: Skill, Speed & Power
Controls: Wiimote

Dream Table Tennis is basically exactly the same as Table Tennis, Singles, just with a few added Dream special features! Use the Wiimote to smash the ball back to your opponent to score

Fitness / Exercise Workout: >>>

Dream Table Tennis, much like the regularly Singles Table Tennis is a great combination for a Cardio and muscle-building workout! Table Tennis involves a continuous play back and forth, requiring you to repeatedly swing to hit the ball, thus getting your heart-rate going throughout, and working on your Cardiovascular System well. Not just that, but as you swing, your Arms and Shoulders will be worked greatly also, thus increasing muscle size in your Biceps, Triceps and Shoulders (Deltoids)! Put added force into your swings to work your Cardiovascular System and muscles even more! This Event is ideal for a Light workout Before, After, or In-Between Intense Training sessions.

points! Press the (A) or [B] button whilst swinging to perform different style hits to make things more difficult for your opponent! Timing is everything; when the returned ball is just in front of you, swing the Wiimote to hit the ball back! (Read Singles Below). In this version of Table Tennis, instead of the winner being the first to 11 points, the winner is the first to 50! Also, the score is added up by the number of rally's that you can maintain, not how many times you beat your opponent with a returned ball; for example, if you and your rival maintain a rally of 25 hits and then your opponent misses the next ball, then you receive 25 points! The most effective way to score big points is to purposely build up a long rally and then Smash the ball to beat your opponent earning you a BIG score! You will also have a Special Moves Meter, which when full, will enable you to perform your Special Move! Once the bar at the bottom of the screen is full, press (A) and [B] simultaneously, and swing the Wiimote to perform a powerful shot! Get 50 points and move on to the next round!

archery

Archery:

Best Type: Skill
Controls: Wiimote & Nunchuck

Archery is a test of your steady handed skills and good judgement with a Bow and Arrow! At first, this event can be fairly frustrating and difficult to manoeuvre accurately, but once you fully understand the sensor movement, you'll master it in no time! At the start of the event, hold the Nunchuck in front of you as if it were the Bow and hold the Wiimote back slightly as if it were the Arrow! Press and hold both (A) and [B] to begin, and then pull the Wiimote (Arrow) back maximise the Target full

screen, ready to line up your shot! Now, moving the Wiimote cursor is simple; just aim at the screen like Skeet; the Nunchuck however may cause some problems! The idea is to align both the Wiimote and Nunchuck cursors within the Target in order to fire a perfectly straight shot at the centre of the Target for a maximum of 10 Points! All you have to do is hold the Nunchuck vertically and slightly tilt it left, right, up or down to move it in that direction! Once you've mastered this, move both cursors together, hold position briefly, and release (A) and [B] to take your shot! In the top right hand corner of the screen is the wind direction and speed, which will drastically affect

your shot! Take this into account during every round! If the wind is saying 'Left 2', then look at the circled areas with the large Target and aim your cursors two circles to the Right to counteract the wind! If the wind is 'Right 6', then aim the cursors six circled areas to the Left! Aim directly opposite of the wind! Practice makes perfect!

aquatics

1.533

Fitness / Exercise Workout: >>>

Aquatics Sports, such as the 100m Freestyle, and 400m Freestyle, are both great Intense Cardio and muscle-building workouts!

Both of these Sport Events will get your Cardiovascular System working significantly, as you'll be continuously shaking both Arms up and down, or left to right, to swim, thus increasing your heart-rate greatly! For the longer 400m Freestyle, the muscles in your Arms and Shoulders, will be worked also, thus increasing muscle size in your Forearms, Biceps, Triceps, and Deltoid! The faster you alternate your Arm movements, the more your Cardiovascular System will be worked, and the faster your muscles will grow over time! These Events are ideal for quick Intense workouts Before or After the more Intense Training sessions.

100m Freestyle:

Best Type: Speed & Stamina
Controls: Wiimote & Nunchuck

100m Freestyle is straightforward swimming race back and forth once across the entire pool! As you're preparing to go, hold [B] to build up Energy and then flick the Wiimote down to dive into the water when "Go!" appears! Now, depending on your character, you'll have to abide to their favourite swimming style in order to swim the fastest; for example a certain character may favour Doggy Paddle, whereas others may lean towards Breaststroke! Check each style beforehand and stick to it!

15.040

Crawl: Forwards/Backwards alternately!
Breaststroke:
Left/Right alternately!
Butterfly: Up/Down together!
Doggy Paddle:
Up/Down alternately!
Crocodile Paddle:
Left/Right together!

As you swim and start to speed up, your Stamina meter within the Heart icon above your character will begin to drop; to maintain pace and never lose Stamina, press [B] once the Heart icon is almost completely empty; this will use

your Stamina Recovery ability and give you a brief added Boost! If you fail to Recover in time, then you'll slow down until it refills again! Swim to the first end of the pool and just before you touch the side, flick the Wiimote down to perform a clean turn! Swim back and repeat the same methods again!

4 x 100m Freestyle:

Best Type: Speed & Stamina
Controls: Wiimote & Nunchuck

4 x 100m Freestyle is exactly the same as 100m Freestyle, only this time, with four characters swimming as a team! (Read 100m Freestyle Above). Swim back and forth across the pool using your Stamina Recovery at the perfect time, and just before you reach the next character in your team, flick the Wiimote down with precise timing for them to receive a Speed Boost when diving in! Repeat this four times and just keep swimming! Read above for more info!

Fencing

Individual Epee:

> **Best Type: Skill & Speed**
> **Controls: Wiimote & Nunchuck**

Fencing Individual Epee is a Fencing event that tests your skills in attacking, evading, and countering your opponent! Use the Anolog Stick on the Nunhcuck to move left or right along the stage; double tap left or right to move faster in that direction, towards or away from your opponent! Use the Wiimote as the Epee and thrust it forwards to hit your rival! Points are scored each time you successfully connect with your opponent; the first to 15 wins! Press the (A) button whilst swinging the Wiimote just before your attacker lunges at you to Parry their hit! This will leave them open briefly; whilst they're regaining stability, quickly thrust them! Press the [B] button just before your opponents attack hits to Feint, causing you to move out of the way, enabling you to Counterattack! Keep moving in and out to throw your opponent off guard and when there's an opening, Lunge in and make the hit!

table tennis

Singles:

> **Best Type: Skill, Speed & Power**
> **Controls: Wiimote**

Singles is a standard game of Table Tennis and the first to 11 Points wins! You score points by smashing the ball and beating your opponent! If you've ever played Wii Sports then you'll find this easy, as it's pretty much exactly the same and requires the same tactics and methods of play! To serve the ball, flick the Wiimote up and then once the balls drops again, swing the Wiimote down to hit it up table! Now it's a simple game just hitting the ball back and forth until one of you misses the returned ball. To trick your opponent and ultimately beat them, alternate your style of shots from normal to Chops and Smashes! Press and hold (A) whilst swinging the Wiimote to perform a Chop shot, which will cause the ball to

head up table at a slower pace, by putting backspin on the ball also, making it difficult for your rival to return with an accurate shot! It can also slow the game down if things get too much! Smash shots however are the key; press and hold [B] whilst swinging the Wiimote to perform a Smash shot, which is a powerful, fast pace Smash up table! With the correct timing and angle, you'll beat your opponent most times! If you hit the returned ball at the perfect time, then the ball will go straight; if you hit it too early, then the ball will head to the left; and hit the ball to late, and it will bend to the right! Always keep this in mind and ensure you time and direct your shots accordingly!

Fitness / Exercise Workout: >>>

Single Table Tennis, much like the Dream Table Tennis is a great combination for a Cardio and muscle-building workout! Table Tennis involves a continuous play back and forth, requiring you to repeatedly swing to hit the ball, thus getting your heart-rate going throughout, and working on your Cardiovascular System well. Not just that, but as you swing, your Arms and Shoulders will be worked greatly also, thus increasing muscle size in your Biceps, Triceps and Shoulders (Deltoids)! Put added force into your swings to work your Cardiovascular System and muscles even more! This Event is ideal for a Light workout Before, After, or In-Between Intense Training sessions.

Wii >>>
Sports

Timing, accuracy and power play a huge factor in all the sports making Wii Sports a gripping experience for all family members! And we are here to ensure that you squeeze even drop of gameplay out of this amazing game.

Fitness / Exercise Workout: >>>

Tennis is a great Light Cardio workout to help Warm-Up or Cool-Down Before, After, or In-Between Intense Training Exercises; and can help increase muscle size in your Upper Body also, including your Arms, Shoulders, Upper Back, and even your Chest! As this Sport requires continuous play back and forth, your Cardiovascular System is worked at a steady rate, which is effective, and helps you train for longer periods in the long run! Switch your Wii Remote holding Hand in between sessions, and swing with your weaker Arm, to increase muscle size in both the Right and Left hand side of your body, as well as increase equal balance in both sides!

Preparation & Personalisation:

Before actually being able to play Wii Sports you're required to set up a 'Mii' character who you will use throughout your gaming experience. Creating multiple Mii players for other family members or friends will enable you to compete against one another for points, the leader board - which is represented in the style of a graph – and ultimately the Pro Status award, which is actually nothing more than a bragging right.

You're able to customise your character greatly from the basics of your name, to your overall height, weight, the style of your hair, facial hair, eyes, nose, mouth and much more in order for your Wii Sports experience to be 100% personalised for you!

Wii Sports Games:
tennis

ennis takes place as a standard doubles match with four players overall using the entire court as your playing field, also incorporating the basic tennis rules and point-scoring system: 15, 30, 45, deuce, match point, advantage and set.

The Wiimote acts as the tennis racket itself and should be held in your hand in the exact same way as the racket should be, with the front facing forwards.

Timing plays a huge factor in this game!

■ To serve the ball, simply move the racket (the Wiimote) up over your head as if you were realistically serving the ball and then swing forwards to smash it up court. Your Mii character will then serve the ball awaiting your next move.

■ Once the ball is up court and gets hit back in your direction, the game is on!

From here on in simply use the Wiimote to keep play going back and forth by producing forehand and backhand swings depending on which player the ball lands to and of course which side the ball is on.

■ To control your front two players you must swing the Wiimote immediately after your opponent has swung and just before the ball has reached your position in order to produce a skilful net shot!

Tennis Tactics

■ Movement:

All Mii movements are automatically taken care of for you; the Mii players will move in the direction of the ball no matter where on the court the ball is, however the front two players will only move slightly for a quick period of time until the ball has past, at which point the rear two players will take over.

■ Timing:

Like we mentioned earlier, timing plays a huge factor in this and all of your shots revolve solely around it! Due to the realism of the game itself, being slightly off with the timing will affect the direction of which the ball will be hit; for example if you swing the Wiimote too early then you'll automatically hook the ball to the left and if you swing too late then you automatically slice the ball to the right.

■ Accuracy:

The accuracy of your shots doesn't really play a significant part in the game however, you can slightly alter the

direction in which the ball lands by manoeuvring the Wiimote further left or right. Performing these kinds of shots whilst simultaneously altering your timing (above) can produce a shot where the ball itself can land in either of the top far corners making it exceptionally difficult for your opponent to reply! For example if you hit the ball early and hook it to the right by cutting the Wiimote across your body, whilst smashing the ball to the right at the same time, it will cause the ball to head to the far right and vice versa for the left!

■ Lobbing & Smashing:

To lob the ball up and over, simply manoeuvre the Wiimote from your side,

starting down low and bringing it up high in the exact same way as actual tennis. Doing this however will make it much easier for your opponent to return your shot with a volley!

To smash the ball down, simply repeat the previous procedure but in reverse; begin with the Wiimote up high above your head and bring it back down with some force, making it hard for your opponent to return your shot!

■ Super Serve:

To perform a fast serve it's all about a quick and fluid motion swing from initially serving the ball in the air to finally smashing it up court. Move the Wiimote up to serve and then with a clean fluid motion, bring it back down immediately after with no hesitation. This may take a few tries for it to be successful and remember practice makes perfect.

If you've successfully employed this power shot then the ball will travel at an incredible speed with a gold trail following it, making it difficult for your opponent to reply with an accurate shot!

baseball

Fastball
105 km/h

There are two teams who either take up the role of pitcher or batsman. The pitcher throws the ball towards the batsman in order to 'Strike' them out, at which point the batsman then has to quickly swing the bat – or Wiimote in this case – in order to smash the ball out into the field.

baseball, just like tennis, is simple, and incorporates the basic rules of the sport, taking it in turns to bat and pitch, whilst also enabling you to score singles, doubles, triples, home runs and foul balls!

Again the Wiimote acts as the bat itself and should be held in the exact same way as real life baseball, remaining faithful to the realism of the sport itself.

Timing plays a huge factor in this sport also, even more so than tennis so keep this in mind!

From here on in everything is automatically taken care of for you and your opponent; the batsman then automatically runs from base to base, whilst the fielders automatically try to retrieve the ball.

Depending on the accuracy, direction and power of the batsman's swing, they can either get caught out immediately, run through the three bases, 1st 2nd 3rd or if the ball is smashed into the crown then you'll receive a home run!

Fitness / Exercise Workout: >>>

Baseball is a great Intense muscle-building workout which can help increase muscle size in your Upper Body; including your Arms, Shoulders, Upper Back, and Chest! This Sport isn't really a Cardio workout, as it is not a continuous playing game like Tennis which will constantly keep your heart-rate going throughout, but instead a stop-start session, which will focus more on muscle increase instead! Put added force and movements into each swing, to really get your muscles working hard! Switch your Wii Remote holding Hand in between sessions, and swing with your weaker Arm, to increase muscle size in both the Right and Left hand side of your body, as well as increase equal balance in both sides also!!

Play ball

The idea is to successfully make it the entire way round the field through all four bases with each team member in order to receive a point for each.

If the pitcher produces a decent throw and the batsman fails to hit it then this is classified as a

Now Wii Know!

If you're in control of the pitcher, then it's your job to throw some fast paced balls at the batsman. To do this, simply hold the Wiimote above your head, slightly behind you – as if you were realistically pitching – and bring it back down in front of you. The faster you do this and the more force you employ, the faster the ball will be!

Strike! If the batsman misses three of these consecutively then they are out and the next batsman takes position.

If the batsman hits the ball inaccurately and either slices it right and hooks it too much left and the ball lands out of the V-shape field lines, then this is classified as a Foul Ball and will have to be reattempted again.

Now Wii Know!

If you've taken on the role of batsman then it's your goal to smash the ball away, up field with as much force as possible in order to clear the fielders. To do this, simply stand to the side and hold the Wiimote above your head behind you as if you would if you were batting. From here, time your swing correctly and bring the Wiimote across your body so that your batting arm ends up across your body. Like pitching, the faster and harder you swing the further the ball will go!

Baseball Tactics:

BATTING:

■ Movement:

Like I mentioned previously, the movement and direction of the Mii characters, whether it's the batsmen or pitchers, are automatically taken care of for you. The batting team will automatically run through the bases until the ball has been retrieved at which point their run will stop, and the pitching team's fielders will automatically head to wherever the ball is on the field.

■ Timing:

For the batting side, timing is the key element for any successfully hit! Pay close attention to when the ball is being pitched and judge when the best time to swing is depending on what sort of a pitch it is. Remember it's not all about power, the timing is absolutely vital and can cause problems in the early stages, however with a little practice, you'll be a natural at it before you know it! Again,

just like tennis, if you swing slightly early then you'll hook the ball off to the right involuntarily, and vice versa if you swing too late, you'll slice it off to the left.

■ Direction:

In this case direction isn't too important when batting; simply hitting the ball is hard enough, so don't worry too much about where you want the ball to land. However, the only necessary thing you must abide to is keeping the ball within the V-shape field, as I mentioned previously, hitting the ball beyond this point will classify as out of bounds or a Foul Ball.

■ Power:

Batting isn't necessarily always about power or speed and force of the Wiimote. Overdoing the power could leave you swinging for the ball too early, but also at the same time, swinging too slow could leave you swinging to late. Obviously the more power and force you employ the further the ball will go, however getting the power and timing correct simultaneously is fairly difficult.

■ Distance:

Distance is a necessity if you're aiming for a Home Run. To gain maximum distance on your swings, simply hold the bat behind you like usual – standing to the side – but make sure that the Wiimote is lower than a regular swing. When the time is right, swing the Wiimote and bring it upwards as if you're scooping the ball up high. Doing this will lift the ball high in the air, and when combined with a decent amount of power, will send the ball towards the opposite end of the field, enabling you to receive several runs or better yet a Home Run.

You can also catch the opposition off guard and successfully counter any Screwball pitches by simply holding the Wiimote still, which will cause the ball to touch the bat lightly and drop to the ground, dribbling a short distance in front! Clever and useful hit when employed correctly!

■ Pro Pitches:

When pitching there are several things to take into account and a variety of three different skilful pitches to choose from – not including the standard straight pitch – which can be used to catch your opposing batsman off guard and ultimately Strike them out!

■ Screwball:

When performing a Screwball pitch, it'll cause the ball to curl significantly to the left and is executed by holding down the [A] button whilst simultaneously pitching with Wiimote.

■ Curveball:

When performing a Curveball pitch, it'll cause the ball to curl significantly to the right and is executed by holding down the [B] button whilst simultaneously pitching with Wiimote.

■ Splitter:

When performing a Splitter pitch, you'll throw the ball at an incredible speed which will drop down at the last minute, making it extremely difficult to return – unless of course the batsman simply holds the Wiimote still! This pitch is executed by holding down both the [A] and [B] buttons simultaneously whilst at the same time pitching with Wiimote.

■ Speed:

Speed is determined by how fast and forceful you are when pitching with the Wiimote. The faster and harder you pitch, the quicker the ball will ultimately travel and therefore the tougher it is for the batsman to return! Check out your pitches speed in mph in the bottom corner and aim to better it next time!

bowling

Fitness / Exercise Workout: >>>

Bowling is an average Light workout to help increase muscle size slightly in your Arms (Biceps and Triceps), and Shoulders! This is ideal for Cooling-Down or Warming-Up Before, After, or In-Between the more Intense Exercises, but doesn't focus on Cardio at all! Switch your Wii Remote holding Hand in between sessions, and swing with your weaker Arm, to increase muscle size in both the Right and Left hand side of your body, as well as increase equal balance in both sides also!

t he exact same rules and regulations as standard 10-pin bowling, incorporating basically everything that you'd expect from a real-life game of bowling.

For those of you who aren't too familiar with the rules and requirements, here's a brief overview:

There are ten sets overall and two parts to each set, giving you the chance to bowl twice every set; the idea is to knock down as many of the 10 pins as possible by employing accurate shots down the lane.

If you fail to knock all pins down straight away then you'll have a second chance to do so, however knocking down all 10 pins isn't a necessity, although it would seriously add to your overall score.

If you manage to successfully knock down all 10 pins on your first bowl then this is classified as a 'Strike' and is worth a total of 20 points – the maximum available points for a single bowl!

If you fail to knock all 10 pins down on your first bowl, but manage to finish off the rest on your second then this is called a 'Spare' and is worth a total of 10 points.

Anything less than knocking down all 10 pins on your second bowl is simply scored by the total number of pins knocked down (5 pins = 5 points).

Bowling Basics:

■ Movement & Lining Up Bowls:

It's not all about slinging the ball as fast as you can down the alley and hoping for the best; movement and lining up your bowl is a necessity if you want to take down the more difficult pins that are left standing on your second bowl. Use the D-Pad – left and right – to adjust your movement in order to accurately line yourself up with the remaining pins. Press and hold left to manoeuvre yourself as far left as you wish and press and vice versa for movement to the right!

■ Body Rotation:

To switch to body rotation simply press the [A] button; once this has been selected, use the D-Pad to rotate your entire body and therefore the direction of your bowl across the lane either to the left or right by pressing and holding left to aim as far to the left as needs be and vice versa for the right. This is a useful technique to use for your second bowl when attempting to knock down scattered pins!

■ Bowling:

Bowling itself is relatively easy once you master the fluid technique. Hold the Wiimote in your bowling hand so that it is directly in front of your face pointing upwards. From this position you must press and hold the [B] button through the entire motion of bowling. Once the [B] button is held, pull the Wiimote back behind you as if you were realistically bowling and then bring it forwards again so that your arm is at a 90 degree

angle to your body straight out in front of you. Once your arm and the Wiimote is straight, release the [B] button to send the ball down the alley! Remember, this must all be performed in a single fluid motion, which may take a few practice bowls to get the gist of things. Do your very best to maintain your arms straightness throughout the entire motion, as even slightly moving your arm left or right will inevitably cause the ball to roll in that direction!

■ Curl & Spin:

To successfully put spin on the ball once you've bowled it, causing it to curl to either the left or right, simply twist your wrist – and in turn the Wiimote – in the direction in which you wish the ball to curl. If you want the ball to spin off slightly to the left then twist your hand to the left and vice versa for the right. The more you twist the Wiimote, the sharper the curve will be!

■ Power:

Power depends on the force and speed in which you perform the final part of the overall bowling motion. If you slowly bring the Wiimote back up to the 90-degree angle and release the [B] button then the ball will travel slowly down the alley, however if you thrust the Wiimote forcefully forwards at some speed then the ball will travel quickly and with a decent amount of power behind it. Do remember though, that the faster you bowl, the more difficult it is to maintain the accuracy and straightness.

■ Accuracy:

Accuracy is vital in a game of bowling and the Wii Sports version is no different. To maintain your accuracy after taking the time to align your bowl, simply keep your arm, wrist and in turn the Wiimote as straight as you can. This will produce a straight and accurate bowl down the alley. Like I mentioned earlier, twisting your wrist will give the ball some spin, however simply lining up your bowl with the D-Pad should do the trick the majority of the time without spin, therefore accuracy is the key element here.

Maintain your arms straightness and follow through to a 90-degree angle for a straight and accurate bowl.

golf

g olf is by far the most difficult and advanced of the Wii Sport games by making it absolutely necessary to take into account power, accuracy, distance, hooking, slicing, wind, rough, bunkers, out of bounds and clubs! The game itself also incorporates all the basic golfing rules and score system, including, 'Hole in Ones', 'Albatross', 'Eagle', 'Birdie', 'Par', 'Bogey', 'Double Bogey', '3 over Par' and so on. The idea of this fun game – like a standard game of golf – is to complete the set courses in the least amount of shots possible.

■ Rules:

The rules of golf are relatively simple, however pulling off a straight, accurate shot and making it to the green in the Par set is the difficult part!
Begin the course by raking your initial shot by driving from the Tee Off and aiming as far along the fairway as possible, avoiding the hazardous areas such as rough, bunkers and out of

bounds areas to leave yourself in a clear position for your following shot. Continue taking your shots until you make it successfully to the green, at which point, switch to your putter which enables you to take an accurate shot along the ground, and then aim for the hole situated somewhere on the green! Do your best to "sink" the ball in fewer shots than your opponent and then move onto the next course!

Fitness / Exercise Workout: >>>

Golf is an average Light workout much like Bowling, which can help increase muscle size in your Arms and Shoulders slightly (if your swing-motions are correct), and is ideal for a Warm-Up or Cool-Down session, Before, After, or In-Between more Intense Training workouts! This Sport isn't a Cardio workout, but instead a stop-start session, which will focus more on muscle increase instead! Switch your Wii Remote holding Hand in between sessions, and swing with your weaker Arm, to increase muscle size in both the Right and Left hand side of your body, as well as increase equal balance in both sides also!

Now Wii Know!

POINT SCORING SYSTEM:

- **Hole in One** – A single shot from driving position
- **Albatross** - 3 shots under Par
- **Eagle** - 2 shots under Par
- **Birdie** - 1 shot under Par
- **Par** – Same amount of shots as that particular Par course – 3 shots for a 'Par 3' etc
- **Bogey** - 1 shot over Par
- **Double Bogey** - 2 shots over Par
- **+3** - 3 shots over Par
- **+4** – 4 shots over Par

... And so on and so fourth!

Golfing Terms:

COURSE EXPLANATION:

■ Fairway:
The fairway is where the majority of your shots will be played, unless however it is a Par 3, at which point you should be able to aim straight for the green from the Tee Off. The fairway is a long strip of well-cut grass, which appears in all courses from the driving range, right up towards the green. The ball will travel a fair distance on this surface so you should ALWAYS aim your shots as far down this stretch of grass a possible! The fairway is a regular Green colour and is extremely easy to locate, as it's usually directly in front of the driving range.

■ Edge of the Green:
The edge of the green is a minute strip of grass located, funnily enough, around the entire edge of the green! This section of turf is slightly more trimmed than the fairway, enabling the ball to travel relatively fast along this type of surface. The edge of the green is basically exactly the same as the green itself and so therefore will require a putter for your following shot. The edge of the green is a light green colour and will always be found towards the very end of the course.

■ Green:
The green is located towards the very end of the course, no matter its Par and is where your final shot or two will take place. The green is an immaculately trimmed and fast-travelling surface, which is always taken great care of and therefore will also require a putter for your following shot, or shots. The course's flag and thus the hole itself is

situated usually in the green meaning that all of your previous shots must take you to this surface! The green is also a light shade of green and is basically identical to the colour of the edge – very easy to locate!

■ Rough:
The rough is an uncared for section of the course which surrounds the entire fairway and green. This section of turf is poorly maintained, resulting in thick, long patches of grass, twigs and foliage, therefore preventing the ball from traveling easily through the rough. It also prevents any decent distance when attempting to take your following shot out from the rough! Do your very best to avoid the rough at all times as it will cause many problems such as loss of speed, distance, lack of accuracy, power and overall shots onto the green! The rough is located on the map as large dark green areas, extending from the fairway and green themselves.

■ Bunkers:
Bunkers are large sand-filled holes and ditches scattered through different sections of the course, both on the fairway and green! Avoiding these obstructions are vital, as they will immediately bring your ball to a complete standstill if made contact

with, and will result in great difficulty in the following shot! Unlike the rough – which is bad enough – the bunkers will prevent your ball from even rolling forwards, instead it will lodge the ball deep in the sand! If this occurs then your following shot should be a simple chip up and over the bunker, back onto the fairway – nothing fancy! Bunkers are marked on the map as yellow sections, so do everything in your power to avoid them at all times!

■ Out of Bounds:

Out of bounds areas are sections of the course that aren't actually classified as the course itself, for example, if you severely hook or slice the ball left or right and the ball travels over the fairway and rough, out of the entire course then this is classified as out of bounds! The water sections of the course will also be marked as out of bounds so avoid these areas at all times. If this occurs then the ball will be placed back on to the nearest part of the course, usually deep in the rough and you will automatically lose a shot or stroke, putting you one shot behind!!
The out of bounds areas are located on the map as the darker parts and are the biggest hazardous sections of the course. Be warned!

Golfing Guidance:

■ Clubs:

Depending on your balls current situation, distance from the hole and surface, whether it being on the green, fairway, rough or bunker, the club best suited for that particular terrain will automatically be selected for you. If you do in fact fancy a change of club for your own personal preference, then you can switch between your selection by pressing either up or down on the D-Pad.

■ Lining up & Positioning your Swing:

To line up your swing and the overall outcome and trajectory of your shot, use the left and right directions on the D-Pad to change the direction in which the ball will travel in order to successfully land the ball on a safe path of the fairway or green!

■ Practicing & Taking your Swing:

Your Mii automatically stands a foot or two away from the ball to begin with enabling you to practice your swing, along with power, accuracy and speed before actually hitting the ball.
To take your swing, stand to your side and hold the Wiimote in the exact same way as you would an actual golf club. Take a look at the stance of your Mii on screen to help with your positioning! Once stood to the side, hold the Wiimote – or club in this case – down, facing the floor directly in front of you. Once in this position, imagine that the Wiimote is an actual golf club and perform a fluid circular motion using both arms and in turn the Wiimote, back behind your head and then forwards, following through so that the Wiimote ends up over your front-facing shoulder.

Once you've practiced that particular swing and mastered the speed, power and accuracy, and feel that you're ready to take your shot, press and hold the [A] button to step up to the ball and perform the exact same motion previously to take your swing!

■ Putting:

To put the ball from on the green, position yourself and hold the Wiimote in the exact same way as if you were taking a regular swing, however this time, only bring the Wiimote up slightly and then forwards a short distance with little speed and therefore power. It's all about accuracy and power with a put, not simply smashing the ball as far up course as possible. Press the [1] button to bring up the greens topography and the contours of the ground. This will help in judging the power and direction of your put by following the lines on screen; the dark lines indicate lower sections of the green and the lighter sections marks the higher points.

■ Power Bar:

The power bar is located on the left hand side of the screen and has three sections to it depending on the required power. Take a look at the line in the map coming from your position and then check how far over the hole it goes. Then judge how much power is required to be taken off in order for the ball not to over shot the mark! If you swing too hard and with too much power and your power exceeds the maximum limit in the power gauge, then the metre will turn red and will begin to violently shake left and right! This will make it physically impossible to control and will inevitably cause the ball to either hook severely to the left or slice severely to the right with a great deal of speed, but no accuracy!

■ Wind:

The wind only plays a minor factor here and only occurs during aerial shots not putting. To counteract this small problem, take note of direction of the wind and then the speed in mps. If the wind is blowing to the right, then use the D-Pad to change the balls trajectory slightly to the left and vice versa if the wind is blowing to the left. Practice with this and get a good understanding of the power of the wind!

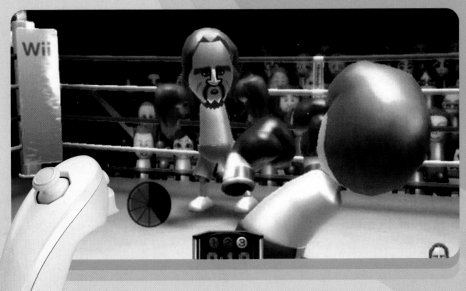

boxing

The Nunchuck is required for this game

just like a regular boxing match, the idea is prevent yourself from being knocked out by blocking and dodging your opponents punches, whilst trying to knock out your opposition by throwing powerful punches, jabs and uppercuts!

The overall fight takes place over a total of three, one-minute rounds. Both you and your opponent can get knocked down several times and can still rejoin the fight if they get back to their feet before the bell, however once the bell rings, the fight is over!

Movement:
There is no movement in the ring at all, and any little movement using your Mii's feet is automatically done for you. The only movement that you're required to perform is in your Mii's fists; therefore the analog movement on the Nunchuck is neither here nor there.

Timing:
Timing plays a relatively big part here, as it's not just about swinging your fists all

over the place whenever you feel like it, especially in later rounds. Time your punches, blocks and dodges well in order to protect yourself the best you can whilst simultaneously inflicting the most amount of damage on your opponent!

Throwing Punches – Attack:
Throwing punches in a game of boxing, as I'm sure you've already realised by now, is a necessity if you want be the champ!

Make sure that you have both the Wiimote and Nunchuck equipped! Hold the Wiimote in your right hand and

the Nunchuck in your left and then hold both pieces of equipment in front of your face in the standard boxing-stance.

Basic Moves List

■ Jabbing Face:

To perform a standard jab to the face, simply punch straight forwards. Your Mii character will then re-enact your jab and throw a blow to your opponents face! Use the Wiimote to throw a right jab and the Nunchuck to throw a left jab!

■ Body Blows:

To perform a body blow, simply punch down at an angle. Your Mii will then land a low blow to your opponent's body! Again use the Wiimote to perform a right-handed body blow and the Nunchuck for a left!

■ Uppercuts:

Uppercuts deal a significant amount of damage to your opponent and are utilised by swinging either the Nunchuck or Wiimote down and up in front of you in a fluid circular motion to perform either a left or right uppercut!

■ Power:

Power is increased by the speed in which you punch or jab forwards! The faster you punch using either the Wiimote or Nunchuck, the harder your punch will be, thus inflicting more damage! This applies for all jabs, body blows and uppercuts!

Defence:

■ Blocking:

To block your opponent's oncoming punches, simply hold both the Wiimote and Nunchuck up in front of your face and remain in this position. There are two types of blocks that you can use; holding both pieces of equipment high in front of your face will block your face, whereas holding them both down in front of you will guard your body and protect you from your opponent's body blows! Blocking is vital here, so use it wisely!

■ Dodging:

Dodging is also a necessity, not so much in the beginning matches, but definitely in later, more advanced fights! To dodge your opponent's punches, simply hold the Wiimote and Nunchuck high in front of your face and sway them side to side simultaneously to manoeuvre your Mii's upper body. Wave the two controllers left to dodge left and vice versa to dodge right! Swaying them back and forth will cause your Mii to move into your opponent or away!

All of these tactics are vital, so play around with them and become familiar with which punch, jab, block and dodge are most effective in a variety of different situations!

Wii Sports Training >>>

Beat Our Team of Experts!

Wii Sports Training gives you the opportunity to practice each skill required for each of the five sports, whether it's accuracy, power or timing, whilst simultaneously giving you a whole new area of game play! Each sport in Training mode has three skills to focus on with a medal ranking of Bronze, Silver, Gold and Platinum! We've spent many frustrating weeks on end trying to obtain the best Platinum scores, and now we'd like to see if you could beat our scores in 'Beat Our Team of Experts!'

Tennis

■ Returning Balls:

Training Info:
During this Training exercise, you must simply return the balls that are being hit towards you from the opposite Mii back into their side of the court. To do this simply hit the balls back and forth using the Wiimote. You must land the ball back in the other half of the court otherwise the exercise is over! There can be no mistakes here!
As your rally builds up and you get more and more into the session, things start to get trickier. The balls that are hit to you become more frequent and faster, the need of movement for net shots, half way shots and back line shots become more of a regular occurrence, and more often the need to switch between forehand and backhand play!

Tips:
Keep your eye on the ball at times; it's easy to get distracted and focus on where the ball that you've just returned lands! Remember to alternate stances when needing to switch between forehand and backhand shots, or close to the net. When returning from the net, hold the Wiimote vertical in front of your face and simply tap it forwards either to the right or left. This will enable you smash it quickly with little movement, and always be prepared on the run back to the line for a sneaky shot that comes you way!

> **PLATINUM PRO:**
> **Our Team of Experts Platinum Medal score was 87! Receiving a total score of 87 therefore will earn you the Platinum Medal ranking! Can you beat us?**

■ Timing Your Swing:

Training Info:
Here you'll see a large orange bar on the opposite side of the court. The idea is to return the oncoming balls into the bar! The beginning shots are relatively easy as the bar is fairly large, however once you get further into this stage the bar begins to shrink and move from left to right more frequently and with more speed,

requiring you to think more about the timing of your shot. There are only forehand shots required here so get into a rhythm to begin with and go from there. The bar will stop on each half of the court briefly, enabling to perform the same shot for a few times, however it will then move to the opposite side; when it does this alter your timing slightly to connect with the bar.

Tips:
For this exercise we've found that keeping your eye on the oncoming ball isn't the most effective way to play, instead keep an eye on the shadow of the ball! When the shadow is directly on the white line, then smash it back up court. This will smash the ball straight, preventing the ball from being struck too early or too late. When the bar decreases in size dramatically you'll need to think more about your timing. Remember this, striking the ball late, thus after the white line will cause the ball to go to the left in a slicing motion, whilst hitting the ball early, thus before the white line will cause the ball to hook to your right!

> **PLATINUM PRO:**
> **Our Team of Experts Platinum Medal score was 53! Receiving a total score of 53 therefore will earn you the Platinum Medal ranking! Can you beat us?!!**

■ Target Practice:

Training Info:
The idea here is to hit the mounted target on the brick wall as many times as possible. After each time you connect with the target, the target will move slightly! The movement will be greater once you get further into the session making things much more difficult. If you fail to hit the target, you can still continue the run by bouncing it back off the wall, however you'll receive no points for this and the wall will begin to give way. If you hit the ball in the same place of the wall repeatedly then the wall will collapse, leaving large holes for the ball to pass through. If this happens then the training is over!

Tips:
The most effective way to play this is to hit the ball lightly at the target or wall; if you overpower the shot then it will be extremely hard to run for the next shot and successfully hit it. Power isn't everything here! Start by serving the ball and then judge whether it needs a late reaction or early one depending if the target is to your left or right. Remember,

early hits are to the left and late hits are to the right. If you end up far away from the targets then produce light shots hooking and slicing your way back to the target itself until you can get a clear shot once again. Do your very best not to hit the same area of the wall too many times, as this will make things a lot more difficult!

> **PLATINUM PRO:**
> **Our Team of Experts Platinum Medal score was 44! Receiving a total score of 44 therefore will earn you the Platinum Medal ranking! Can you beat us?!!**

Baseball

■ Hitting Home Runs

Training Info:
Here you'll be pitched 10 balls at lightening speed. The idea is to smash them as hard as you can over a total of 121m in order to score a Home Run. The pitcher can perform any of three pitches; 'Fastball' etc so be on the ready at all times and master each one! Pull back on the Wiimote so that it's behind your back and when the ball comes speeding in your direction, simply swing it forwards! There's are no movement controls to perform simply stand, wait and hit!

Tips:
Timing is everything here! Remain in the batting stance until the pitcher lobs the ball towards you, wait for a further second or two and swing! The harder you bat, the further ball will travel. The most effective way to get distance on your swings is to hold the bat down slightly, and when the balls heads your way, forcefully swing the Wiimote forwards and up in the air! This will give power and height, which will then in turn give the distance that you need! Getting 10 Home Runs is all well and good for the Gold Medal and Gold Gods, but if you want to be a Platinum Pro, then you need to fill them Home Runs with 'Out of the Park' scores 'X'!!

> **PLATINUM PRO:**
> **Our Team of Experts Platinum Medal score was 10 home runs and a score 5,769m! Receiving a total score of 10 home runs and a score 5,769m therefore will earn you the Platinum Medal ranking! Can you beat us?!!**

■ Swing Control:

Training Info:
The Swing Control training is all about your accuracy and therefore timing of your swings. On screen you'll be shown a large triangle shape starting from the base at which you bat, extending outwards onto the field. Directly in the centre of this triangle is a small dark blue area, on either side of that are two light blue triangles and either side of them are two larger white triangles. Now these coloured sections equal points and the idea of this exercise is to score as many points as possible. This is the point scoring system as follows:

> **Dark Blue: 11 Points**
> **Light Blue: 6 Points**
> **White: 3 Points**
> **Hitting the ball within the field: 1 Point**

The idea is land the majority the balls within either the dark blue or light blue areas to rack up big points! 10 balls will be pitched at you, and you must smash them back out onto the field, within the set areas! The first four target area will be directly in front of you. After these four, the target area will move to your left for a further three and then to the right! Alter your timing to adjust to these changes!

Tips:
Again this is all about timing, although even more so this time round! In the same way as tennis, hitting the ball early will cause it to land to the left, whereas striking the ball late will cause it bend to the right. For the first four pitches you'll want to find a middle ground so that you hit it straight, while the second set positioned to your left you'll want to hit the ball slightly earlier to hook it and vice versa for the right target area! Forget about power for this training session, instead primarily for the accuracy. This will take a few tries to suss out the timing, but once you've mastered the straight area, adjust the timing ever so slightly for the following two directions!

PLATINUM PRO:
Our Team of Experts Platinum Medal score was 73! Receiving a total score of 73 therefore will earn you the Platinum Medal ranking! Can you beat us?!!

■ Batting Practice:

Training Info:
You'll be pitched a total of 30 balls, which the pitcher will alternate every now and then with Screwballs, Fastballs etc so be prepared at all times. The idea here is to simply hit as many balls as possible. The balls get lobbed your way in quick succession, with little time to think about your swing, so be ready at all times. Your score is shown in the top left hand corner of the screen, and if you want to be a Platinum Pro, then you must successfully hit all 30 balls into the V-shaped field! No matter how you connect with the ball, if it lands in the set field then you'll score a point, however if you miss the ball or hit it out of the V-shape then you fail to score the point and your combo comes to an end!

Tips:
To master this training exercise, simply incorporate everything that you've learnt throughout the previous two sessions! Like I mentioned above, it doesn't mater how you hit the ball, its simply about landing it in the V-shaped field, so time your swing correctly and find a middle ground so that the ball lands as central as possible. Start low and swing high so that the ball has more of a chance to straighten itself out if you slightly miss hit it! Keep your eye on the ball at times and be prepared for the occasional fastball, which usually comes on the final pitch to throw you of guard!

PLATINUM PRO:
Our Team of Experts Platinum Medal score was 30! Receiving a total score of 30 therefore will earn you the Platinum Medal ranking! Can you beat us?!!

Bowling

■ Picking Up Spares:

Training Info:
The idea here is to simply knock down the remaining pins during each stage. They start off easy and get progressively harder as you go on. In the latter stages the pins will be spread out over a greater area of the lane, requiring you to alter not just the direction of your bowl, but the spin also! There are a total of 20 stages to this bowling exercise and you get five failures; any more than five fails in knocking down the remaining pins will bring the training session to a close!

Tips:
Practice your straight bowls and remember to alter the direction of your bowl if you naturally spin to one side! Use both the D-Pad to change your positioning and the (A) button to change the direction of the ball itself. Use spin for latter stages by twisting your arm to either the left or right for the more spread out pins. Follow this simple solution for Platinum Medal:

■ Stages:

Stage 1:
Remaining Pins: 1
Pick up the spares: Bowl straight down the centre!

Stage 2:
Remaining Pins: 1 & 2
Pick up the spares: Bowl straight down the centre!

Stage 3:
Remaining Pins: 6, 9 & 10
Pick up the spares: Use the d-pad to change your position and aim for the left hand side of pin number 6. The ball will follow through onto pin 9, whilst pin 6 smashes into pin 10!

Stage 4:
Remaining Pins: 2, 4, 5 & 8
Pick up the spares: Bowl straight into pin

2 so that the ball will follow through into pin 8, whilst taking out the other two simultaneously!

Stage 5:
Remaining Pins: 1, 3 & 6
Pick up the spares: Aim for the right hand side of pin number 1 so that the ball will hit pins 1 and 3, whilst knocking pin 3 into pin 6!

Stage 6:
Remaining Pins: 1, 3 & 8
Pick up the spares: Bowl to the left hand side of pin 1 so that pin 1 will smash into pin 3 and the ball will follow on into pin 8!

Stage 7:
Remaining Pins: 2 & 8
Pick up the spares: Adjust yourself so that pins 2 and 8 are in line and then simply bowl straight into pin 2.

Stage 8:
Remaining Pins: 1, 2, 4 & 7
Pick up the spares: Move to the far right hand side of the lane and use (A) to adjust the direction of the ball. Aim diagonal to your left and throw the ball at the far left hand side of pin 1. The ball will then follow through onto pins 2, 4 and 7!

Stage 9:
Remaining Pins: 1, 2, 3, 4 & 5
Pick up the spares: Aim for the left hand side of pin 1, which then hit pin 3. The ball will follow on into pins 2 and 5 whilst pin 2 will smash into pin 4 out of the way!

Stage 10:
Remaining Pins: 1, 2, 5 & 9
Pick up the spares: Aim for the right hand side pin 1. Pin 1 will then smash into pin 2 whilst the ball will follow on into pins 5 and 9!

Stage 11:
Remaining Pins: 2 & 7
Pick up the spares: Move to the far right hand side of the lane and aim for the left hand side of pin 2. The ball will follow into pin 7!

Stage 12:
Remaining Pins: 1, 2, 3, 5, 6, 9 & 10
Pick up the spares: Aim for the far right hand side of pin 1 so that it smashes into pin 2, whilst the ball follows into pins 3, 5, 6 and 9, with pin 6 taking out pin 10!

Stage 13:
Remaining Pins: 1, 3, 5 & 9
Pick up the spares: Aim slightly to the right of pin 1 and bowl relatively slowly straight so that pin 1 hits pin 3 whilst the ball follows into pins 5 and 9!

Stage 14:
Remaining Pins: 2, 4 & 9
Pick up the spares: Aim for right hand side of pin 2 so that it smashes into pin 4 whilst the ball rolls on into pin 9! Try putting a sight right spin on in!

Stage 15:
Remaining Pins: 2, 4, 5, 7, 8 & 9
Pick up the spares: If you take a look at the layout of the pins, it's basically a smaller version of the standard 10 pin bowls. Line yourself up so that you're level with pin 2 and bowl relatively hard into it, knocking the remaining pins out with the ball!

Stage 16:
Remaining Pins: 2, 7 & 8
Pick up the spares: Aim for the far left side of pin 2 so that ball follows on into pins 7 and 8!

Stage 17:
Remaining Pins: 9 & 10
Pick up the spares: Bowl straight into both pins!

Stage 18:
Remaining Pins: 2, 7 & 10
Pick up the spares: This is a very difficult stage and will require some luck as well as skill! Aim for the very far left side of pin 2 – zoom in using 'Up' on the d-pad for a more accurate indication – and bowl with a great deal of power! The 2 pin should then spin off to the right and smash into pin 10 whilst the ball rolls on into pin 7!

Stage 19:
Remaining Pins: 5 & 0
Pick up the spares: Again, another fairly difficult stage! Aim for the far left hand side of pin 5 – zoom in – and bowl with a great deal of power! The 5 pin should then spin off to the right, into pin 10!

Stage 20:
Remaining Pins: 1
Pick up the spares: Bowl straight down the centre! Easy!

> **PLATINUM PRO:**
> **Our Team of Experts Platinum Medal score was 20! Receiving a total score of 20 therefore will earn you the Platinum Medal ranking! Can you beat us?!!**

■ Power Throws:

Training Info:
During this exercise you'll be required to knock down as many pins as possible! The beginning stage you'll start with the standard 10 pins and then each time the number of pins will increase with another back row; 15 pins, 21 pins and so on so forth. Simply bowl as hard and as straight as you can in order to knock them down! The earlier stages are relatively easy however, the latter stages, i.e. 91 pins test your skills dramatically!

Tips:
What can we say? Power!! Throw the ball as hard as you possibly can down the lane and aim for the initial red pin! This will cause a scatter effect no mater the size or how many pins!

> **PLATINUM PRO:**
> **Our Team of Experts Platinum Medal score was 734! Receiving a total score of 734 therefore will earn you the Platinum Medal ranking! Can you beat us?!!**

■ Spin Control:

Training Info:
This training session is a true test of your spin skills! There are a total of 20 stages, each one getting progressively more difficult. Each stage has a section of the lane blocked by a barrier or barriers! It's your job to skilfully curl the ball round these barriers in order to hit the pin at the far end! You have five failures; any more than five fails then the training comes to an end!

Tips:
Practice beforehand twisting the Wiimote both left and right before attempting this exercise. Try to master the technique of spinning the ball early down the lane and late. To perform an early spin release the ball low to the ground and twist the Wiimote; to perform a later spin further down the lane, release the ball high in the air and twist!
Follow this simple solution to master the stages:

■ Stages:

Stage 1:
Remaining Pins: 1
Barriers: Centred near to the start
Move to either the far left or right side of the lane, rotate and bowl straight for the pin! Requires no spin!

Stage 2:
Remaining Pins: 1
Barriers: Left side near to the middle.
Move to the far right hand side of the lane, rotate and again bowl straight the pin to the right of the barrier! Requires no spin!

Stage 3:
Remaining Pins: 1
Barriers: Both left and right sides near to the middle.
Bowl straight down the centre between the two barriers! Requires no spin!

Stage 4:
Remaining Pins: 1
Barriers: Right side near to the middle
Move to the far left hand side of the lane, rotate and bowl straight for the pin! Requires no spin!

Stage 5:
Remaining Pins: 7
Barriers: Move slightly to your right so that when your rotate to the left, the pin is in clear view for a straight bowl! Requires no sin!

Stage 6:
Remaining Pins: 7
Barriers: One to the right near to the start and another further up to the right.
Move to the far left hand side of the lane and bowl straight for the pin! Requires no spin!

Stage 7:
Remaining Pins: 6
Barriers: One to the right side near to the beginning and one to the left further up.
Now this is the first stage where spin is required! Move slightly to your left and rotate slightly to your right so that you're aiming between both barriers. Bowl at a fair bit of speed and twist your arm and in turn the Wiimote dramatically to the left! This will head straight past the first barrier and curl to the right of the second!

Stage 8:
Remaining Pins: 5
Barriers: Both to the left and right sides near to the end.
Bowl straight down the centre! Requires no spin!

Stage 9:
Remaining Pins: 1
Barriers: Left side near to the start.
Move to the far right hand side of the lane, rotate slightly to your left and bowl whilst twisting the Wiimote to the left. This will add left spin round the right side of the barrier!

Stage 10:
Remaining Pins: 1
Barriers: One long barrier blocking the entire lane near to the start.
Simply bowl straight for the pin, but release high in the air to throw the ball up and over the barrier!

Stage 11:
Remaining Pins: 10
Barriers: Right hand side near to the start
Move to the far left hand side of the lane, rotate to your right and add a little bit of spin to the right so that the ball curls around the right hand side of the barrier!

Stage 12:
Remaining Pins: 1
Barriers: Three barriers, each in the centre; one to the start, middle and end. This is an extremely difficult stage and requires a great deal of spin and power at the last minute in order to successfully hit the pin! To add spin at the very last minute, you need to release the ball as late as possible whilst twisting the Wiimote significantly!! Stand to either the far left or right side – we'd advise the right side as the majority of people are right handed and therefore natural spin to the left – and rotate to the right hand side of the final barrier. From here bowl at some speed and release high in the air, putting a great deal of left spin on it simultaneously! The ball will then curl to the left after the final barrier and hit the pin!

Stage 13:
Remaining Pins: 1
Barriers: Right side at the start and one central, slightly left near to the end. There are two ways that you can do this however, if you're right handed then we'd advise the first option. Move slightly to your left, aim between both barriers and bowl with spin to the left so that the ball will curl round the right hand side of the second barrier! You can also stand to the far left and curl it round the left side of the second barrier!

Stage 14:
Remaining Pins: 10
Barriers: Both left and right near to the start and one t the left further up. Move to your left slightly, rotate to your right and aim between the first two barriers and to the right of the third. Bowl straight through the first two and add a little left spin to curl the ball around the right side of the final barrier!

Stage 15:
Remaining Pins: 5
Barriers: One to the left side near to the start and another on the left further up. Move to the far side, rotate to the left and aim for the right side of the second barrier. Bowl at some speed with left spin to curl round the end barrier!

Stage 16:
Remaining Pins: 1
Barriers: One centred near to the start and two further up to both the left and right.

Move to either the far left side and rotate to your right. Aim to the left of the first and second barrier on the right and bowl with some speed with a slight right spin! The ball will head straight past the first barrier and curl to the right in between the following two!

Stage 17:
Remaining Pins: 7
Barriers: Both left and right sides near to stat and two further up, again left and right.
Move slightly to your right, rotate to your left and aim between both sets of barriers. Add left spin to your bowl so that it curls to the left after the second set of barriers!

Stage 18:
Remaining Pins: 7
Barriers: One to the left near to the start and another t the right further up. Move to the far right, rotate left and aim between the to barriers. Put some right spin on it to curl around the second barriers into the pin!

Stage 19:
Remaining Pins: 7
Barriers: One to the left near to the start and another small one to the left further up.
Again, another really difficult stage here! Move to the far left side and rotate between the two, just to the right of the second barrier. Bowl with some speed and add a significant amount of left spin onto your bowl in order to curl around the right side of the final barrier!

Stage 20:
Remaining Pins: All
Barriers: N/A
A straightforward 10-pin bowls stage! Simply bowl and get a strike!!

> **PLATINUM PRO:**
> **Our Team of Experts Platinum Medal score was 20! Receiving a total score of 20 therefore will earn you the Platinum Medal ranking! Can you beat us?**

Golf

■ **Putting:**

Training Info:
Here you'll be given 10 different distances from the hole, each with there own contours and topography, which you'll have t maser in order to sink the balls. You get a total of five failures, any more and the training will come to an end! They start of relatively easy, however once you get on through the stages, power, accuracy and taking the topography into account will all become necessary!

Tips:
Instead of holding the Wiimote like an actual golf club, try holding down by your side and simply flicking it up into the air slightly to make things easier. Doing this will enable your swing and therefore power to be much more

precise! Use the d-pad to rotate and the (1) button to view the greens topography!

The following solutions are all 10 stages and exactly how to master them!
Note: We've realised that he final two stages may vary slightly!!

Round 1:
Direction: Hit straight
Power: Power bar – Dot 1

Round 2:
Direction: Hit straight
Power: Power bar – Dot 2

Round 3:
Direction: 12 nudges to the left
Power: Power bar – Dot 1

Round 4:
Direction: 12 nudges to the right
Power: Power bar – Dot 1

Round 5:
Direction: 10 nudges to the left
Power: Power bar – Dot 2

Round 6:
Direction: 12 nudges to the right
Power: Power bar – Dot 2

Round 7:
Direction: 1 nudge to the left
Power: Power bar – Dot 3 ?

Round 8:
Direction: 7 nudges to the left
Power: Power bar – Dot 3 ?

Round 9:
Direction: 15 nudges to the right
Power: Power bar – Dot 3 ?

Round 10:
Direction: 8 nudges to the left
Power: Power bar – Dot 3 ?

PLATINUM PRO:
Our Team of Experts Platinum Medal score was 10 with all five lives still available! Receiving a total score of 10 with all five lives available therefore will earn you the Platinum Medal ranking! Can you beat us?

■ Hitting The Green

Training Info:
This time round it's al about chip shots! You'll be given 10 different chip shot

scenarios, fairways and roughs, and the idea is chip the ball onto the green as close to the flag as possible! The points are added in distance; the further away from the flag you are, the poorer the shot and at the end of all 10 stages, your overall distance is tallied up and therefore your score! You are automatically deducted 30m if you fail to reach the green or overshoot it! There's no wind, which does help, however the green topography still counts. You can also get hole in one's, which significantly lower your overall distance, although this is mostly due to luck!

Tips:
In the map you'll notice small white dots spread out through the directional line of where the ball will land. These small dots correspond with the small dots on your power bar! Follow these as power guidelines! For example, if the flag on the map is halfway between dots one and two then hit the ball between the first and second dot on the power bar! This will give you the exact power and distance you need! When you're taking your shots from the rough, remember to add more power to get the lift!
Again hold the Wiimote in the same way as before – down by your side – and swing lightly upwards for perfect power every time!

PLATINUM PRO:
Our Team of Experts Platinum Medal score was 34m. Receiving a total score of 34m therefore will earn you the Platinum Medal ranking! Can you beat us?

■ Target Practice:

Training Info:
This training exercise is a test of your driving skills! You'll be given two large target zones, one on the second power dot and one on the 3 ? power dot. The furthest one away is larger than the first with a higher point scoring system on it, 10 for the outer area, 25, 50 and 100 for the centre! If you want Platinum then you have no choice but to go with this one! You have 10 balls to smash wayward up towards the targets and the total number of scored points is added at the end! Be careful and check the wind direction and strength regularly as it changes on nearly almost every drive!

Tips:
Always use the power dot indications to get a perfect drive! Remember that the score is counted where the ball lands, not where the ball rolls onto so using the power dots in both the map and bar

work perfectly! Take into account the wind; we've worked out that whatever strength the wind is, tap the opposite direction that amount of times to make up for it i.e. if the wind is 15 mph to the left, then tap 15 times to the right, and always make sure that add a little extra power! Stay within the bar limit, no matter how strong the wind is and never let it overpower to the red bar as this will lose al accuracy! Accuracy is the key here!

PLATINUM PRO:
Our Team of Experts Platinum Medal score was 835. Receiving a total score of 835 therefore will earn you the Platinum Medal ranking! Can you beat us?

Boxing

■ Working The Bag

Training Info:
Punch the bags using combos and power punches, uppercuts and body blows to smash them off their hinges! The bags will continuously reappear until the clock runs out. There are three different types of bags, brown, white and black. The browns are easy, whites are slightly more difficult and the blacks take some punishment! Just punch away!

Tips:
Remember to alternate your punching styles throughout to your advantage. The brown bags are easy, a few right to left punch combos will do it, as will a powerful right or left body blow swing, or an uppercut. The white bags are slightly tougher, weaken them first with a few basic hits and then go out with a few uppercuts and body blows, and smash the black bag with your most powerful punches repeatedly to speed things up! The most effective and quickest way to destroy all bags is to follow up with the opposite hand that you just used, for example if you struck with a left hook, then follow up with a right, as this will save a great deal of time!

■ Dodging:

Training Info:
Your trainer will continuously throw tennis balls your way and it's your job to dodge them or as many as you can! The number of balls thrown and the order that they are thrown in start off easy, simple left to right, however once you get further into the exercise, things get more difficult as two balls are thrown in different direction, greater speed and in more random order! Each time to successfully dodge a ball, you'll receive one point to add to your score, however each time you get hit, you gat a point deducted! Careful, these soon add up!

Tips:
To dodge, hold both the Wiimote and Nunchuk up in front of your face and move them both simultaneously to either the left or the right depending on which way you want to dodge! To get a rough understanding on what direction the balls are heading, take note of which hand the balls in and the positioning of

your trainer! They are as follow:
If the ball is in his right hand then doge far left as this indicates that the ball will head either right or centre!

If the ball is in his left hand then dodge far right as this indicates that the ball head either left or centre.

If he strafes left the dodge right and if he strafes right then dodge left, no matter what hand the ball is in!

When he throw two balls simultaneously then wait a split second and dodge as far out of the way as possible as the balls take up the majority of the area! Practice a few times and understand his movement and stances in order to tell what way to dodge next!

■ Throwing Punches:

Training Info:
Once again it's you and your trainer! Your trainer will hold up two mitts, one in his left and one in his right, and it's you task to punch them when he raises

them! The exercise starts off relatively easy, like all the others, but once again gets progressively harder as he switches between mitts more frequently, changes heights and holds both up simultaneously! Punch the mitts as many times as you can before the cock runs out and do not accidentally miss and connect with the trainer! Hitting the trainer will deduct a point in the same as the previous tennis ball session!

Tips:
Always swing with the hand closest to the raised mitt; if the trainer holds up his right hand then swing with your left and vice versa! Your trainer will move slightly every now and then, which will inevitably cause you to accidentally hit him unless you dodge or strafe slightly. If he moves slightly to the left, then follow his movement and dodge to the right so that there's no mess ups! Stick to standard left and right jabs and don't try anything too fancy such as body blows or uppercuts; there's no need! Punch as accurately and as quickly as you can to get as many hits in during the time available!

Wii sports resort

The following is a complete Master's guide for Every Stamp available in Wii Sports Resort, assigned to every Game!! Much like the Platinum Medals in Wii Sports; Stamps in Wii Sports Resort are the secrets that ultimately, we all want to achieve!! So here they are...

Wii Sports Resort Games:

swordplay

Duel

Duel Stamps:

"On the Edge"
■ **How to Achieve**
Simply Block every attack, and Draw all 3 Rounds. Do Not defeat your Opponent and knock them over the edge. But Do Not allow yourself to be beaten either. Once you've Drawn all 3 Rounds, the Final Round 4 Arena will be unlocked. Unlocking this Podium will earn you the Stamp!

"Straight to the Point"
■ **How to Achieve**
Attack your Opponent repeatedly to push them further back to the edge of the Ring. Once they're on the very edge, Block their next Attack, leaving them open for a Counterattack; and then Thrust the Wii Remote Forwards in a Stabbing motion, to perform a Straight Lunge. Knock them out of the Ring using this Lunge attack to earn the Stamp!

"Stalemate":
■ **How to Achieve**
Simply Block every attack thrown your way and Draw all 3 Rounds. Do Not defeat your Opponent and knock them over the edge. But Do Not allow yourself to be beaten either. Once you've Drawn all 3 Rounds, the Final Round 4 Arena will become available. You must now Draw this Round also to earn the Stamp! If you Win or Lose; you will not receive the Stamp – it must be a Draw to end the Duel evenly.

"All Too Easy"
■ **How to Achieve**
This is almost impossible to do on the first 3 Rounds. However, it can be easily done on Round 4's smaller Podium! Draw all 3 Rounds to unlock the Final Round 4 Podium; and then Block your Opponents first attack, leaving them open for a Counterattack. Execute a powerful Strike now by swinging Horizontally across the body, to knock your Opponent out of the Ring in a single hit, and earning you the Stamp!

"There Can Only Be One"
■ **How to Achieve**
To challenge the Champion, you must first increase your Ranking Level to 1, 500 Points, by defeating the many other Opponents thrown your way. Lose however, and you'll lose Points – so be careful! Keep Winning to increase Rank, and at 1,500 Points, the Champion will become available. Now all you have to do is defeat the Champion to earn the Stamp! Block regularly, learn to Parry; and master Counterattacks if you want to win!

Speed Slice

Speed Slice Stamps:

"Slice and Dice"
■ **How to Achieve**
This Stamp is easiest to achieve during the beginning stages when your Rank is low, as this is when your Opponents are at their slowest. As you advance, your Opponents become faster, requiring quicker thinking. So we advise you to get this Stamp straight away! Slice every Object in the correct direction before your Opponent does; and Do Not miss a single one. Slice them all, and the Stamp is yours!

"No Object Unsliced"
■ **How to Achieve**
Getting this one is inevitable, so don't worry about going for it. Ultimately after playing a few games, you will eventually Slice every Object available, and inevitably earn this easy Stamp!

"Focus Your Mind"
■ **How to Achieve**
This one is all about guess-work and a lot of luck; as there's no way to tell which direction you're going to have to Slice. This will take a few attempts to get right, however you will eventually guess correctly. When the Object has been thrown, wait for it to disappear upwards off the screen, and then before it falls back down again; Slice in any Direction, and hope for the best! If you're lucky and

guess correctly, then you'll receive this Stamp! Persevere, and you will eventually get it.

"Double Digit"
■ How to Achieve

This one is pretty tricky, as you only have 0.1 second to Slice at the precise moment! Look out for the Alarm Clock Object and get ready. The Digits on the Display will count down for about four seconds until it disappears, and you must Slice at the precise moment when the Digits are the same i.e. 8.8, 7.7, 6.6, 5.5 etc to earn this Stamp! Don't worry about beating your Opponent, simply focus on getting timing right. You must be quick however, as the Alarm Clock will disappear again shortly. 6.6 is probably the easiest one to go for. Count down with the Clock, and then Slice at the precise moment when both Digits are the same, to earn this Stamp! Again, persevere – you will get it.

"A Cut Above"
■ How to Achieve

To challenge the Champion, you must first increase your Ranking Level to 1, 500 Points, by defeating the many other Opponents thrown your way. Lose however, and you'll lose Points! Keep Winning to increase Rank, and at 1,500 Points, the Champion will become available. Now all you have to do is defeat the

Champion to earn the Stamp! Be quick, Do Not hesitate; and perform short flicking motions to save valuable time!

Showdown
Showdown Stamps:
"Not a Scratch"
■ How to Achieve

This Stamp is easiest to achieve in the beginning Stages when you first start, as your Attackers have Weak Defences, and poor Sword skills in the earlier Stages. Not just that, but Stage 1 for example is much shorter than the latter Stages. Defeat every attacker, and Do Not take any hit! Block regularly, and Clear the Stage with all three Hearts still remaining to earn this Stamp!

"Stage 10 Clear"
■ How to Achieve

To achieve this Stamp, simply Clear ALL the initial 10 (Normal) Stages. The first few Stages are easy; however as you advance, they get progressively more difficult and require much more skill! Block often, Parry regularly, and Counterattack every Blocked-strike to take down foes easily, whilst remaining protected at all times. To Block, make sure to hold the Wii Remote (Sword) perpendicular to your Opponent's Sword! Complete all 10 Stages, and the Stamp is yours!

"Perfect 10"
■ How to Achieve

The key to achieving this Stamp is to take your time, and not to get impatient and rush through the Stage. Block at all times

throughout the entire Stage, and only ever Counterattack! If you get hit and lose a Heart; then Restart and try again. Wipe out all attackers and clear Stage 10 (Normal) with all three Hearts still remaining to earn this Stamp!

"The Final Showdown"
■ How to Achieve

To unlock the Final Showdown Stage, you must Clear ALL of the initial 10 (Normal) Stages first, to unlock the following 10 (Reverse Stages). Then you must Clear ALL 10 (Reverse) Stages also to unlock the Final Showdown Stage. The Final Showdown is a challenging Stage, and requires all of your Sword skills, including Blocking, Counterattacking, and Parrying to complete! Clear the Final Showdown Stage with at least one Heart remaining to earn this Stamp!

"Untouchable"
■ How to Achieve

This Stamp is by far the hardest one to achieve! The exact same methods apply as 'The Final Showdown' Stamp explained above; however this time, you Must Not take a single hit throughout the entire Stage! Your Sword skills must be perfect; and Blocking, Counterattacking, and Parrying are vital. Use everything that you've learnt throughout all 20 Stages to Clear the Final Showdown with all three Hearts still remaining, to earn this challenging Stamp!

Wakeboarding

Wakeboarding Stamps:
"100-Point Jump"
■ How to Achieve

Master the Landing after each Jump, and this Stamp is easy! To Land perfectly, the Board Must be completely Flat when it touches the Water. Zigzag from left to right, and repeatedly Jump-Trick over the Waves by flicking the Wii Remote. Each time you Land, the Boat will speed up, enabling you to execute more advanced Tricks that are ultimately worth more Points. After about six or seven successful Jumps, you should be getting big Air, and earning 100 Points on every Trick! Execute a 100 Point Trick and the Stamp is yours!

"Seven Jumps"
■ How to Achieve

If you've achieved the '100-Point Jump' Stamp explained above, then you will more than

likely achieve this Stamp also! The same rules apply. Continue to Trick, and Land perfectly for 7 consecutive Jumps in a single run to earn this Stamp! This means that you must string together 7 Tricks without hitting anything or landing unevenly.

"Surf Skimmer"
■ How to Achieve

Again, if you've achieved the 'Seven Jumps' Stamp explained above, then you will most likely achieve this Stamp also; if however you can keep the consecutive string of Tricks going for a further three Jumps. Zigzag across the Waves, and successfully land 10 consecutive Jump-Ticks, to earn this Stamp!

"Clear Run"
■ **How to Achieve**

To unlock the Expert Difficulty Level, you must first complete a few Beginner challenges, to increase your Ranking Level to 1,000 Points. 500 Points unlocks the Intermediate Level, and a following 500 unlocks Expert. To achieve this Stamp, build up your Jump combos, and keep a consecutive string of Tricks going, to score Big! In Expert however, you will also have to avoid numerous Objects. Judge your Jumps correctly to avoid the Red and Green Pillars on either side of the Boat; and manoeuvre yourself carefully through, or over the top of the small Blue Objects that appear in front of the Boat! If you hit any of these Objects, then Restart and try again. The key to success is to not always go for every Jump, especially if there's an Object coming up! But instead, to follow the Waves past them until it's safe again to Jump. Avoid Every Object, and earn a Score of 1000 + Points, to receive this Stamp!

"Circumnavigator"
■ **How to Achieve**

For this one, you must simply execute 50 successful Jump-Tricks in Free Cruising Mode. You don't have to string them together like

usual; but you do have to Land each one for them to count! Press the Minus Button (-) at the Start screen to enter Free Cruising Mode, and have some fun! Make sure however, that you keep count of how many Tricks you perform. After executing 50 + successful

Jumps, you Must continue Cruising all the way around Wuhu Island for them to be accepted; and then complete any Level (Beginner, Intermediate or Expert) in order to receive the Stamp! Simply ending the Free Cruise will not do.

Frisbee >>>

Frisbee Dog

Frisbee Dog Stamps:

"Mid-Air Catch"
■ **How to Achieve**

After practicing for a few games, getting this Stamp is inevitable. To achieve, you must accurately throw the Frisbee directly at the Target, so that it lands in the Purple Centre Circle (Bulls-Eye). To do this, you must master the Angle of your Throws, to cause the Frisbee to curl either Left or Right, depending on where the Target is. To curl the Frisbee Left, Angle the Frisbee Downwards! To curl the Frisbee Right, Angle the Frisbee Upwards! To throw it Straight, keep it Flat. Power plays a huge part also. Practice with a variety of Angles, and hit the Target's Centre to earn this Stamp!

"Practice Makes Perfect"
■ **How to Achieve**

This Stamp can actually be achieved in three throws! So completing it in 10 throws is easy. With correct Angling of the Frisbee, you can hit all three Balloons in the same line, one after the other. To hit the Middle row of three Balloons, throw the Frisbee straight with no Angling. To hit the Balloons on the Right, Angle the Frisbee Upwards to curl it Right. And to hit

the Balloons on the Left, Angle the Frisbee Downwards to curl it Left. Pop all 9 Balloons in less than 10 Throws, to earn this Stamp!

"10 x 10"
■ **How to Achieve**

This one is difficult! To achieve this Stamp, you must successfully direct the Frisbee into the Outer Turquoise section of the Target, for All 10 throws! If you fail to hit the Turquoise section for any of your throws, then Restart, and try again. There are two ways in which you can do this. Either perfect your Accuracy, Power and Angles; and manually aim for the Outer Turquoise section; or, aim directly for the Centre Target, but slightly alter your Angling Up or Down to cause the Frisbee to veer off slightly to the Left or Right, where the Turquoise sections are found. When the

Balloons appear, ignore them; as trying to hit them as well could hinder your accuracy! Practice, and perseverance is key.

"Dead Centre"
■ **How to Achieve**

Again, this one is difficult! For this Stamp, you must accurately throw the Frisbee directly into the Purple Centre Circle of the Target, for All 10 throws! If you fail to hit the Centre for any one of your throws, then Restart, and try again. Like we explained above, you must perfect your Angling, Power, and Accuracy to achieve this Stamp; and even then, it will take a lot of skill to get right. Again, ignore the Balloons, as they will only hinder your accuracy if you try hitting them! Stick with it, and eventually you'll earn with Stamp!

"Perfect Score"
■ **How to Achieve**

This Stamp is by far the most difficult! You must get a 100% score by accurately landing All 10 Frisbees in the Purple Centre Circle, just like 'Dead Centre' explained above; however

surface, and lands safely on the other side. This can only be done if the Frisbee is thrown Flat; the Water section isn't too large, and there are no high Walls, Cliff-faces / Rocks etc obstructing the bounce!

this time…you must pop Every Balloon as well!! Incorporate everything that you've learnt, and focus predominantly on Angling and Wrist actions.

■ TIP: If the Balloon is on the Right, but the Target is on the Left; then you must Angle the Frisbee Downwards so that it curls Left - however you must release the Frisbee further Right, in order to hit the Balloon first. As you do this violently flick your Wrist back (Left) to extend the curvature of the Frisbee; which with enough practice and skill, will cause the Frisbee to travel to the Right to begin with, thus popping the Balloon; and then veer sharply off to the Left, to hit the Target! The same rule applies if the Balloon is on the Left, and the Target is on the Right; only in reverse. This is a difficult skill to master; however perfect it, and this challenging Stamp is yours!

Frisbee Golf
Frisbee Golf Stamps:

"Under Par"
■ How to Achieve

Scoring Under Par on Any Course is acceptable; so we advise you to play the 3-hole Course, as it's the shortest! If you've mastered Angling and Power via 'Frisbee Dog', then this Stamp will be easy. Throw the Frisbee down the Fairway, and into the Target Area on the Green to complete each Hole. By the end of all three Holes, you Must complete at least one Hole in Less throws than the set Par, i.e. a Par 4 Hole must be completed in Three throws or less to get an end score of -1. Get an end result of -1 or less, to earn this Stamp!

"Skip to Safety"
■ How to Achieve

This is a difficult Stamp, as there are only a few areas in which you can do it successfully! The idea is to skilfully Skim the Frisbee across any Water section, so that it bounces on the

We therefore advise you to attempt the 'Resort C' Three-Hole Course, as Hole 3 has a clear open Lake just before the Green… Get close to the Lake, and then aim for the Water using either a Mid-Range Disc or a Putter – Mid-Range Discs bounce further and higher, so this is probably your best bet! Now throw the Frisbee flat and with enough power to bounce on the Lake, and onto the Green. Complete the Hole after to earn the Stamp!

"Rolling Goal"
■ How to Achieve

This Stamp can be achieved on most Holes! Simply throw the Frisbee from outside of the Green, and get it to Bounce before it hits the Target Area. Get close to the Green, and then check the Distance to the Target in the top right hand corner of the screen. Use the Putter if it's around 30 Yards; and the Mid-Range Disc

around 90 Yards. To make the Frisbee Bounce, judge the Distance and Power; and then manually aim Downwards, so that it has time to Bounce on the Green, before reaching Target Area in the same throw, to earn this Stamp!

"Hole-In-One"
■ How to Achieve

This Stamp is Only possible on a short Par 3 Hole! Par 4 Holes and higher are too long and cannot be completed in a single throw. We therefore advise you to attempt the 'Classic B' Three-Hole Course; as Hole 1 is an extremely simple Par 3… Select the 'Driver' Disc, and throw it with Power up towards the Target Area on the Green. If you're accurate enough and manage to successfully hit the Target Area in a single throw, the Stamp is yours! Complete the remaining two Holes to receive the Stamp!

"A Clean 18"
■ How to Achieve

To achieve this Stamp, simply complete the 18-hole Course without Ever throwing the Frisbee Out Of Bounds, or into Water. The Out Of Bounds area circles the entire Course, beyond the Fairway, Green, and Rough. Slicing and Hooking the Frisbee to the far Left or Right, is Out Of Bounds! As long as you throw straight down the Fairway and onto the Green, you'll have no problems. If it does go Out Of Bounds, or into Water Hazards, then Restart and try again. Also, it doesn't matter what Score you get at the end; so simply focus on avoiding the Out Of Bounds areas and Water Hazards for all 18-holes, to earn this Stamp!

archery

Archery Stamps:

"Bulls in a Row"
■ **How to Achieve**

This Stamp is easiest to achieve on 'Stage 1' of the 'Beginner' Difficulty Level, as there is no Wind, and the Target is extremely close. Aim

ever-so slightly above the Centre Bulls-Eye (one Target 'Ring' will do), and release, to hit the Bulls-Eye every time! Repeat this method, and hit the Bulls-Eye with all Three Arrows, to earn this Stamp! Fail to hit the Bull with any of your Arrows; then Restart, and try this Stage again!

"Stay on Target"
■ **How to Achieve**

To achieve this Stamp, simply hit every Target with All of your Arrows, on any Difficulty Level. We advise you to attempt the 'Beginner' Difficulty Level however, as it's the easiest. There are 4 Stages, with three Arrows per Stage; therefore you must successfully hit 12 Targets overall. It doesn't matter where on the Target you hit, just as long as you do in fact hit the Target. To succeed, just remember to take into account the Distance of the Target, and the Wind Strength and Direction; then alter your Aim accordingly!

"Rack 'Em Up"
■ **How to Achieve**

If you want to increase your Ranking Level and Advance to Pro Class, then you will inevitably get this Stamp at some point. Simply hit any Target in any Difficulty Level or Stage, 100 + times. Therefore as long as you keep playing, and practicing; you will eventually hit 100 Targets, and earn this Stamp before you know it!

"The Secret Target"
■ **How to Achieve**

This one is even more difficult than the final 'Sharpshooter' Stamp! In every Stage of every Difficulty Level, there is a hidden Secret Item to hit – usually some sort of Fruit.
Finding them is challenging enough; however hitting them is even harder! In order to hit the Secret Targets, you Must have a good understanding of the long Distances that separate you and the Target; as well as Wind Strength and Direction. This will take time to master, however with the following Secret Locations; at least you won't waste time searching for them. The rest however, is up to you!

"Sharpshooter"
■ **How to Achieve**

This is a difficult Stamp, as your accuracy must be 100% throughout for every Stage! Luckily, you can achieve this on the 'Beginner' Difficultly. To earn this Stamp, you must successfully hit All 12 Targets in the Bulls-Eye, for maximum Points. This requires a lot of skill, and an advanced understanding of Distance, Wind Strength, and Direction. The first three Stages can be mastered quickly and easily; however the Final fourth Stage is the most challenging. Stick with it, and learn from previous mistakes – trial and error is the key here! Judge how far out you were previously, and then alter your Aim accordingly for the next round.

■ **Beginner Difficulty Level:**
1: (Orange) Orange: On your Right hand side, to the Left of the Waterfall.
2: (Green) Melon: On your far Left hand side, in between two Trees, up on the Cliff-Face Ledge.
3: (Cream) Cantaloupe: This one is completely hidden and cannot be seen until you fire an Arrow close to it! It's directly behind the Target's Left Support Structure. Aim up and over the Support Beam to get a closer look.
4: (White) Cake: On your far Right hand side, down on the Grass, at Ground Level.

■ **Intermediate Difficult Level:**
1: (Orange) Orange: This one is hidden also, and cannot be seen until you fire an Arrow close to it! It's in the Tennis Courts beyond the Palm Tree on your Right hand side. Aim to the Right on the Palm Tree to reach the Courts.
2: (Green) Melon: Up high, on the Overhead Bridge on your far Left hand side.

3: (Cream) Cantaloupe: In front of the Castle, at Ground Level, to the Left hand side of the Tree. It's almost camouflaged with the wall behind.
4: (Brown) Bread: Up high on top of the Cliff, to the Left of the Tree, on your far Right hand side. You can just see the top of it.

■ **Expert Difficulty Level:**
1: (Orange) Orange: On the Sandy Beach on your far Right hand side. It's further than you think.
2: (Green) Melon: On your Right hand side, just over the top of the raised Grass Mound, in between the two large Rock-faces. You can just see the top of it.
3: (Cream) Cantaloupe: On your Left hand side, up high on the Ruin's Rooftop.
4: (Red / Black) Alarm Clock: This one is hidden and cannot be seen until you fire an Arrow close to it! It's on your far Right hand side (as far as you can go), in the Lava beyond the Pathway, to the Right hand side of the large Rock-Pillar.

basketball

3-Point Contest

3-Point Contest Stamps:

"Five in a Row"
■ How to Achieve

After a few practice runs, this one isn't too difficult. Perform the exact same motions as if you were actually throwing a Basketball, for maximum accuracy i.e. hold both Hands up with the Wii Remote, and flick your Wrist with the appropriate force, at the top of the extension. Find fluid rhythm, and successfully sink Five consecutive Balls in a row, to earn this Stamp!

"Bonus Ball Buff"
■ How to Achieve

To earn this Stamp, successfully sink all five Multicoloured Bonus Balls (the fifth Ball in all five rows) into the Basket! If you fail to sink a Multicoloured Ball, then Restart, and try again. If you fail to sink a Normal Ball, then don't panic – this Stamp only requires you to sink the Bonus Balls! However, you need to get into a nice rhythm using all the Balls, and then sinking the Bonus Balls should come naturally. And remember; as you move around the 3-Point Line, you Must alter your Aim and Power accordingly, to coincide with the slight change in direction, and angle, to the Net!

"Speed Shooter"
■ How to Achieve

For this one, you must successfully Score 20 Points or more, with at least 10 Seconds left on the Clock, after throwing all 25 Balls. All Normal Balls are worth 1 Point each; however the Bonus Balls are worth 2 Points! Therefore

if you successfully sink all five Bonus Balls whilst completing the 'Bonus Ball Buff' Stamp explained above; then you only need to sink a further 10 Normal Balls to earn this Stamp. Both speed and skill are key here! Be quick; score 20+ Points with 10 Seconds left, and the Stamp is yours!

"You Got Game"
■ How to Achieve

This is where things get tricky! To achieve this Stamp, successfully sink Every single Ball, before the time runs out! There's no room for mistakes, so you're going to have to use every bit of skill that you've learnt, if you want to sink all 25 Balls! DO NOT rush each throw - take your time, and master Power, Angling, Wrist Flicking actions, and Release Time of the Ball. As you move around the 3-Point Line, slightly alter everything that we mentioned above, in order to sink the Balls at different angles. If you fail to sink a Ball, then Restart, and try again. With enough practice and perseverance, you will get this Stamp eventually!

"Speed Demon"
■ How to Achieve

If you manage to achieve the 'You Got Game' Stamp explained above, then hopefully, you can get this Stamp also! You must successfully sink all 25 Balls like before…however this time round, you must also have 15 Seconds or more remaining on the Clock at the end! Incorporate everything that you've learnt so far, and learn from past mistakes – for example, if you always seem to throw to the Left, then alter your trajectory slightly to the Right; or if you always seem to throw the Ball beyond the Net, then try flicking your Wrists less forcefully to reduce the Power. Everyone throws differently, so it's up to you to realise your own mistakes, and then counteract these problems manually. Stick with it, and you will get it eventually!

3-On-3 Game

3-On-3 Game Stamps:

"3-Point Goal"
■ How to Achieve

Master the '3-Point Contest' explained above, and this Stamp is easy! Simply score a 3-Point shot from beyond the 3-Point Line (Light Brown Semi-Circle) to achieve this Stamp! Pass the Ball to begin with, and then pass it back to a Player who's beyond the 3-Point Line. Now go for the 3-Point shot, but wait for a split second in midair so that the Defender doesn't block it. Sink the Ball, and the Stamp is yours!

"Slam Dunk Master"
■ How to Achieve

To achieve this easy Stamp, simply execute five successful Slam Dunks! The only way to go for a Slam Dunk is by being almost directly beneath the Basket. If you're too far away, then you'll simply jump for a 2-Point shot instead. To get close to the Net, incorporate accurate Passes, and Dribbling skills. Pass the Ball around to confuse your Opponents, and then when a Player is in open space, quickly Pass the Ball, and Dribble to the Net, by moving the Wii Remote Up and Down, as if you were Dribbling a real Basketball. When in range, go for the shot, and you'll enter Slam Dunk mode. To complete the Dunk, raise the Wii Remote up to make your Player Jump, and then when he / she is at the highest point, swing the Wii Remote Down, to Slam the Ball into the Net! Perform five successful Slam Dunks in a single Match to earn this Stamp!

"3-Point Master"
■ **How to Achieve**
Again, master the '3-Point Contest', and this Stamp is easy! If you've already achieved the '3-Point Goal' Stamp explained above, then we advise you to go for this one also. To get this Stamp, successfully sink five 3-Point shots from outside of the 3-Point Line (Light Brown Semi Circle) in a single Match! And remember; hesitate in midair slightly before you throw, to avoid the Block.

"Buzzer Beater"
■ **How to Achieve**
This Stamp is easiest to achieve in the beginning Stages, when you first start. To earn this Stamp, you must score the 'Winning' Basket when the Buzzer sounds at the end of the Game. Therefore the Scores Must be an

even Draw before the Buzzer! The easiest way to do this is to keep the scores at 0-0 for the entire Match. Hold onto the Ball, until your 20 Second Time Limit is up; at which point the Ball is passed over. Steal the Ball, Block regularly, and Do Not let them score. Continue to do this for the entire Match until there's 10 Seconds left on the Clock. Hold the Ball at this point, and wait for the Timer to count down to 1 Second – at which point, go for the final 'Winning' shot! 2-Pointers and 3-Pointers work well, as the game still plays as you're in midair! Jump up at the Buzzer, and successfully sink the Ball when the timer runs out, to score the Winning Point, and earn the Stamp!

"Defeat the Champions"
Defeat the champions in a game! The current Wuhu champions are faster, jump higher and

shoot better than any other team. Increase your lead by scoring 3-point goals.
■ **How to Achieve**
To challenge the Champions, you must first increase your Ranking Level to 1, 500 Points, by defeating the many other Teams thrown your way. Lose however, and you'll lose Points! Keep Winning to increase Rank, and at 1,500 Points, the Champion Team will become available. Now all you have to do is defeat the Champions to earn the Stamp! The key to beating the Champions is to Fake every shot! To do this, move the Wii Remote Up and Down slowly before throwing, making it look as if you're about to throw, thus confusing your Opponents; and then when they Jump to Block, wait for them to land, and then Jump and Throw for real! You should score every time this way.

table tennis

Match

Match Stamps:
"Not the Face"
■ **How to Achieve**
This Stamp is to easiest to achieve in the beginning Stages; as your Opponents cannot return Power Shots, which is key to earning this Stamp. When your Opponent plays a Soft Ball, or Lobbed Ball, you can return with a Power Shot, by forcefully swinging the Wii Remote! To earn this Stamp, you must aim the Powered Ball directly at your Opponent, by timing your swing, and judging whether it requires a Backhand or a Forehand shot; as well as whether to swing early to Hook it, or late to Slice it. Think about the position of you and your Opponent, and then swing accordingly to smash them in the Face, and earn this Stamp!

"Back From the Brink"
■ **How to Achieve**
This one is difficult! To get this Stamp, you need Slice the Ball on the return hit, so that it twists and turns in midair; Bounces on the very edge of the Table where the White Lines are, and then spins off in the opposite direction, towards your Opponent! This is a challenging Trick-shot to execute correctly so listen carefully. Basically, you need to hit the Ball with a Backhand shot, and violently flick, and twist your Wrist upwards, to perform this type of shot. Not just that, but you have to time your swing perfectly in order to get the Ball to land on the outer White Lines! If done correctly, the Ball will Bounce on the Lines, and twist-spin back onto the Table. Do this and Stamp is yours!

"30-Stroke Rally"
■ **How to Achieve**

This Stamp can only be achieved once you've advanced to 300+ Points in Rank, as your Opponents before this Level cannot keep a lengthy Rally going! To achieve, you must keep a continuous Rally going for 30 shots or more. Hit the Ball Straight with every shot, and avoid using Skill shots, like Curve Balls, Lobs, Power Shots etc, as you may accidentally beat your Opponent before the Rally is complete! Use Backhand / Forehand shots to keep the Ball as central as possible, and continue to keep the Rally going for 30+ shots to earn this Stamp!

"A Worthy Opponent"
■ **How to Achieve**
To earn this Stamp, you need to Draw every Round, so that the final Score reaches 20-20. In Table Tennis, the Winner is determined by the Player who increases their Score by +2 Points, once they've passed the Match Point Score of 5. Therefore if your Opponent has 5 Points, and you have 7, then you win the game. In order to stop this happening, and to Draw every Round, you must prevent yourself and your Opponent from getting ahead by more than 1 Point. Therefore you need to Win One Point, and then let your Opponent Win the next, so the Score always remains at a maximum of 1 Point difference! Continue to do this for every Round i.e. 10-10,11-10,11-11,12-11,12-12 and so on and so forth, until both Players reach the end Score of 20-20; at which point, you'll earn the Stamp!

"Defeat the Champion"
■ **How to Achieve**
To challenge the Champion, you must first increase your Ranking Level to 1, 500 Points, by defeating the many other Opponents thrown your way. Lose however, and you'll lose Points! Keep Winning to increase Rank, and at 1,500 Points, the Champion will become available. Now all you have to do is defeat the Champion to earn the Stamp! Use a variety of

Forehand and Backhand shots, and regularly switch between Slice shots, Hook shots, Lobs, Power Shots, and Trick-shots, to beat your Opponent, and earn the Stamp!

Return Challenge

Return Challenge Stamps:

"Score 50 Points"

■ How to Achieve

This Stamp is pretty straight forwards, and is even easier on the beginning Stages, when you first start. Simply Return the Balls that are hit to you, and earn an overall Score of 50 Points! Each Ball that you successfully Return is worth 1 Point. Successfully hitting the Cans that appear, are worth 3 Points each! Continue to Return the Balls and earn 50 Points to achieve this Stamp! Miss a Ball, and the game ends.

"Score 100 Points"

■ How to Achieve

Exactly the same as 'Score 50 Points' explained above. If you're already going for the 'Score 50 Points' Stamp, then we advise you to go for this Stamp as well. Simply keep the Return Rally going for a further 50 Points, and get your overall Score to 100 Points, to earn this Stamp!

"Score 200 Points"

■ How to Achieve

Again, exactly the same as the above two Stamps almost. To earn this one, you need to Score 200 Points! The Balls will be hit at tremendous speeds now, and you'll have to deal with Slice shots, Power shots, and all kinds of Trick-shots if you want to last. You'll constantly be asked to change from Forehand to Backhand shots, so be on the ready at all times. Get a Score of 200 Points, and the Stamp is yours!

"Can Do"

■ How to Achieve

To achieve this Stamp, successfully hit a total of 30+ Cans in a single game! We advise you to start going for this one early on, when the

Balls are travelling at slower speeds. Leaving it late in the game will prove difficult. To hit the Cans, you need accurately judge your shots depending on where the Cans are; for example, to hit a Can on the Left side, position yourself on the Right, and swing early with a Forehand shot, to Hook the Ball across the Table to the Left. Whereas if the Can is on the Right side, then position yourself on the Left, and swing early with a Backhand shot, to Hook the Ball to the Right. Hit 30 Cans and the Stamp is yours!

"Honourable Master"

■ How to Achieve

This Stamp is much more difficult than it sounds, as the Server Never moves! He stays in the same place throughout the entire game, so you must manually direct the Balls past them, to either their Left or Right side. To do this, you Must master the Forehand / Backhand shots, and Swing-Timing also. If you swing early, then you'll Hook the Ball; swing late, and you'll Slice the Ball. The most effective way to do this is to either swing as late or as early as possible every time, to cause the Ball to miss the Server with every shot! Ignore the Cans, and simply focus on not hitting the Sever. Score 100+ Points without Ever hitting your Opponent, to earn this Stamp!

Golf Stamps:

"Under Par"

■ How to Achieve

Scoring Under Par on Any Course is acceptable; so we advise you to play the 3-hole Course, as it's the shortest! Hit the Ball down the Fairway, onto the Green, and into the Hole to complete each Course. By the end of all three Holes, you Must complete at least one Hole in Less throws than the set Par, i.e. a Par 4 Hole must be completed in Three throws or less to get an end score of -1. Get an end result of -1 or less, to earn this Stamp!

"Chip It In"

■ How to Achieve

This Stamp can Only be achieved by hitting the Ball from Outside of the Green, with a Club that is not a Putter. To do this, master the Distance, and Power that you exert. Check the Map, and you'll notice several 'Dots' on the 'Line' leading towards the Hole. If the Hole is on the First Dot for example, then you must swing with the same amount of force to correspond with the Dots on the Power Bar, i.e. One Dot up!   If the Hole is on the Second or Third Dot, then you exert Power to Two or

Three Dots etc. As long as you hit the Ball straight with the correct Power, you should be fine. Chip the Ball in, and the Stamp is yours!

"King of Clubs"

■ How to Achieve

Similar to the 'Under Par' Stamp above, you must complete an entire Course in 9 Under Par (-9 shots) to earn this Stamp! We therefore advise you to play an 18-Hole Course; as 18 holes should give you enough time to reduce your Score! It is possible on a 9-Hole Course; however Every Hole must be completed in One Under Par! At least with 18 Holes, you only have to do this for every other Hole, allowing you to Par the others in between. Get an end result of -9 or less, to earn this Stamp!

"Ace of Clubs"

■ How to Achieve

The same rules apply as 'King of Clubs' above, only this time, you will have to get One Under Par on Every Hole! You must complete an entire Course in 18 Under Par (-18 shots) to earn this Stamp. An 18-Hole Course is the only way to really do this. Master the Map and Power Bar; Wind Direction and Strength; and of course, whatever you do, DO NOT hit the Ball Out Of Bounds or into Water Hazards, as

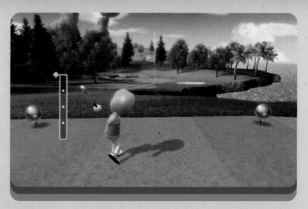

this will cost you 3 Missed Shots!!! Get an end result of -18 or less, to earn this Stamp!

"Hole-In-One"

■ How to Achieve

This Stamp is Only possible on a short Par 3 Hole! Par 4 Holes and higher are too long and cannot be completed in a single shot. We therefore advise you to attempt the 'Classic B' Three-Hole Course; as Hole 1 is an extremely simple Par 3... Even on the simplest Par 3 Hole, this Stamp is difficult! If you're accurate and sink the Ball in a single shot, the Stamp is yours! Master Wind Direction / Strength; the Roll distance onto the Green; and make sure to hit the Ball Straight, with just enough Power so that the Power Bar doesn't Bend (Hooking or Slicing considerably!) Complete the remaining Holes to receive the Stamp.

bowling >>>

10-Pin Game

10-Pin Game Stamps:

("Gobble Gobble")
■ **How to Achieve**

For this Stamp, simply Bowl three consecutive Strikes in a row, to score a 'Turkey'! After bowling one Strike, the following two should come naturally. Repeat the same techniques as for the first Strike; and exert the same amount Power, and Direction, to unlock this Stamp! Remember to Bowl Straight, and hard, to knock over all 10 Pins.

"Split-Frame Spare"
■ **How to Achieve**

To achieve a 'Split-Frame Spare', you must throw the first Ball so at least two Pins are still standing, with a gap in between the two. You must then skilfully knock down the remaining Pins for a Spare! If the gap is small, then it's pretty simply; however if the Pins far apart, then it's almost impossible! To successfully knock down both Split-Pins, hit the closest Pin first with force, on either its Right or Left side; so that the Pin then spins off and hits the second Pin! For example; hit the closest Pin on the Right hand side to cause it to spin off to the Left. Or hit the closest Pin on the Left hand side to spin off to the Right!

"Pro Bowler"
■ **How to Achieve**

Practice is key! For this one, you must get a Strike or a Spare for almost every throw; except one and the final Third throw in the last Frame; to earn a total end Score of 200+ Points! To do this, you must master Power, Direction, Wrist-control for Spin, and Split-Pins. Use everything that you've learnt, and score

200+ Points to earn this Stamp. If you miss any more that two Strikes or Spares, then Restart and try again, as you will be unable to achieve the 200 Point Score!

"No Pin Standing"
■ **How to Achieve**

This one is much like the 'Pro Bowler' Stamp above; however this time, you Must get a Strike or a Spare on Every throw! Missing even one Strike / Spare will result in failure! So if you miss a Pin; Restart and try again. Missing a Strike or Spare on the final Third throw of the last Frame however is still acceptable. Although missing one in any of the previous Frames isn't! If you've already achieved the 'Pro Bowler' Stamp, then hopefully you should be able to get this one also.

"King-Pin"
■ **How to Achieve**

This Stamp requires 100% perfection, and accuracy! You Must get a Strike for Every throw, for all Frames, including the final Third throw on the last Frame; to get a maximum Score of 300 Points! Even Spares do not count – every throw must be a Strike!! If you fail to get a Strike for any of your throws, then Restart

and try again. Practice regularly, and perfect your bowling skills, including Power, Direction, and Straight Throws. Persevere, and you will eventually earn this challenging Stamp.

100-Pin Game

100-Pin Game Stamps:

"100-Pin Strike"
■ **How to Achieve**

For this Stamp, simply knock down All 100 Pins in a single throw for a Strike! It's not actually as hard as it sounds. As long as you hit the first Red Pin at the very front of the Triangle, the added Domino effect will take care of the rest! Although there are 100 Pins instead of 10, the same methods apply in knocking them all down. Throw the Ball with added force directly at the first Red Pin, and watch the rest topple, to earn this Stamp!

"Split-Frame Spare"
■ **How to Achieve**

This Stamp requires the exact same technique as the 'Split-Frame Spare' explained for the '10-Pin Game' above. Only this time it's much more difficult, as the Alley is considerably wider! Therefore if the Split-Pins are far apart from one another, then achieving this Stamp is impossible!! If they're close together however; you have a chance. Throw the first Ball and leave at least two Pins standing, with a gap in between. Knock down both Split-Pins by hitting the closest Pin first on either its Right or Left side; and then hope that it spins off and hits the second Pin!

"Gutter Guard Genius"
■ **How to Achieve**

This Stamp will take a few attempts. Trial and error is the answer here! To earn this one, you must throw the Ball to the side, so that it hits of the Gutter Guard (Side Walls), and then bounces back at an angle and knocks down All 100 Pins for a Strike! To do this, move slightly to your Left when you begin, and position yourself directly in the Centre of the Alley (using the small Dots on the floor as your guideline). Now Rotate your Throwing-Directional Line around to either the Left or Right, and aim for the Second small White 'Wii Sports' Sign along. Throw the Ball with power at the second Sign, and it will bounce back and hit the first Red Pin, every time! Get a Strike by hitting the Gutter Guard, to earn the Stamp!

"Secret Strike"
■ **How to Achieve**

If you've played the original Wii Sports, then you'll know about the Secret Button! At the end of both Gutter Guards (Side Walls) is a Secret Button, which if you manage to hit, will cause an explosion, knocking down All 100 Pins instantly! To reach the Button, you must carefully roll the Ball along the top of the Gutter, so that it travels to the far end. To do this, move all the way to the far Right hand side (if you're Right Handed) but stop two or three clicks away to the Left. Now Rotate your Directional Line two or three clicks to the Right. From this position, throw the Ball, but Release it at the top of the extension, to throw it up high onto the barrier; and then enforce a significant amount of Left-Spin by flicking the Wii Remote Left, to cause the Ball to Curl in that direction, all the way along the barrier to the opposite end! If you're Left Handed, then move to the far Left, and put Spin on to the Right. Master your Spin-control, and positioning; and you'll get it eventually!

"No Pin Standing"
■ How to Achieve

This Stamp is a Challenge! However if you've mastered your Straight throws; and have achieved the 'No Pin Standing' and 'King-Pin' Stamps explained in the '10-Pin Game' above; then you should be able to get this one also. Remember; just because there are 100 Pins, theoretically the exact same results occur as the Pins fall; plus the added Domino effect will help significantly! Throw every Ball directly at the first Red Pin with added force, and score either a Strike or a Spare for Every Frame, to earn this Stamp! Missing Only the final Third throw on the last Frame is acceptable.

Spin Control
Spin Control Stamps:
"The Bare Minimum"
■ How to Achieve

Once you fully understand how to manually control your Spins with appropriate Force and Direction; this Stamp is easy! To put Spin on your throws, simply flick the Wii Remote with force in either direction, to Spin the Ball Left or Right, depending on where the Barriers are positioned. Successfully Curl every Ball around the Blockades, and knock down at least One Pin for every Frame, to earn this Stamp!

"Split-Frame Spare"
■ How to Achieve

You've completed this Stamp twice now, so you should know exactly what to do! Throw the first Ball around the Barriers, and leave at least two Pins standing, with a gap in between. Knock down both Split-Pins now by hitting the closest Pin first on either side, causing it to spin off, and hit the second!

"The Obvious Target"
■ How to Achieve

For this Stamp, you simply have to hit the (1) Pin at the front of the Triangle, for Every Frame! This isn't too difficult once you master Spin-control. If you fail to hit the (1) Pin for any Frame, then Restart and try again. All you

have to do is learn how to Curl the Ball around the Barriers with enough Spin so that the it realigns itself to the Centre of the Alley by the time it reach the Pins!

"Spin Doctor"
■ How to Achieve

To achieve this Stamp, you must earn a score of 170 Points at the end of all Frames, without Ever touching Any of the Barriers! Even slightly clipping them, or brushing past will result in failure. To succeed, you must perfect your Spin-control, and fully understand how to Curl left and right. You must also get a majority of Strikes and Spares to earn the 170 score. The most effective way to do this, is to move to either the far Left or far Right depending on where the Barriers are, and Curl the Ball inwards, past the Barriers, to hit the first Centre Pin every time! Practice is key.

"No Pin Standing"
■ How to Achieve

If you've mastered the 'Spin Doctor' Stamp above, then you're well on your way to achieving this one also! Use the exact same techniques as above, only this time put even more effort in, and get a Strike or a Spare on Every Frame! Again, missing the final Third throw on the last Frame is acceptable, however nothing else. Use everything that you've learnt so far, and perfect your Spin Control. Score a Perfect game almost, and the Stamp is yours!

POWER CRUISING

Slalom Course
Slalom Course Stamps:
"Bonus Ring King"
■ How to Achieve

This is by far the easiest to achieve on the first (Beach) Course, as there are fewer Waves; the Waves are smaller, and the Time Bonus Rings are positioned far apart from one another. All you have to do is navigate your way through All Time Bonus Rings – this includes the smaller x2 Rings also! Pass

through All Big and Small Rings; then finish the Course to earn the Stamp!

"Score 5000 Points"
■ How to Achieve

This Stamp is inevitable! Especially if you practice regularly; and want to increase your Ranking Level. To earn this one, simply continue to play each Course and score Big Points to earn decent Rank Points! Eventually, after enough games and over time, you will inevitably accumulate a total score of 5,000 Points, thus earning you this Stamp!

"Master Cruiser"
■ How to Achieve

For this Stamp, you must score 170 Points or more, on All 6 Courses. In order to do so, you must pass through Every Time Bonus Ring, and Every x2 Bonus Ring also! If you miss a high Time x2 Ring, then you might as well Restart and try again; especially on the latter Course, where you really do need to be quick, and hit all Rings. As you advance, the Waves become more frequent, and much bigger. The Bonus Rings also appear closer together and at sharper angles. And, in the last two Courses, you'll have to Boost-Jump over the Waves in

order to Jump through the x2 Bonus Rings in Midair! That you take all of this into account, and Do Not miss a single Ring, if you want to score 170+ Points, to get this Stamp!

"Jump Master"
■ How to Achieve

To unlock the final Course, simply complete the previous Courses a few times first. The final 'Shoals' Course will test your Boost-Jumping skills significantly, as the majority of the Bonus Rings require you to Jump through them. Not just that, but they are also closer together, and at sharper angles. As you approach a Midair Bonus Ring, save your Boost until you reach the oncoming Wave;

then Boost over the top, straight through the Rings! Successfully pass through Every Bonus Ring – x2, Water, and Midair Rings – and then complete the Course to earn this Stamp!

"All the Time in the World"
■ How to Achieve

To earn this Stamp, explore the Seas surrounding Wuhu Island, and find Every single Time Balloon scattered around in Free Cruising Mode, in a single run! Search thoroughly and locate them ALL within the 5:00 minute time limit to earn this Stamp!

canoeing

Speed Challenge

Speed Challenge Stamps:

"Beginner Licence"
■ How to Achieve

There are a few Stages (Distances) assigned to each Difficulty Level. Complete the first Set Distance to unlock the next, and then complete the Longer Distance to unlock the one after that, and so on and so forth. Complete all Stages in the Beginner Level and then complete the 200m Course to unlock the Intermediate Difficulty Level, and earn this Stamp! Avoid the Water-Grass and other Objects, as they will slow you down considerably!

"Intermediate Licence"
■ How to Achieve

Much like the 'Beginner Licence', this Stamp requires you to complete all of the Set Distances for the Intermediate Stage to unlock the 300m Course; and then you must complete 300m to unlock the Expert Difficulty Level, and earn this Stamp! Throughout this Course, avoid the Water-Grass, Water-Lily's, underwater Sharks, and other Objects also! You will also have to cut some corners if you want to make it in time.

"Expert Licence"
■ How to Achieve

Again, complete the set number of Distances for the Expert Level, and then complete the 400m Course at the end, to earn this Stamp! Throughout this Course, avoid the mini Water-Rapids in the first section, which will slow you down and send you off course if you touch them! And also, later on in the Stage, giant Acorns that I suppose are dropped by overhead Birds, will come crashing down into the Water, causing a massive Ripple effect, which again will send you drastically off course! Avoid these at all costs.

"Ducky Come Home"
■ How to Achieve

This Stamp is easy to achieve, especially since you have an Unlimited amount of Time! Select Practice Mode by pressing the (-) button, and then search the Lake for Every

single Baby Duck swimming around. As you approach each Baby Duck, an ! mark will appear above them, indicating that they will now follow you wherever you go. Find All Baby Ducks scattered about, and then return them to their Mother (the Large Duck) somewhere in the area, to earn this Stamp!

"Cut the Red Tape"
■ How to Achieve

For this Stamp, you must reach the Red Tape in all three Difficulty Levels! What Red Tape??... Well; once you've completed all Distances for each Level, 200m, 300m, and 400m; you can play them again, and travel even further past the usual Finishing Line! Roughly about 30 or 40m beyond where the usual Finish Line is located; is a 'Red Tape' Finishing Point!! In order to reach this however, you must be extremely quick and perfectly accurate with your Left-Right Strokes. You also need to avoid Every Obstacle, and cut Every corner if you want to make it in time. Pass through the Red Tape on all three Difficulty Levels to earn this Stamp!

cycling

Road Race

Road Race Stamps:

"Breathless"
■ How to Achieve
This one is easy. All you have to do, is cross the Finish Line with all three Energy Hearts depleted, and roll over the Line when your Mii turns Blue, and begins to slow down to take a Drink. It doesn't even matter what Position you finish in. Ride to the Finish Line, and on the final Straight, repeatedly shake the Wii Remote an Nunchuck in quick succession, to

tire yourself out; and then roll over the Finish Line 'Breathless', to earn this Stamp!

"First of Many"
■ How to Achieve
This Stamp is easiest to achieve on the 1-Stage Races, when you first start, as your Opposition are at their slowest here. To earn this Stamp, simply finish in 1st Position, and Win and Race! To do this, keep a steady pace going throughout, and Never run out of breath by losing all three Energy Hearts, as doing this will bring you to a Standstill, thus losing valuable seconds! Also, stay directly behind another

Cyclist to get a Windbreak (which gives you a Boost of Speed), and avoid Strong Winds, and Banana Peels on the ground at all times!

"1-Stage Master"
■ How to Achieve
To earn this Stamp you must Win all six 1-Stage Races in 1st Position! Remember; keep a steady pace going throughout, and Never run out of breath by losing all three Energy Hearts! Use other Cyclist to get a Windbreak Speed Boost, and avoid Strong Winds, Banana Peels, and other Objects at all times!

"3-Stage Master"
■ How to Achieve
Almost the same as '1-Stage Master'. This time however, you must Win both 3-Stage Races in 1st Position to earn this Stamp! Unlock and complete All six 1-Stage Races to unlock the 3-Stage Races.   This Stage is slightly more difficult than the last, and your Opposition will be slightly faster. They will also not run out of breath as much as they did in the 1-Stage Races, or be affected as much by the Strong Winds or Hazardous Objects. Cycle well, and win both Races to achieve this Stamp!

"6-Stage Master"
■ How to Achieve
Again, unlock and complete All 1-Stage and 3-Stage Races to unlock the 6-Stage Race. To earn this Stamp, you must Win the 6-Stage Race in 1st Position! Take it easy for the majority of the Race, and catch up and overtake the Cyclist in front slowly. Do Not power through the beginning part of the Race, and run out of steam. Keep it steady, and minimise the distance gradually. Stop peddling on Downhill sections to regain Energy, and use everything that you've learnt so far to Win the Race, and earn the Stamp!

air sports

Skydiving

Skydiving Stamps:

"High Five"
■ How to Achieve
For this one, successfully Link up with 4 other Mii's in the same Group to get a 'Perfect' Link-Up, and then Rotate the Group around so that everyone's Face is in the Shot! Tilt the Wii Remote Down and Forwards to approach a Group, and then touch a Mii to automatically Link-up. You must now move the Wii Remote around to Link-up with the remaining three Mii's before the Timer runs out. Once all four are Linked-up; turn the Wii Remote around

and Upside Down, to Rotate the Mii's, and get their Faces in the shot, to earn this Stamp!

"Birdwatcher"
■ How to Achieve
To achieve this Stamp, you must take a Photo when a Bird is in the Shot flying across the screen! This Stamp is just luck of the draw. There's no control over when the Bird will appear, so your best bet is to just keep Linking-up with other Mii's and taking Photos; and eventually you will inevitably get one with a Bird in it!

"30-Person Formation"
■ How to Achieve
This is a challenging Stamp, as you must

successfully Link-up with 29 Mii's by the end of the Dive! Navigate through the Skies, and quickly Link-up with Every Group that you come across. If you want to reach the 29 mark, then you must Link-up with All 4 Mii's in each Group, every time. That's a total of 7 Groups of 4 Mii's, and then a single Mii shot! Hold the Wii Remote Flat to slow down, giving you more time during the Dive. Once you've successfully Linked-up with 29 Mii's, you then need to join them in the Final Formation, by

navigating through the three large Rings at the end of the Dive! Get 29 Mii's and Finish the Formation to earn the Stamp!

"Sympathy Snap"
■ How to Achieve

For this Stamp, you must avoid Linking-up with Every Group of Mii, so that you end up with No Pictures at the end of the Dive! To do this, start by holding the Wii Remote Down and Upside Down to avoid the first closest Group; and then freefall at speed to avoid the rest! If you manage to end the Dive with no Pictures, then the Photographer will appear for a Special Shot with just you and him. In order to take the Picture and earn the Stamp, you must successfully navigate though the Photographer's Final Formation Ring! This is tricky, as he's constantly moving. Quickly approach the Photographer and then pass through his Ring, to enter Formation; snap the Pic, and earn the Stamp!

"Score 200 Points"
■ How to Achieve

If you've achieved the '30-Person Formation' Stamp above, then you should be well on way to getting this one also! You must earn 200+ Points by the end of the Dive, by Linking-up with All 4 Mii's in Every Group for a 'Perfect' Link-up, and turning them all around so that their Faces are in Every shot, for added Bonus Points! Do Not waste time and miss a Group. And at the end of the Dive, make sure that you complete the Final Formation. The more Mii's you Link-up with, the more Points you

will ultimately earn for the Final Formation. Earn 200+ Points, and the Stamp is yours!

Island Flyover

Island Flyover Stamps:

"Visit Wedge Island"
■ How to Achieve

To achieve this Stamp, simply Read any (i) Location on Wedge Island! Wedge Island is the small Island in the Southeast part of the Map, where the Golf Course is located. You'll have to clear a large area of Water first to reach it, as it's not part of Wuhu Island! There are 6 (i) points on Wedge Island. Fly through Any one to earn this Stamp!

"Popfest 150"
■ How to Achieve

For this Stamp, you must find and Pop 150 Balloons around the Island in a single flight! ▨ In order to make the Balloons appear however, you Must first locate and Read a minimum of 10 (i) points around the Island! ▨ After finding 10 (i) locations, the Balloons can then be found in many different places i.e. on Planes, Cars, Boats etc. Some will be simply Floating around the Island; others may be held by Mii's, and some appear from within

larger Balloons. Search everywhere and Pop 150 Balloons with your Popper-Balls to earn this Stamp!

"Follow That Plane"
■ How to Achieve

This one is pretty simply once you actually realise how to locate Miguel's Guide Plane! As you begin, press the (1) button on the Wii Remote to fire a Flare and get Miguel's attention. Search around now in the Sky, Ground, and Water; and try to locate Miguel's Flare signal! Keep firing Flares until you notice his signal somewhere in the distance. It's a bright White / Blue circular Flash! Approach Miguel's Plane, and he'll tell you to 'follow'. Stick with him, and follow his Plane for 3:00 Minutes or more, to earn this Stamp!

"Wuhupedia"
■ How to Achieve

This is a difficult Stamp! But luckily for you…we've provided an easy-to-follow Map of Wuhu Island, with All 80 (i) Locations marked on it!! In order to achieve this Stamp however, you must find All 80 (i) points, in all three Times of Day; Daytime, Evening, and Night. That's 240 (i) points overall. * To unlock the Evening Time, you must first locate and Read a minimum of 20 (i) points around the Island! And to unlock the Night Time, you must locate and Read a minimum of 40 (i) points around the Island! * Use the Map provided to locate All 240 locations to earn this Stamp!

"Balloonist Extraordinaire"
■ How to Achieve

For the final Stamp, you must locate and Pop Every White Balloon scattered around the Island! Remember, Balloons can be found on Planes, Cars, and Boats etc; simply just Floating around the Island; held by other Mii's, and even released from larger Balloons. Search everywhere and Pop All White Balloons with your Popper-Balls to earn this Stamp! Once you Pop a Balloon, it will change Colour, indicating that you've already Popped it. ▨

Wii Fit
fitness guide!

No one can question Nintendo's genius from Pokémon to the Wii, no one does it better! Yet who would have thought that Nintendo could not only make gaming good for your health, but also fun and challenging. Loose weight, cut your BMP and make the most of the awesome Wii Fit!

>>>

Setting up & getting Started!

How to Synchronise the Wii Balance Board with your Nintendo Wii Console?

o set up the Wii Balance Board, you must first insert the four Batteries that came with your purchase of the Wii Fit package. Flip the Balance Board over and remove the small Battery cover of the underside. Insert the four Batteries as shown, and then press and hold the small Red 'Sync' Button to the side. Now flip open the small SD Card Slot cover on the front of the Nintendo Wii console, and then press and hold the Red 'Sync' Button inside also, to successfully Synchronise the Balance Board with the console. Replace both covers, and then place the Balance Board flat on the floor, so that the Power Button is facing away from the Television. Your Wii Balance Board is now ready to use!

Creating Your Mii Character and Getting Started >>>

When the Wii Plaza starting screen loads, click the 'Register' icon and click 'Create' to create a New User Data. Next, click a Mii Character that you would like to use for your Wii Fit experience, and then listen to the brief explanation about Balance and Posture. You'll be told how most people (without training) lean on one Leg for support. This is bad, as your overall Body Weight is distributed unevenly, causing uneven balance and posture on one side. With practice and training, you'll learn how to stand straight with perfect posture so that your Weight is distributed evenly through both legs.

You'll then be asked to take a 'Body Test', which measures your Center of Gravity (COG), your Body Mass (BMI), and your Athletic Ability, including overall Balance, Stillness, and Posture. Once completed, you'll be given your overall Wii Fit Age, which you want to be as low as possible! First, enter your 'Height', and be as accurate as you can. Next, enter the 'Year' that you were Born (age), and then type in your Birthday (Date and Month).

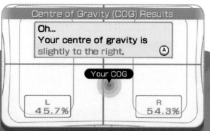

Body Test >>>

Before beginning, select how Heavy your Clothing is. Lightweight Clothing includes Shorts, a T-Shirt, and no Shoes for instance; whereas Heavyweight Clothing includes Trousers, a Top, and Shoes.

Now, stand on the Wii Balance Board with your Feet spread evenly apart, and stay relaxed whilst loosening your Shoulders. Stand as still as you possibly can and try your best not to move a muscle to get the most accurate result. The Balance Board will now 'Measure' your Centre of Gravity and indicate on screen where your COG is. Don't worry if it's not perfectly centered – it never is, especially for first timers! The majority of people stand to the side, with most of their weight on one leg. To counteract this, stand perfectly straight and try to put even pressure on both legs. If you're posture is usually hunched or slouched, then straighten your back manually for maximum effectiveness!

After this you'll have to manually set your COG in the small centre Circle. Stand upright and shift your body weight so that the Red Dot is in the centre circle, and then hold this position for 3 seconds to register. This position gives you the perfect posture, so try to remember it for future reference!

You'll now be given your Body Mass (BMI) results based on your Height and Weight measured by the Balance Board. If you're BMI results land you in the 'Healthy Weight', then you're on the right track to a perfect body. If you're 'Underweight' or 'Overweight' then don't worry – that's what Wii Fit…and ourselves are here to correct!

You'll then be asked to take a 'Basic Balance Test', which measures your Athletic Ability, Balance, Stillness and overall Posture. There are a variety of different Balance Tests that you may given, and they are given at random, so you never know which one you're going to get. However, they are as follows …

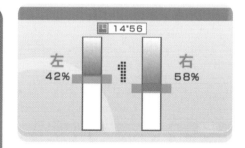

Agility Test:

Shift your COG to the front, back, left and right as you try to hit the Blue Tiles with the Red Dot.

■ **How:** …Shift your Body Weight in all directions to guide the Red Dot into the Blue Squares. Unlike the previous test above, you don't have to hold the position; instead all you have to do is touch the Blue Squares with the Red Dot to cause the next to appear, and then repeat the same procedure again. As you advance, the Squares will start to move, making them more difficult to hit. You have 30 seconds to hit as many Blue Squares as you can. Remember, this is an Agility Test, so be quick!

basic balance tests...

Basic Balance Test:

Try to keep your Left and Right balance at 50-50.

■ **How:** …Shift your Body Weight from Left to Right to get the end of the Red Bars into the small Blue Bars on both the right and left hand side of the screen. To do this, you must put more pressure on one side of the Balance Board than the other. The Blue Bars will become smaller as you advance, making it more difficult to hit.
Hold the correct position for 3 seconds to move onto the next. You have 30 seconds to complete 5 different Balances.

Single Leg Balance Test:

Place your preferred Foot on my centre, stand on just One Leg, and try to keep your balance. (If you need to, use objects or other people to support yourself)

■ **How:** …Stand on your strongest, most stable Foot, and lift your other Leg up. The most effective and balanced way to do this is to bend your Leg behind you and hold it at your buttocks. If you're finding it difficult to hold your balance, then position a Chair in front of you, and hold on to it with your hand for support! All you have to do here is simply stand as still as you possibly can, and try your best not to move or shake uncontrollably. Keep the Line on screen as centered as you can for best results, and hold this position for 30 seconds. Every 10 seconds, the Bar will become narrower, making it more difficult to remain inside the Bar. Keep still and balanced throughout!

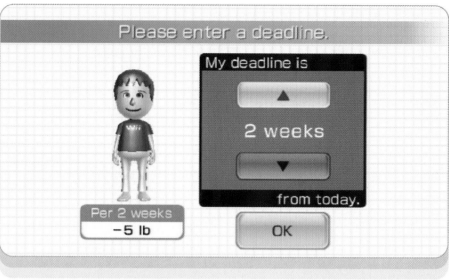

Stillness Test:

Try to keep as Still as possible throughout the duration of the Test.

■ **How:** … All you have to do here is stand still on the spot whilst your Stillness is recorded. This however is more difficult that it first looks – especially for newcomers! The most effective way to remain as still as you possibly can, is to stand with your Legs evenly apart, and actually Grip the Balance Board with your Toes for support (no shoes). Keep your back straight and your feet firmly in place, and aim to keep the Dot as centered as possible on the middle Cross [+]. As you advance through the Test, the screen will begin to move, making it more difficult, as you'll be unable to see how still you are – again DO NOT move at this point. Remain still at all times. Shortly after, the square will completely disappear for the final 10 seconds. Hold your stationary pose and you're done.

Walking Test:

Stand with your Feet spread equally apart, and Walk in place for 20 Steps just like you would walk normally.

■ **How:** …This Test records your Left and Right Balance as you walk on the spot. Simply walk in place as you usually would, Left, Right, Left, Right, for 20 Steps, and try to keep your weight distribution on each Foot as even as you possibly can. If you put more weight and pressure on one side as you walk, then your Left-Right Balance will be uneven. There's no real way to know how your Left-Right Balance and weight distribution will turn out for this one, as it all depends on your current balance. Your best bet is to keep a steady walk going throughout, and then alter it slightly next time depending on what side your balance veers

off to – i.e. if you're balance is more to the Right, then put more pressure on your Left Leg as you walk, and vice versa. If your results are extremely uneven and you're having trouble with this one, then try lightly jogging on the spot instead, alternating your Steps in quick succession! This will keep you light on your toes, with little pressure on both feet, and increase your Left-Right Balance dramatically.

Setting Yourself Goals & Assigning a Password to your Profile

After completing the set Balance Tests, you'll be told that you can set yourself 'Goals'. This is good, as it gives you something to strive for. If you're Underweight, then set yourself a Goal to gain a few Lbs in a few Weeks, whereas as if you're Overweight, set yourself a Goal to lose a few Lbs in a few Weeks. And then aim for that target!

If you're uneasy about your Weight or your current progress on Wii Fit, and you don't want others to view your personal details, then you can assign a Password to your Mii Profile, so that Only you can access it! To do this, simply enter a Four-Digit Password …and memorise it. Keep this Password to yourself and keep your information secure. Each time you want to access your Mii Profile and continue with your Wii Fit training, simply re-enter the Password and you're in.

calendar screen & Wii Fit training room

the following Calendar Screen allows you to check your current progress each and every day as you Train, as well as being able to check your BMI, Weight, and Wii Fit Age via an easy-to-follow Graph. Here you can also take part in a Daily Body Test to see how you've advanced each day. You can also alter any User Setting that you want to change. Once you're done here, click the 'Training' icon to enter the Training Room, where your Wii Fit Training can finally begin!

Now you'll be given a choice of which Trainer you would like to Train you. Don't worry, there's no real difference at all – only the Gender. Select a Male or Female Trainer and you'll be taken to the Training Room where you'll be told briefly about each category of Exercise, including Yoga, Muscle Workouts, Aerobic Exercises, and Balance Games. You'll then be given your brand new 'FitPiggy' which counts your overall training Time and helps keep track of your activities, both Daily and Overall.

■■■ IMPORTANT FACT ■■■

Before we start and before attempting any of the other exercises, it is vital that you begin with, and master, your Yoga training skills first! This is a necessity, as Yoga will help to increase and perfect your overall Balance and Posture, which is a must have if you want to master the other exercises such as Muscle Workouts and Balance Games. You NEED Balance and Posture to successfully complete the other exercises to the best of your ability, so spend a few days finely tuning and controlling your Balance with Yoga first - and then move onto the other exercises, which will then enable you to achieve those all important High Scores more easily!

Wii Fit yoga

perfecting your Yoga training skills stimulates your muscles that are not usually used in your everyday life, and helps to increase your body's overall Flexibility, Balance and Posture. Yoga is an absolute necessity if you want to master all of the other Training Exercises, as you will require well-trained Balance if you want to get the most out of your Wii Fit experience!!

This is the perfect way to increase your overall Balance and Flexibility, which is vital for all the other exercises.

Deep Breathing

INFO: Using the basic Breathing method can help improve your Metabolism.

■ How to Execute

Stand upright on the Balance Board with your Legs spread evenly apart, and keep your back and overall Posture as straight as you can for maximum effectiveness. Place your Hands on your Stomach so that your Elbows are at a 90 degree angle, and then Inhale slowly and deeply through your Nose, as the large outer Blue Circle decreases. As you do this, you'll want to stay as still as you possibly can so that the Red Dot remains in the centre Yellow Circle. The less the Red Dot moves, the better your Stillness and Posture is, and ultimately the more effective this workout will be! Also, the less the Red Dot moves, the higher your

Score will be. Inhale deeply and then Exhale slowly when the Blue Circle increases. Follow your Trainer as he / she does this for perfect breathing timing. If you're having trouble breathing through your Nose, then breathe through your Mouth instead, and as you perfect this Yoga technique, start to increase the time it takes you to Inhale and Exhale. This Yoga pose will aid you dramatically in future Exercises.

Warrior

> INFO: **Helps tone your Thighs and Hips, and may also align your Pelvis.**

■ How to Execute:

Stand upright on the Balance Board with your Legs spread evenly apart, and then take one large step back off of the Board with your Left Leg, extending it behind you, whilst

keeping your Right Leg firmly in place on the Board. Exhale as you do this. Now turn your Left Leg so that your Left Foot is pointing to the Left, and then turn

your Pelvis out to the Left, and lean over to the Right, whilst maintaining your outstretched Arms at all times. Bend to the side as far as you can, and hold this position to feel you're your Waist and Abdominal muscles stretch on the Left hand side of your Body! For maximum effectiveness, you should bend in a straight line whilst keeping your Legs and Arms completely still, so that your Body stays aligned throughout. Inhale and Exhale slowly and gently following the large outer Blue Circle just like before, and remain as still as you possibly can, so that the Red Dot stays within the Yellow Circle. The more control over your Stillness, Posture and Breathing, the less the Red Dot will move, and the more effective this exercise will be. Whilst Inhaling, slowly return back to the Upright position and keep your Arms up. Now switch sides when told to do so, and repeat the same procedure again on the other side. Bend to the left this time, and feel the Right hand side of your Body stretch. Inhale and Exhale slowly, and again hold this position for a few seconds. Return to the upright position again, and then finally, whilst Exhaling, lower your Arms back down to the original starting position and relax to complete the Half Moon Pose!

Half Moon >>>

> INFO: **Stretches your Waist muscles and can help improve Posture.**

■ How to Execute:

Stand upright on the Balance Board with your Legs and Feet pinned together, and straighten your Legs and Back fully to automatically tighten the muscles in your Lower Body. Expand your Chest outwards now and loosen your Shoulders whilst keeping your Arms down by your sides. Whilst Inhaling, raise both of your Arms out to the sides, and then upwards, high above your head until the Palms of your Hands meet one another. Straighten your Arms upwards, and link your Fingers together at the top of the extension. Stretch your Spine manually at this point and hold this position. Now, whilst Exhaling, bend

and face that direction, whilst keeping your Right Leg in place, so that your Right Foot is still facing forwards. Your Left and Right Heel should now be aligned with one another. Inhale deeply, and stretch and straighten both Arms out to the side, so that one is pointing towards the Television, and the other is point away. Whilst Exhaling, bend your Right Knee forwards and lower your Waist, while keeping your Left Leg firmly in place, so that you're putting pressure and force onto the Balance Board. As you do this, push with your Left Leg and take the pressure on your Right Leg. Relax your Upper Body here and try to distribute your weight evenly through both Legs. To master this Pose, look forwards and focus on the Fingers of your Right Hand. Find a comfortable position, and hold it for the required time whilst remaining as still as you can. The idea here is to keep the end of the Red Bar within the small Blue Bar halfway up. If the Red Bar is lower than the Blue Bar, then exert more pressure onto your front Right Leg to raise the Bar into the Blue; whereas if the Red Bar is higher than the Blue Bar, then accept slightly more body weight onto your rear Left Leg, to lower the Bar into the Blue! Breathe in time with the large Blue Circle as you do this, and then pivot back around and return to the original starting position with both Feet back on the Balance Board when told to do so. Switch Legs now and take a step back with your Right Leg this time, and repeat the exact same procedure again to complete the perfect Warrior Pose!

Tree >>>

INFO: **Helps strengthen your Legs and Back.**

■ How to Execute:

Stand upright on the Balance Board with your Legs close together, and then raise your Left Leg up, bend it at the Knee, and place the Sole of your Left Foot on the inside of your Right Thigh. Hold this position and maintain your balance as you do so. Once you're steady, bring your Hands together in front of your Chest so that your Palms meet, as if you are 'Praying' ; and then lift both of your Arms up towards the ceiling, high above your head. Keep your Back perfectly straight at this point, relax your Shoulders, and manually stretch

out your Spine. Once you're in this position, maintain Balance on one Leg, then Inhale and Exhale slowly and deeply for around 30 seconds. Keep as still as you possibly can and try your best not to shake or wobble uncontrollably, and aim to keep the Red Dot within the small Yellow Circle whilst breathing in time with the Blue Circle! If you're having trouble doing this and maintaining a steady balance, then feel free to support yourself by placing a Chair in front of you, and holding on with one hand. If you do this however, then make sure that you still keep one Arm raised up high in the air, as this will help stretch out your spine, and strengthen your Back!! When the 30 seconds are up, follow the Trainer on screen, and Exhale whilst lowering your Arms back down in front of your Chest. Now slowly lower your Leg back down to the original starting position in one fluid motion. Switch Legs here, and lift your Right Leg up, and place the Sole of your Right Foot on the inside of your Left Leg this time. Repeat the same procedure again here to strengthen your other Leg, and complete the perfect Tree Pose!

straight, then simply lean forwards as far as you can go instead. Your Back must remain perfectly straight! Again, hold this position briefly. Now, whilst Inhaling, raise both Arms upwards so that your Palms meet one another, and then bend your Knees and hold this position. Your Thighs should be almost parallel with the floor, and your Pose should almost resemble that of the Squat position! If done correctly, you'll feel the burn on your Thighs (Quads). For maximum effective of this exercise, try to make the transactions from one Pose to the next, in one fluid motion. The smoother your movement, the more successful it will be. As you can see, the usual Yellow Circle has changed to a thinner Oval shape, therefore you can have more movement from your Front to Back motions, however your Left and Right movements are now limited! In order to keep the Red Dot within the Yellow Oval, try your best to keep your side-movements from Left to Right to a minimum, and maintain your COG balance throughout. Shaking from side to side as you attempt this Pose will cause the Red Dot to move significantly so keep your Feet firmly in place to counteract this. Hold this Pose for the required time, and remember to follow the Blue Circle for perfect breathing timing throughout. When told to do so, Exhale whilst straightening your Knees back out, and bring your Arms back down to the original starting position to complete the perfect Sun Salutation Pose!

Sun Salutation

INFO: **Helps tone your Arms and Thighs.**

■ How to Execute:

Stand upright on the Balance Board with your Legs pinned together, and then bring your Hands together in front of your Chest so that your Palms meet, as if you are 'Praying'. Whilst Inhaling, raise

both of your Arms up high above your Head, and straighten your Arms upwards fully. Maintain your Balance and total control, and then bend backwards slightly to curve your Spine. Hold this position briefly, and then whilst Exhaling, lean forwards and bend down to touch your Toes with both Hands. As you do this, make sure that you keep your Back perfectly straight! If at the moment you are not flexible enough to reach your Toes whilst keeping your Spine

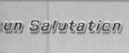

Standing Knee

INFO: **Helps towards improved Flexibility in your Thighs.**

■ How to Execute:

Stand upright on the Balance Board with your Legs pinned close together. Press your Right Foot down firmly onto the Board and exert more pressure for added balanced; then lift and raise your Left Leg so that your Knee is at Waist height.

Try it Out

Hold your Knee in place with your Hands, and maintain balance throughout. If you're finding it difficult to remain still and keep the Red Dot within the Yellow Circle, then remember to support yourself with your free Hand. If you do this however, remember to keep one Hand free to hold your Knee in place! Gripping the Board with your Toes may also help. From this position, Inhale, and stretch out your Spine by straighten your Back manually. This Pose is all about good Posture – therefore the straighter you are from your standing-Leg, all the way up; the more effective this exercise will be! Now, whilst Exhaling, hold your Knee, and pull it in tight towards your Chest. Hold your Knee up close your Chest briefly, and then release and lower it back down to Waist height again, but DO NOT drop it completely. You must now repeat this for a few repetitions. Inhale and Exhale in time with the outer Blue Circle, Inhaling as you release and lower your Knee, and Exhaling as you pull it in tight to your Chest. Once you've completed the required repetitions, Exhale and return to the original starting position by dropping your Leg back down onto the Board. Switch Legs now, raise your Right Knee this time, and repeat the same procedure again to complete the perfect the Standing Knee Pose!

Chair >>>

> **INFO: *Helps straighten your Back and Legs, as well as your Abs.***

■ How to Execute:

Stand on the Balance Board with your Legs spread evenly apart, and manually tighten and tense your Buttocks and Abdominal muscles for added effectiveness. Manually straighten your Back to stretch your Spine, and keep your Shoulders relaxed throughout. Whilst Inhaling, raise your Arms up and out in front of you, straighten them fully, and hold them in place at Shoulder height, so that they are parallel to the floor. Keep your Back completely straight at all times, and look straight ahead, focusing on your Fingers to help maintain Balance. Now whilst Exhaling, bend your Knees and drop down into an almost Squat position, so that it almost looks as if you are sitting – hence the name, 'Chair'. As you bend your Knees and drop down, rise up onto the tip of your Toes also for increased intensity! Manually contract your Abdominal muscles also as you do this, and make sure that your Thighs remain almost parallel to the floor as you hold the Pose. Keep your Back straight and your Shoulders relaxed, and continue to hold this 'Chair' Pose for around 30 seconds. Follow the Blue Circle to perfect your Breathing timing, and remain as motionless as possible to keep the Red Dot within the Yellow Circle. Inhale and Exhale slowly and gently to keep it as steady as you can, and then when told to do so, Inhale deeply, and rise back up slowly to the standing position. Exhale now, and lower your Arms and Heels back down to the original starting position, to complete the perfect Chair Pose!

Skip

Palm Tree >>>

> **INFO: *Helps tone your Ankles and stretch your Back.***

■ How to Execute:

Stand upright on the Balance Board with your Legs spread evenly apart, and then whilst Exhaling, raise your Arms up high above your Head, and straighten them fully. At the top of the extension, rise up onto the tip of your Toes, so that your Heels are off of the Board, and your Toes are the only thing remaining on the Front half of the Board. Stretch your fingers out wide, and manually straighten your Back to stretch and align your Spine. Now from this position, bring both of your Arms down in front of your body, and then follow through, and rotate them down and around behind you, so that the Palms of your Hands are now facing upwards, towards the ceiling. Keep your Arms perfectly straight as you do this, and remain steady on your Toes at all times. If done correctly, your stance should now resemble that of a 'Sky-Diving' Pose! Hold this position for around 30 seconds, and remember to follow the Blue Circle to help control your breathing, and ultimately your Balance. Maintain your stillness as best you can to keep the Red Dot within the Yellow Circle, and if the Red Dot is in the upper half of the Circle, then you're exerting too much pressure on the front of the Board, therefore try leaning backwards slightly to centre it; whereas if the Red Dot is in the lower half of the Circle, then you're not exerting enough pressure, therefore you should lean forwards even more! Once you've held the Pose for the required time, Exhale slowly and gently, and then lower your Arms, and drop back down onto your Heels, to return to the original starting position and complete the perfect the Palm Tree Pose!

Triangle

> **INFO:** *Helps straighten your Lower Body and tone your Waist.*

■ How to Execute:

Stand upright on the Balance Board with your Legs spread evenly apart, and then take one large step back off of the Board with your Left Leg, extending it behind you, whilst keeping your Right Leg firmly in place on the Board. Now turn your Left Leg so that your Left Foot is pointing to the Left, and then turn and face that direction, whilst keeping your Right Leg in place, so that your Right Foot is still facing forwards. Your Left and Right Heel should now be aligned with one another. Now, whilst Inhaling, stretch your Arms out wide and extend them fully, so that one Arm is pointing towards the Television, and then other is pointing away. Whilst Exhaling, twist your Upper Body around, and bring your Left Arm up and around over your Body, and then bring it down and rest your Left Hand on your Right Ankle. Once you have a comfortable position, raise your Right Arm straight up above you, and point it towards the ceiling. Look up at this point, and focus on the Fingers of your Right Hand. To master this Pose correctly, your Left Side should be completely parallel and at a 90 degree angle to your raised Right Arm! Hold your Ankle and push down onto the Balance Board with your Right Foot, whilst exerting added pressure with your Left Hand if needs be. Inhale and Exhale deeply and slowly following the Blue Circle as you do so, in order to keep the Red Bar within the Blue Bar halfway up. To perfect this, you'll want to exert about 60% of your overall body weight onto your Right Leg! Once completed, follow the Trainer, and pivot back around to the original starting position. Switch Legs now, take a step back with your Right Leg this time, and repeat the same procedure again to complete the perfect Triangle Pose!

King of the Dance

> **INFO:** *Helps tone your Hips and may also align your Spine.*

■ How to Execute:

Stand upright on the Balance Board with your Legs close together, and bend your Left Leg behind you so that your Foot is at your Buttocks. Hold your Left Foot with your Left Hand so that your Thumb rests on the Sole of your Foot, and then find your balance. Now raise your Right Arm up in the air above your head, and extend it fully. Whilst Inhaling, lower your Arm down, straight in front of you, so that it is now completely parallel to the floor, yet still maintaining the full extension. As you do this, bring your Left Leg back slightly, and raise it up past your Buttocks for increased balanced. This will align your COG. To do this smoothly, use your Hand to pull your Foot upwards! In this position, look forwards and focus your gaze on the Fingers of your Right Hand. Whilst Exhaling, raise your Left Leg even further, so that your Left Foot is now up almost at Shoulder height. Remember,

Downward-Facing Dog

> **INFO:** *Stretches your Back and can help to strengthen your whole Body.*

Downward-Facing Dog

■ How to Execute:

This Pose is completely different to anything that you have done so far. Start by dropping down onto all fours (your Hands and Knees), and place Only your Hands on the Balance Board. Keep your Legs off of the Balance behind you, and then once you're comfortable, Exhale and raise your Buttocks high into the air. As you do this, press down into the floor with your Heels so that both Feet are now flat on the floor. Doing this will straighten both your Back and your Legs simultaneously! Straighten your Arms fully at this point, and make sure that your Elbows are facing outwards to the side. In this position, lower your Head, and focus on your Stomach. If done correctly, your Body should resemble an Upside Down 'V-shape'. To begin with however, look up at the Television and get a feel for the amount of pressure you need to exert onto the Balance Board to keep the Red Bar inside the small Blue Bar. Once you understand how much force you need to use, lower your Head once again and focus on your Stomach like before. To get the most out of this Pose, and to master the position properly, push down and exert more pressure with your Arms, and then manually point the lower part of your Spine (Coccyx) up towards the ceiling! To do this effectively, your Arms, Back and Legs must be all completely straight, and your Heels must remain flat on the floor. If you're having trouble with this due to lack of Flexibility, then bend into the V-shape as much as you can, until you feel the strain. Place equal weight and pressure on your Arms and Legs, and manually pull your Stomach in, and contract your Abdominal muscles. If you're below the Blue Bar, then you need to exert more pressure onto the Balance Board with your Hands, whereas if you're above the Blue Bar, then accept more body weight into your Legs instead! Inhale and Exhale slowly and gently throughout and breathe in time with the Blue Circle. Relax your Shoulders and hold this V-shape position for around 30 seconds. When told to do so, lower your Arms and Knees back down to the original starting position on all fours, to complete the perfect Downward-Facing Dog Pose!

this is an advanced Pose, so Flexibility is key here! If you're unable to get your Foot this high, then simply raise it as far as you can go, and remember to keep your balance throughout. Tighten your Stomach and Abs now and hold this position for around 30 seconds. If done correctly, all of your Limbs should be parallel with one another, and should be at a 90 degree angle to everything else. Both Arms should remain straight at all times, as should your Right Leg. Your Left Thigh shoulder be at a 90 degree angle to your Right Thigh, and your Left Leg should be bent at the Knee, again at a 90 degree angle! Once you've mastered this, hold it for the required time, and breathe slowly and gently, in order to maintain balance throughout, and to keep the Red Dot within the Yellow Circle. Remember, if you're finding it difficult to balance, then feel free to support yourself by placing a Chair in front of you, and holding on with your free Hand! When told to do so, Inhale, and raise your Upper Body and Right Arm back up; and then Exhale as you lower your Arms and Leg back down to the original starting position, in one fluid motion - the smoother the transaction, the better. Switch Legs now, raise your Right Leg this time, and repeat the same procedure again to complete the perfect King of the Dance Pose!

Bridge >>>

> **INFO: Helps straighten your Torso and may also tone your Hips.**

■ How to Execute:
There's no need for the Balance Board here, however you will be better off on a soft surface, such as a Yoga Mat for example. If you do not have a Yoga Mat, then set a few Towels down instead. Also, if you have any sort of Back problems, then take extreme care when performing this Pose, and only curve your Spine slightly. Do not overdo it and injure yourself!!

Lie flat on your Back, facing up towards the ceiling, with your Legs and Arms held outwards in a relaxed position. Now bend your Knees

upwards, and bring your Feet closer towards your Buttocks, so that your Heels and Toes are now flat on the floor. Whilst Inhaling, bring your Hands to your Heels, and hold your Ankles with both Hands if you can. You'll require increased Flexibility to do this, therefore if you cannot reach your Heels with your Hands, then simply rest the Palms of your Hands on the floor instead, as close to your Heels as you can possibly go. Once you have this position, Exhale now, and slowly raise your Hips up off of the floor, whilst keeping your Hands and Feet held firmly in place. If done correctly, then your Calves should be perfectly straight, pointing your Knees upwards towards the ceiling, and there should be an almost semi-circular arc beneath you, from your Calves, through to your Thighs, and following through to your Upper Back! Keep your Arms and Head still at all times; and to help maintain good posture throughout, focus your gaze on the ceiling as you do so, and breathe slowly and gently in time with the Blue Circle! Hold this Pose for around 30 seconds, and then return to the original starting position when told to do so, to complete the perfect Bridge Pose!

Cobra

> **INFO: Helps straighten and increases Flexibility in your Back muscles and may correct Posture.**

■ How to Execute:
There's no need for the Balance Board here, however you will be better off on a soft surface, such as a Yoga Mat for example. If you do not have a Yoga Mat, then set a few Towels down instead.

Also, if you have any sort of Back problems, then take extreme care when performing this Pose, and only curve your Spine slightly. Do not overdo it and injure yourself!!

Lie face down on the floor, and tuck your Arms in slightly, so that your Elbows and Palms of your Hands are resting on the floor beneath you. Expand your Chest now and Inhale. Whilst Inhaling, stretch your Elbows out, and extend your Arms fully, and then push your Upper Body off away from the floor so that your Back is now Curving upwards. As you do this, you must keep your Feet, Legs and Wait completely still, pinned to the floor, as this will help Curve your Spine even more! To help increase the curve more comfortably, raise your head and look upwards. Lock your Arms at the Elbows and keep your Shoulders still at all times - try your best not to raise them, as this will take the strain off your Back, and decrease the intensity of the exercise! Keep your Arms as straight and extended

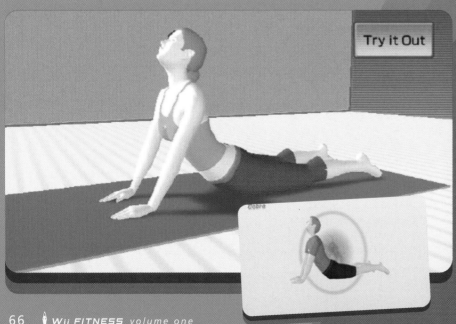

as possible, use your Inner Thigh muscles to hold the Pose, and maintain that perfect Curvature from your Lower Spine (Coccyx) all the way up to your Neck, for that all important perfect technique! Inhale and Exhale deeply and slowly with the Blue Circle, and hold this Pose for around 30 seconds. Exhale when you're finished, and slowly return to the original starting position to complete the perfect Cobra Pose!

Crocodile Twist

> **INFO: Helps exercise and stretch the muscles in your Back.**

■ How to Execute:

There's no need for the Balance Board here, however you will be better off on a soft surface, such as a Yoga Mat for example. If you do not have a Yoga Mat, then set a few Towels down instead.

Lie flat on your Back, facing upwards towards the ceiling; and then whilst Inhaling, stretch out both of your Arms, and place them flat on the floor, out to your sides. Whilst Exhaling, hold your Right Knee with your Left Hand, bend your Right Knee, and cross it over your Body, so that it ends up your Left hand side. To do this, manually pull your Right Knee across your body using your Left Hand. Push your Right Knee down firmly onto the floor, and make sure that your

Right Foot is pointing to the left, in the same direction as you crossing Knee. In this position, turn your Head to the Right now, and focus your gaze away from your body. You should now feel the strain on the Right hand side of your body, as it stretches slowly whilst holding this Pose! For increased intensity, manually push your Right Shoulder down into the floor, and hold it in place to real feel the strain! Hold this position for around 30 seconds, and Inhale and Exhale slowly and gently in time with the Blue Circle, to perfect your breathing as

you do this exercise. Return to the original starting position when told to do so, and then switch Legs. This time, bring your Left Leg across your Body to the

Shoulderstand >>>

> **INFO: Helps strengthen your Abs and Back, as well as align your Legs.**

■ How to Execute:

There's no need for the Balance Board here, however you will be better off on a soft surface, such as a Yoga Mat for example. If you do not have a Yoga Mat, then set a few Towels down instead. Also, if you have High Blood Pressure, or any other Medical Conditions of the same nature, then take extreme care when performing this Pose, and do not strain yourself too hard, and cause unnecessary problems!

Lie flat on your Back, facing up towards the ceiling, and hold your Arms down at your sides, resting the Palms of your Hands on the floor beside you. Keep your Legs pinned together, and then whilst Inhaling, raise both of your Legs up in the air; then Exhale, and raise your Back upwards also. Bend your Legs behind your Head now, keeping your Arms and Hands firmly in place on the floor. If you can touch the floor behind your Head with your Toes, then do so, as this will seriously increase the intensity even more! In this position, bring your Chin up to your Chest, and hold this

Right, and repeat the same procedure as before, to feel the strain on your Left hand side now, and complete the perfect Crocodile Twist Pose!

position for a second or two. Now pull your Waist and Stomach up, and raise your Legs upwards, so that your Feet are now pointing up at the ceiling. Extend your Legs fully as you do this, and support yourself by holding your Waist / Buttocks. Use your Shoulders for support also, and maintain a good balance throughout! Once you have a steady and stable position, hold this Pose for around 30 seconds, and breathe in time with the Blue Circle. Straightness and stillness is everything here! The more control you have over your body, and the straighter your Legs and Back are, the more effective this exercise will be. After the required time, Exhale slowly, and lower your Legs back down behind your Head. Push your Hands into the floor for added support now, and then slowly lower your Back and Legs back down to the original starting position; and relax, to complete the perfect Shoulderstand Pose!

Wii Fit muscle Workouts

With enough regular training, mastering all of the Muscle Workouts will ultimately increase your muscle size and overall body strength! These Muscle Workouts train all of your muscles in the Left and Right side of your body equally, to develop a well-balanced body overall.

This is the perfect way to increase your muscle size and get that all important Toned-look.

Single Leg Extension

Reps: 5/6

Skip

Single Leg Extension

INFO: *Helps tighten the Torso, Hips and Triceps, and can also improve your Co-ordination too.*

■ How to Execute:

Stand upright on the Balance Board with your Legs spread evenly apart, and then raise your Left Leg so that your Left Knee is up by your Waist / Hip area. As you're balancing on your Right Leg, hold your Left Arm at a 90-degree angle behind you so that your Left Hand is pointing down towards the floor, and hold your Right Arm at a 90-degree angle in front of you so that your Right Hand is pointing up towards the ceiling. Once you're in position, remain standing on your Right Leg, and then swing your Left Leg backwards, and your Left Arm upwards. As you do this, extend both your Left Leg and your Left Arm fully so that your stance resembles that of a 'Flying Superman' Pose! Swing your Right Arm backwards also, and extend this

fully as well. Once you've done this, bring your Left Leg back up to your Waist / Hip area, and return to Arms to the original 90-degree angle starting positions. Repeat this back-forth motion for the required amount of Repetitions, and remember to breathe steadily as you do so. If done correctly, then you should almost look as if you're Running on the spot in Slow Motion!! Maintain balance on your Right Leg throughout, and if needs be, remember to support yourself by holding onto a Chair in front of you, using your Right Hand, to help keep the small Red Dot within the Yellow Oval at all times, for maximum effectiveness. If you do this however, then still remember to swing your Left Arm as usual. Once you've completed the required amount of Reps', switch Legs now, and balance on your Left Leg this time; then swing your Right Leg backwards, and your Right Arm upwards, to complete the perfect Single Leg Extension workout!

Press-Up & Side Stand

INFO: *Helps tighten your Chest, Shoulder and Arm muscles.*

■ How to Execute:

Get down onto all fours, and place Only your Hands on the Balance Board. The first part of this exercise is the 'Press-Up'. Extend your Legs backwards fully, raise your Lower Body off of the floor, and support yourself using your Arms. If you have trouble doing Press-Ups, then keep your Knees on the floor instead, to

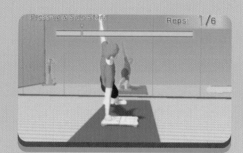

reduce your weight, making this workout a little easier for you! The timing for this exercise is a little different to anything that you've attempted so far, so listen up. Once you're in position, wait for the first 'Whistle' sound, and then lower your Body down towards the floor, whilst bending your Elbows outwards as you do so. Whatever you do, DO NOT touch or rest on the floor as you go down, as this will completely take the strain off the Triceps muscles in your Arms! Lower yourself down, and hold this position for a second or two until you hear the second 'Whistle' sound, indicating to push back up. Follow your Trainer on screen, and push back up to the original position, using your Arms, but remember to keep your Body as straight as you possibly can, and try not to raise your Buttocks too high.

Now here comes the 'Side Stand'. Once you return to the top Press-Up position, again listen out for the 'Whistle', and then cross your Right Leg over your Left Leg, and then raise your Right Arm out to the side, and then high up above your Head, so that your Hand is now pointing up towards the ceiling. To increase effectiveness even more, look up and focus on your raised Hand. Hold this position for a second or two again, and then when the next 'Whistle' sounds, uncross your Legs, and return to the Press-Up position.

Basically there are four 'Whistles' to listen out for – two to start and end the Press-Ups, and two to start and end the Side Stand! At the top of the screen is a continuous Bar – when the Red Bar start, go down for the Press-Up, and when it ends, push back up. When the Green bar starts, begin your Side Stand, and when it ends, return to the Press-Up position. Easy.

Once you've done this, complete another Press-Up just like before, but this time, cross your Left Leg over your Right Leg, and raise your Left Arm upwards! Return to the Press-Up position, and continue to

repeat this method or Press-Up, Right Side, then Left Side, to complete the perfect Press-Up & Side Stand workout!

Torso & Waist Twists

INFO: Helps tighten your Side Abdominal muscles to give you a more toned Waistline.

■ How to Execute:

Stand upright on the Balance Board with your Legs spread evenly apart, and then stretch your Arms out to your sides, extending them fully. The first part of this exercise is the 'Torso Twists'. Keep your Legs and Hips completely still as you do this workout, and Only move your Upper Body, from your Torso up! Movement in your Lower Body will reduce the intensity of this exercise. Now, listen out for the 'Whistle' sound,

and Rotate your Upper Body around to the Right as far as you can go, so that you're now facing to the Right. As you do this, keep your Arms straight and extended at all times, and keep focusing in the direction of your Body. Go with Upper Body your movement. When you hear the second 'Whistle' sound, Rotate all the way back around, so that this time you're now facing to the Left. Repeat this procedure for the required amount of Repetitions, and continue to Rotate from Right to Left, using Only your Upper Body. As you do this, try to control your movement as best you can so that the small Red Dot remains within the Yellow Circle at all times! Once you've done this, lower your Arms down to your sides, and get ready for part two.

Now for the 'Waist Twists'. For this exercise, you'll want to Twist your body, not Bend it! Raise your Arms back out to the sides again, and fully extend them like before. Now, listen for the 'Whistle' sound again, and then Twist your Upper Body down to the Right hand side, so that your Left Hand is now down by the Right hand side of your Body, and your Right Arm is pointing up towards the ceiling. Try to keep your Back as straight as you possibly can, and manually keep your Buttocks tucked in as you do so.

Jackknife >>>

INFO: Helps tighten your Abs to give you a fitter, more toned Physique.

■ How to Execute:

Lie flat on your Back, and place Only your Feet on the Balance Board, with your Legs slightly bent at the Knees. Stretch both of your Arms out behind your Head, and extend them fully. When the first 'Whistle' sounds, remove your Feet from the Balance Board, and raise both of your Legs and Upper Body simultaneously off the floor, and then touch your Legs (Shin area is best) with your Hands. Keep your Arms extended at all times as you do, and maintain the slight bend in your Legs also. If done correctly, then your Body should now form an almost perfect 'V-Shape'! Hold this position for a second or two until the second 'Whistle' sounds, and then lower both

your Arms and Legs back down to the original starting position. As you do this, make sure that your movement is steady and controlled, and make sure that your Feet land back on the Balance Board to complete each Repetition. The smoother the transaction, the more effective this exercise will be, and the more your Abdominal muscles will work! Repeat this procedure for the required amount of Reps', to complete the perfect Jackknife workout!

Remember to keep your Arms fully extended and in the fixed position, so that when you Twist, your Arms follow your Body movement. When Twisting to the Right, you'll feel the strain in your Side Abdominal muscles, in the Left side of your Body! When the 'Whistle' sounds again, Twist back up to the original standing position. On the next 'Whistle', repeat the same procedure, but this time Twist down to the Left, so that your Right Hand is now down by your Left side, and your Left Arm is pointing up towards the ceiling, to feel the strain in your Right Side Abdominal muscles this time! Repeat this for the required amount of Repetitions and maintain the small Red Dot within the Yellow Circle, to complete the perfect Torso & Wait Twist workout!

Rowing Squat

*INFO: **Helps tighten your Thighs and Back to give you a strong posture.***

■ How to Execute:
Stand on the Balance Board with your

feet spread Shoulders width apart, and then hold your Arms out in front of you, at Shoulder-height. Wait for the 'Whistle' sound, and then Squat down by bending your Knees at about a 120-degree angle, as if you're about to sit down. Do not enter the full-Squat position, but instead maintain that 120-degree angle throughout, as this will help increase the Lactic Acid in your Thighs (Quads) and Hamstrings! As you're Squatting down, stick your Buttocks out, and keep your Back completely straight for maximum effectiveness! To help with this, focus straight ahead of you. As you Squat, pull your Arms back from in front of your body simultaneously, so that your Elbows are now tucked in tight to your sides. Manually contract your Upper Back muscles as you pull your Arms in, to

tighten and work your Trapezius, and Latissimus Dorsi muscles in the upper part of our Back. As you do this, maintain the correct posture so that the Red Dot drops and remains within the Blue Bar on the right hand side of the screen. Hold this Rowing Squat position for a second or two until the Blue Bar turns Yellow, and then return to the original standing position with your Arms out in front of you. Count if necessary to understand when best to Squat, and stand, with perfect timing. Execute the required amount of Repetitions to complete the perfect Rowing Squat workout!

Single Leg Twist

*INFO: **Helps tighten your Side Abdominal muscles to give you a more toned Waistline.***

■ How to Execute:
Stand upright on the Balance Board, and then remove your Left Leg, holding it back behind you slightly to the side, so that you're now standing on only your Right Leg. Raise your Right Arm up in the air now, and hold it slightly out to the side, then hold your Waist / Hip with your Left Hand. If done correctly, you should look as if you are Flying in the 'Superman' pose! This is now your starting position. When the 'Whistle' sounds, raise your Left Knee up to your Waist / Hip area, and bring your Right Arm down across your body simulta-neously, touching your Left Knee with your Right Hand. Once you've done this, raise your Arm back up, and lower your Leg back down behind you. Repeat this technique for the required amount of Repetitions, in quick succession. Do not hesitate or hold this position like usual, instead it's all about quick movements! As you do this, always keep your Left Leg off of the floor, and never drop it completely, as this will take the strain off of your Leg, and reduce the intensity of the exercise significantly! Maintain steadiness and

Lunge >>>

*INFO: **Helps tighten your Thighs and Hips to give you firm Legs and slimmer Hips.***

■ How to Execute:
Stand on the Balance Board with your Legs spread evenly apart, and then take one large extended step back off the Board with your Left Leg, but keep your Right Leg firmly in place. Now place your Hands behind your Head, and interlock your Fingers – this will help maintain the perfect Lunging technique for the following exercise! Wait for the 'Whistle' to sound, and then bend your front Leg at a 90-degree angle at the Knee and push downwards, but make sure that your Knee doesn't pass your Toes. As you do this, bend your rear Leg at a 90-degree angle also, so that your stance now resembles the 'Wedding Proposal' pose! Keep your back straight at all times, and do not lean forwards! Exert added pressure onto your front Leg so

that the Pink Bar on the right hand side of the screen rises up past the Blue Line. If the Bar doesn't reach the Blue Line, then you're not putting enough force onto your Front Leg, so exert more. Hold this position for a second or two, and then rise back up; wait the next 'Whistle', and again, Lunge forwards. If done correctly, you'll feel the burn and Lactic Acid build up in your Right Thigh (Quads)! Complete the required amount of Repetitions, and then switch Legs, taking a step back with your Right Leg this time, and Lunging with your Left Leg, to feel the burn in your Left Thigh. Repeat this procedure for the required amount of Reps' to complete the perfect Lunge workout!

Sideways Leg Lift

> **INFO:** *Helps tighten the Side and Shoulder muscles for that well-toned look.*

■ How to Execute:

Stand upright on the Balance Board using only your Right Leg, and then lean slightly to the side, so that your Left Leg is now off of the Balance Board by a few inches, but not as much as the previous Single Leg Twist workout. Hold your Waist with your Left Hand, and keep your Right Arm down by your side. Wait for the 'Whistle' to sound, and then raise your Left Leg out to the Side, whilst simultaneously raising your Right Arm out to the side and then upwards, ending at the same angle as you leg extension! If done correctly, the full extension of this exercise should almost resemble the 'Flying Superman' starting position of the previous Single Leg Twist workout. Again, balance and

steadiness is key here! If you find yourself wobbling uncontrollably, then feel free to support yourself by holding onto a Chair in front of you, using your free Left Hand, to help maintain the small Red Dot within the Yellow Oval. If you do this however, then still remember to raise your Right Arm as usual! Do not hold the extended position, but instead quickly thrust both your Leg and Arm outwards and upwards in quick succession to real feel the burn. Complete the required amount of Repetitions and then switch Legs. Stand on your Left Leg now, and raise your Right Leg and Left Arm this time, repeating the same techniques as before, to complete the perfect Sideways Leg Lift workout!

Chest, and manually contract, pull in, and tighten your Abdominal muscles for maximum effectiveness! Whatever you do, DO NOT allow your Stomach to drop to floor, as this will take every bit of strain away from this exercise! If you're having trouble holding yourself up and maintaining this position, then feel free to raise your Buttocks up into the air, creating an 'Upside-down V-Shape' with your body. This will reduce your overall weight and minimize the pressure greatly, making the workout a little easier. That's pretty much it! You now have to simply hold this position for the required amount of time. Try not to wobble too much, and try to keep the Red Dot as central to the Cross [+] as you possibly can for maximum results!

Tricep Extension

> **INFO:** *Helps tighten your Triceps to give you leaner, more toned Arms.*

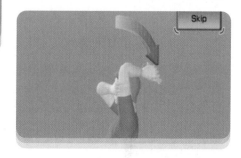

■ How to Execute:

There's no need for the Balance Board here, however you will be required to hold and use the Wii Remote, to pick up on your movements instead!

stillness as best you can, and try not to wobble on the spot, so that you can maintain the Red Dot within the Yellow Oval at all times. If you're having trouble with balance, then feel free to support yourself on a Chair in front of you, using your Left Hand which is usually placed on your Hip. If you do this however, then remember to still raise and lower your Right Arm as usual! Switch Legs now so that you're standing on only your Left Leg, and raise your Left Arm in the air this time. Repeat the same procedures as before to complete the perfect Single Leg Twist workout!

Parallel Stretch

> **INFO:** *Helps tighten your Torso's deep muscles to give you a flexible, well-postured body.*

■ How to Execute:

This exercise is solely about Stamina, and your overall Endurance, and is completely different to anything that you've attempted so far! This can be a painful exercise, especially when you reach the 'Stretch Challenge' later on!!

Get down onto all fours, and place Only your Forearms on Balance Board, so that your Hands are extended beyond the Board. To help with the following Endurance exercise, either interlock your Fingers, or clench your Fists, and tense, holding them close together! Now stretch your Legs backwards and extend them fully, making sure that your Stomach is well away from the floor, and your entire body is perfectly straight. Expand your Shoulders now to raise your

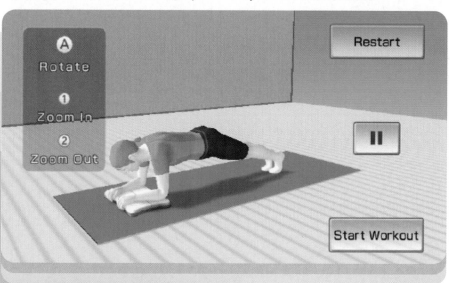

Stand upright on the spot with your Legs close together, and hold the Wii Remote in your Right Hand. Raise and stretch your Right Arm upwards, and extend it fully, so that the Wii Remote is pointing up towards the ceiling. Now bring your Left Hand across your body and support your Right Arm by holding your Elbow with your Left Hand. Wait until you hear the first 'Whistle' sound, and then Bend your Right Elbow downwards so that your Forearm and Wii Remote Hand is now pointing down behind your Head. As you do this, keep your Upper Arm perfectly still at all times. The only part of your Arm that should have movement is your Elbow and Forearm! On the second 'Whistle', raise and extend your Arm back up to the original position again, but as you do so, manually tense and contract your Triceps muscle for maximum effectiveness! Point the Wii Remote back at the ceiling, and then repeat the same procedure again for the required amount of Repetitions. Continue to

Bend and Extend whilst manually contracting, and then switch Arms when told to do so. Hold the Wii Remote in your Left Hand this time, raise and extend it fully, and support your Elbow with your Right Hand. Now lower your Left Forearm down behind your Head by bending your Left Elbow, and then raise it back up once again. Execute the required amount of Reps' to complete the perfect Tricep Extension workout!

Once you've mastered this technique properly and feel that you could probably start to add more weight to your workout and increase the intensity, then try holding a Bag of Sugar in your raised Hand also, alongside the Wii Remote of course. Master this, and then try using Bottles of Water instead! Bottles are perfect for this exercise, as you can fill them up or decant them as much as you want, to increase or decrease the weight to best suit you! Give it a go, and feel those Triceps muscles burn!

Single Arm Stand

> INFO: **Helps tighten the Abs and Thigh muscles and can improve Co-ordination too.**

■ How to Execute:

There's no need for the Balance Board here, however you will be required to hold and use the Wii Remote, to pick up on your movements instead!

Hold the Wii Remote in your Right Hand, and then raise your Right Arm upwards above your head, so that the Wii Remote is now pointing up towards the ceiling. Keep the Wii Remote held up high with your Arm fully extended, and then sit down on the floor. Lay down now facing up to the ceiling, and maintain the upright position of the Wii Remote at all times! Your Raised Arm should always be in the air, perpendicular to the floor. When the 'Whistle' sounds, raise your Upper Body off of the floor, and pull yourself up by manually contracting your Abdominal muscles. From this position, push down with your free Left Hand, and push your Body back up to the original standing position. This entire movement should all be done in one fluid motion! The smoother the transaction from laying down, to standing up, the more effective this workout will be! As you do this, remember to keep the Wii Remote pointing up at all times so that the Red Line overlaps the central Blue Line at all times on screen. The less movement you have in your Raised Arm, the better your results will be at the end of this exercise. Listen out for the 'Whistles' and continue to lay down, and stand up for the required amount of Repetitions. When told to do so, switch Arms now, and hold the Wii Remote in your Left Hand this time. Push up using your free Right Hand, and remember to keep the Wii Remote up at all times, as you complete the transactions in one fluid motion, to complete the perfect Single Arm Stand workout!

Arm & Leg Lift >>>

> INFO: **Helps tighten the Shoulder and Hip muscles to improve body balance.**

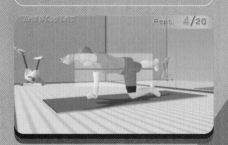

Reps: 4/20

■ How to Execute:

There's no need for the Balance Board here, however you will be required to hold and use the Wii Remote, to pick up on your movements instead!

Hold the Wii Remote in your Right Hand, and then get down onto all fours, whilst still holding the Wii Remote. Once you're down on your Hands and Knees, make sure that the Wii Remote is pointing forwards at all times. Wait for the first 'Whistle' to sound, then raise your Right Arm and Left Leg simultaneously, and stretch and extend them both outwards fully,

so that your Right Arm is outstretched in front of you, and your Left Leg is outstretched behind you. Your Stillness indicator on screen is slightly different to anything that you've seen so far, so listen up. As you extend your Arm outwards in front of you, make sure that the Wii Remote is pointing straight ahead at perfect Head height, so that the Red Line overlaps the Blue Line perfectly! The steadier your Arm and Wii Remote Hand is, the straighter the Line will be! If you shake or wobble, then the Line will become squiggled, and your overall result will be low. Keep your Arm and Hand as straight as you possibly can, and keep it pointing straight ahead at all times, in order to maintain the Red Line on top of the Blue Line, for maximum effectiveness and result! When the second 'Whistle' sounds, lower your Right Arm and Left Leg back down to the original starting position, and then repeat the same procedure again for the required amount of Repetitions. Switch Arms and Legs now, and hold the Wii Remote in your Left Hand this time. Raise and extend your Left Arm and Right Leg now, and repeat the same technique as before, for the required amount for Reps' to complete the perfect Arm & Leg Lift workout!

Stretch Challenge

INFO: *Challenge your Trainer.*

Press-Up Challenge >>>

INFO: *Challenge your Trainer.*

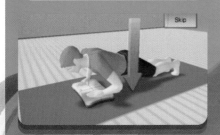

Jackknife Challenge >>>

INFO: *Challenge your Trainer.*

■ How to Execute:
This challenge is all about your overall Stamina and Endurance when challenging your Trainer with the ultimate Parallel Stretch workout!! The beginning stages are pretty simple, however once you advance onwards through the difficulties, and reach the 'Champion' level, then things really start to burn!! Read the 'Parallel Stretch' section above for more details.

Just remember to fight the pain, and stick it out to the very end! Endurance and Stamina is everything here – focus your attention on something else to take your mind off of the exercise, and once competed... have a long rest.

■ How to Execute:
This challenge is all about your overall Stamina and Endurance when challenging your Trainer with ultimate Press-Up workout!! The beginning stages are pretty simple, however once you advance onwards through the difficulties, and reach the 'Champion' level, then things really start to burn!! Read the 'Press-Up & Side Stand' section above for more details.

Just remember to fight the pain, and stick it out to the very end! Endurance and Stamina is everything here – focus your attention on something else to take your mind off of the exercise, and once competed... have a long rest.

■ How to Execute:
This challenge is all about your overall Stamina and Endurance when challenging your Trainer with the ultimate Jackknife workout!! The beginning stages are pretty simple, however once you advance onwards through the difficulties, and reach the 'Champion' level, then things really start to burn!! Read the 'Jackknife' section above for more details.

Just remember to fight the pain, and stick it out to the very end! Endurance and Stamina is everything here – focus your attention on something else to take your mind off of the exercise, and once competed... have a long rest.

Wii Fit aerobic exercises

This is the perfect way to get your Cardiovascular System working and burn off those hateful Calories.

the Aerobic Exercises are Cardio-based Endurance workouts that can burn Calories and Fat at a fast rate over several minutes of intense training. Putting that little extra effort in and pushing yourself even harder throughout these exercises will burn Fat much faster, and can ultimately even help strengthen your Bones!

Hula Hoop >>>

INFO: Sway your Hips to spin the Hula Hoop. This can help improve Pelvic Alignment.

■ How to Execute:

Stand upright on the Balance Board with your legs spread evenly apart, and when the game begins, start to rotate your Hips around to the Left (anticlockwise) to start spinning the Hula Hoop around your Mii character on screen. For maximum effectiveness, keep your Legs completely still, and Only rotate your Hips / Waist area around. To help with your rotational movements, hold your Hands on your Hips also, and manually move your Hips around using your Hands, for increased rotations! Remember, the faster and larger your rotations, and the smoother your movements, the more Spins you will ultimately complete.

As you progress, the two Mii characters ahead will start to throw more Hula Hoops at you, from either the Left or Right side. You MUST catch these Hula Hoops if you want to earn Big Points, as your Spins will be doubled each time you catch a new Hoop. For example, one Spin with one Hoop is worth 1 Spin; whereas one Spin with two Hoops is worth 2 Spins, and one Spin with 3 Hoops is worth 3 Spins; and so on and so forth! Therefore Spinning with multiple Hoops will seriously increase your overall score come the end! Keep a close eye on the other two Mii characters ahead, and when you notice one of them throw the Hula Hoop, stop spinning, and lean to either the Left or Right depending on which direction the Hoop is coming from, by shifting your body weight to that side, in order to catch the oncoming Hoop! Once you have it, return to the centre of the Balance Board, and continue to spin with two Hoops. Again, wait for the next Hoop to be thrown, and do the same again. Continue to rotate, spin, and lean to catch the new Hoops, and then continue to Spin for the required amount of time to complete the session. Remember, the more Hoops you have, and the more fluid your rotational movements are, the higher your score will be!!

Super Hula Hoop

INFO: Sway your Hips to spin the Hula Hoop. This can help improve Pelvic Alignment.

■ How to Execute:

Super Hula Hoop is pretty much the exact same as the Hula Hoop game explained above, and requires the exact same techniques and motions as before (read above for more details in Rotational movements etc).

The only difference this time however, is that this game is more of an endurance session, as you'll be required to Spin over a few Stages, for a few minutes each time, which as you can guess can seriously increase your overall score come the end! Not just that, but you will also have to Rotate / Spin in the direction that you are told to Spin on screen. For example, at the beginning of each Stage, you'll be told to Spin in a specific direction at which you MUST abide to. If you're told to Spin to the 'Right', then you MUST rotate your Hips / Waist around to the Right, and not to the Left. If you rotate to the Left, then the Balance Board will not accept your

rotational movements, and you will score no Spins, ultimately causing the Hula Hoop to drop! The same applies if you're told to Spin to the Left – you MUST rotate to the Left in order for your movements to be accepted, and for the Spins to count! Pay attention at the beginning of each Stage to understand which direction you must rotate in, and then continue to Spin in that direction for the required amount time, remembering to lean to either the Left or Right to catch the oncoming Hoops, thus increasing your overall Spins! Move onto the next Stage, and repeat the same process again. Continue to do this for each Stage, and rack up those all-important Spin Points to score Big!!

Rhythm Boxing

> **INFO: Throw Punches in time to the Rhythm. This workout will help you burn your Body Fat.**

■ How to Execute:

You must use both the Wii Remote and Nunchuck for this session, holding the Wii Remote in your Right Hand and the Nunchuck in your Left Hand.

For this workout, you'll be required to throw a combination of different Punches in order to score Points. If your timing is perfect, then you'll score Double Points for each successful action! As this is Rhythm Boxing, timing is everything, so pay close attention to the 'Tap, Tap, Tap' Beat at all times, and Punch in perfect unison with the Beat to Double up your Points. To begin with, pay close attention to your Trainer Mii on screen who performs the combination first. He will only show you the once, so look closely! Once you understand the Punch-Block combination, you will then have to repeat the motions exactly, to complete the routine. The combinations involve actions like 'Right-Block, Left-Block' for example. 'Right-Block' requires you to Step off of the Board with your

Right Leg, and then Punch using your Right Hand. Block simply requires you to step back on, and stand on the Balance Board with both Feet, remaining still as the Punch-Bag strikes you, thus Blocking the strike. 'Left-Block' requires you Step off of the Board with your Left Leg, and Punch using your Left Hand. Again, step back on the Balance Board, and remain still with both feet firmly in place, to Block. This combination should all be completed in one fluid motion, in perfect time to the 'Tap, Tap' Beat for maximum Points!

As you progress through the session, the routines and combinations will become longer and more challenging! For example, instead of a simple one-two combo, you'll be required to remember and repeat more intense combinations such as 'Right, Left, Right Left, Block, Block, Right, Left'. Also, instead of just stepping off of the Board to the front, you will have to step off to the back also, so pay close attention to the Footwork movement at all times!! These types of combos require a greater sense of Rhythm and a heightened short-term memory! Once you understand the routine, repeat the combination a few times until you move onto the next routine.

There are three different Stages to Rhythm Boxing – Beginner, Advanced and Super Advanced. The Beginner Stage is 3

Minutes long, and involves basic routines of one-two Punch-Block combinations, thus helping you to get into the session. Advanced is 6 Minutes long, and incorporates more advanced routines, and longer combinations of Punch-Block-Step combos for example, for the more Rhythmic players. And Super Advanced is a 10 Minute session, involving the most complex routines and combinations, that test your memory, and brain-to-body movement significantly! In this Stage, you will also have to 'Dodge' the Punch-Bags jabs, instead of just Blocking them. To do this, hold the Wii Remote and Nunchuck together in front of you, and then sway them both simulta-neously to the Right and Left, to Dodge in that direction! Also, you may have to step off of the Board with your Left Leg for instance, but actually Punch using your Right Hand, and vice versa; so always pay attention to the Footwork movements as well!

Remember, pay close attention to the Trainer Mii first, then remember the combination, and repeat it with the exact movements (Handwork and

Footwork) in perfect time to the Beat, to score Big Double Points! And at the very end of the workout, you'll be given a 'Bonus Time' Freestyle moment for a few seconds, which enables you to repeatedly Punch in any way you choose, to rack up those all important last second Points. Repeatedly Punch, Left-Right in quick succession until the timer runs out, and get your heart-rate pumping!! This is a great Cardio Endurance workout, and by putting that little extra effort and movement into your routine, and exerting added force when Punching, can seriously work on your Cardiovascular System, and burn off those hateful Calories, and ultimately Fat, quickly and easily!!! So get Boxing.

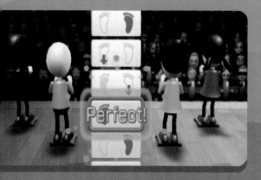

Step Basics

> **INFO: Step to the Front, Back, Left and Right to help improve your sense of Rhythm.**

■ How to Execute:

Step Basics is all about perfect timing, rhythm, and co-ordination. Much like Rhythm Boxing, you must listen carefully to the Beat of the music, in order to know exactly when to Step on and off of the Balance Board with perfect timing. Pay close attention to the Footwork movement that appears on screen, and follow them exactly.

You'll begin with the 'Pink Feet' actions, which simply indicates when to Step on and off of the Board. When the 'Right Pink Foot' is highlighted by the Pink Box, you must Step onto the Board with your Right Foot. This is quickly followed by the 'Left Pink Foot' action, requiring you to then Step on with your Left Foot now. After this, the 'Right Pink Arrow' pointing Down requires you to Step back off of the Board with your Right Foot, whilst still keeping your Left Foot in

place. This is quickly followed by the 'Left Pink Arrow', indicating that you must now Step back off of the Board with your Left Foot as well. This motion will repeat itself for a while. This 'Pink Foot-Pink Arrow' motion simply requires you Step on and off of the Balance Board with your Right Foot, then Left Foot, for the required amount of times. After this, you'll have to change your first Stepping Foot, from Right to Left, requiring you to Step on first with your Left Foot now, and then your Right; then Step back off of the Board with your Left Foot, quickly followed by your Right Foot. Again, this repeats itself for a while, until the actions change.

The next actions that appear are the 'Blue Feet' icons with the Arrows pointing to either the Left or Right. When the 'Blue Foot' appears with the Arrow pointing to the Right, this indicates that you must Step off of the Board to the Right, first with your Right Foot, and then with your Left Foot. After this, another two 'Pink Feet' actions will appear, requiring you to Step back onto the Board to the Left, first with your Left Foot, and then with your Right Foot. Immediately after this, the 'Blue Feet' actions will appear again, this time with the Arrows pointing to the Left. You must now Step off of the Board to your Left, first with your Left Foot, and then with your Right Foot. Again this is followed by another two 'Pink Feet' actions, indicating that you must now Step back onto the Board to your Right, first with your Right Foot, and then your Left. This repeats itself like always so continue to follow the 'Blue Feet' and 'Pink Feet' actions as you go. To make this sound a little easier, simply pay attention to what Foot is shown on and off of the Balance Board on screen. If the Left Foot is off, then take your Left Foot

off. If the Right Foot is off, then take your Right Foot off. If both Feet are off to the side, then Step off completely to the side. And if both Feet are on, make sure that you're standing on the Board with both Feet. And remember to pay close attention to the Arrow directions, as this explains what Foot you need to lead with, and in which direction you need to Step!

Listen carefully to Beat of the music, and Step in time with the Beat at all times. If you Step 'almost' in time, then you'll receive a 'Good' rating for each Step, earning you 1 Point; however if you are 'perfectly' in time with the Beat, then you'll receive a 'Perfect' rating, which Doubles you score to 2 Points! Miss a Step, and you'll receive 0 Points. You must master this, and the timing, in order to receive the 'Perfect' rating for the majority of your Steps, if you want to earn Big Points! 'Good' isn't enough – you must be 'Perfect'!

Step Plus

> **INFO: Step on and off the Wii Balance Board in time to the rhythm to burn off Calories.**

■ How to Execute:

Step Plus is pretty much the exact same as the Step Basics game explained above, and requires the exact same techniques and movements as before (read above for more details in Step movements etc). Only this time, more advanced movements will be required, as well as the previous Pink and Blue Feet actions!

Like we said, the session begins exactly the same as it did before, with the 'Pink Feet' and 'Blue Feet' actions coming first. Remember, Step on and off of the Board with the appropriate Foot for the 'Pink Feet' actions, and then Step off of the Board, to the side, with the appropriate Foot when the 'Blue Feet' actions appear, following the Arrow directions as you do so. Again, timing is everything here!

Shortly into the session, you'll be told to 'Clap' along with the Beat of the music. Now this isn't necessary, however if you want a more intense workout, then we advise you to do so, as this will obviously increase your body movement, and therefore increase your Cardio workout even more!

A short while later, you'll be introduced to a new action – the 'Green Foot' icon, which requires you to 'Kick Out' with force, using the shown Leg. This is an advanced action, so it may take a few attempts to perfect. When the 'Right Green Foot' action appears, you must Kick Outwards with your Right Leg. Immediately after this, the 'Green Arrow' action will appear, indicating that you must drop your Kicking Leg down behind you, off of the Board. This is followed by a 'Pink Arrow', stating that both Feet should now be off of the Board. After this, stand back onto the Board with the appropriate 'Pink Foot' icon, and then follow up with another 'Green Foot' Kick with the other Leg! Again this will repeat itself for a while until you move on. In simple terms, you need to Step on the Board with one Foot, and Kick with the other; then Step back off the Board, Step back on with the other Foot, and Kick with the next Foot before Stepping back off, and repeating the same procedure again!

Now, this is where things start to get a bit confusing, and rather quite tricky, as you'll be introduced to the 'Purple Feet' actions! These 'Purple Feet' actions require you to Step on and off of the Board from the Side-stance this time. Pay close attention to what Foot is shown, and the direction in which the Foot is pointing. When the 'Right Purple Foot'

appears facing to the Left, you must turn and face to the Left, and then Step onto the Board using your Right Leg. This is quickly followed by a 'Purple Left Foot' action, indicating that you now need to step onto the Board with Left Foot, again to the Side. You must now Step back off to the Side using your last placed Foot, quickly followed by your first placed Foot. Therefore if you lead with your Right Foot, and then your Left, you'll Step back off of the Board with your Left Foot, and then your Right; and vice versa. So it's Right, Left, Left, Right, or Left, Right, Right, Left. Again, follow the Arrow directions at all times to fully understand the movements. You'll then turn to the Right, and lead with your Left Foot, thus repeating the same procedures as before, only this time in reverse.

A short while in, the Beat of the music will increase, and Speed-up, therefore you must slightly alter your movement and Step-speed in order to hit those

'Perfects'! The actions will repeat themselves now. Continue to follow the Pink (front and back steps), Blue (side steps), Green (kicks), and Purple (side-facing steps) actions for the remainder of the session, and remember to master your timing on every Step, to earn those all important 'Perfect' ratings, and seriously increase your overall score come the end!!

Jogging & 2P Jogging

> **INFO: Put the Wii Remote in your pocket and Run in place to help burn away your Body Fat.**

■ How to Execute:

There's no need for the Balance Board here, however you will be required to use the Wii Remote, to pick up on your movements instead! Place the Wii Remote in your Pocket, and make sure that it is secure, so that it will not fall

Free Step >>>

> **INFO: Do Aerobics while you watch TV. Just follow the sound of the Wii Remote.**

■ How to Execute:

Free Step is the perfect light or intense Cardio Workout that will seriously get your heart-rate, and Cardiovascular System working well! There are three Levels to choose from – 10 Minutes, 20 Minutes, and 30 Minutes. There are no confusing actions to perform this time, like the previous two Step games; instead it's simply about Stepping on and off of the Balance Board for the required amount of time, 10, 20 or 30 Minutes, in order to complete the required amount of Steps – 800, 1600, or 2400 Steps. This workout is actually so easy to follow, that you can even switch Channels whilst playing, and watch something else on TV for the required amount of time. All you have to do is listen out for the Sounds on the Wii Remote indicating exactly when to Step on, and off of the Board.

At any time during the workout, you can change the 'Pace' of the music using Up and Down on the D-Pad, to either speed up or slow down your

Steps. Increase the Pace for a more intense workout, or decrease the Pace for a lighter workout. You can also change the Sound of the Wii Remote Step-indicator by pressing the (A) button. But as a brief bit of advice, refrain from using the 'Voice' sound, as it's extremely irritating! Instead, use the 'Rhythm 2' sound, as this is by far the easiest to listen to. Not just that, but the Tone increases each time you need to step back onto the Board, which is very handy, especially if you've changed channels!

Listen carefully to the sound of the Wii Remote, get a nice rhythm going, and keep a steady Step pace going for the required amount time to complete the workout. And remember, after every 100 Steps, switch your Stepping foot, and lead with your other Leg, as this will shift your body weight evenly over time!

out when Jogging!! If you have small Pockets, or no Pockets at all, then hold the Wii Remote in your Hand instead!

Jogging is by far one of the best Cardio workouts in the game, especially when running the Island Lap, as it allows you to Jog on the spot at your own pace, for the entire distance of the Island, which usually takes around 5 Minutes! This is the perfect chance to get your heart-rate going over time, and your Cardiovascular System working well! All this is ideal for burning off Calories and Fat.

All you have to do for this exercise, is simply Jog on the spot for the required distance. You have a choice of three Distances to choose from - Short, Long, and Island Lap. To get the most out of this exercise, you MUST stay at a constant steady pace of about 60% of your overall top speed. DO NOT run! Remember, this is a Jogging exercise, not a sprint. At the end of the session, you'll be given your 'Burn Rate' in Percentage '%'. In order to get your Score into the 90s or 100% you must continue to Jog at the same pace throughout the entire Lap, and try your best not to stop and start, or slow down and speed up. Doing this will minimize your Burn Rate significantly, thus lowering your Score! In order to keep your % high, you must have total control over your Jogging speed. As well as that, you must also stay behind the lead Mii character ahead of you at all times! DO NOT overtake him / her, as you will then have to stop at every crossroad until they catch up to you, thus reducing your Burn Rate, mentioned above. The most effective way to keep a steady pace going, is to find a decent pace at around 60% of you overall top speed, then stay close behind the lead Mii, and if you notice that they are gaining distance on you, then speed up slightly; whereas if you notice that you are catching up too much, then slow down slightly. Use the Mii in front as

Free Jogging >>>

> **INFO:** *Go for a run while you watch TV. Let the Wii Remote guide you.*

■ How to Execute:

There's no need for the Balance Board here, however you will be required to use the Wii Remote, to pick up on your movements instead! Place the Wii Remote in your Pocket, and make sure that it is secure, so that it will not fall out when Jogging!! If you have small Pockets, or no Pockets at all, then hold the Wii Remote in your Hand instead!

Free Jogging is by far the best and most effective intense Cardio workout in the game, as it allows you to Jog on the spot at your own pace, for either

10, 20 or 30 Minutes! This is a great Endurance workout that can help increase your Stamina if done regularly, and is the perfect chance to get your heart-rate going over long periods of time, and your Cardiovascular System working hard! All this is ideal for burning off Calories and Fat.

Free Jogging is pretty much the exact same as Jogging and 2P Jogging, only this time, instead of running just one Lap, you'll now be running for a certain period of time instead; either 10, 20 or 30 Minutes. Also, there is no lead Mii to follow or use as your pace / distance guide this time, so maintaining a steady pace and an average 60% top speed, is all down to you now! You'll be running the Island Lap, and should be able to complete 2 Laps in 10 Minutes on a perfectly-paced Lap. Much like Free Step, you can switch Channels and continue to Jog whilst watching something else; however we advise you not to do this, as you will be unable to see how fast your Mii is running, and if and when you slow down or speed up, which is the main purpose of this exercise. Therefore we advise you to keep the game on and pay close attention to your Mii's running speed at all times, in order to get a high % result come the end! If you decide to do this, then you can have a little fun also, and try to find all 15 Mario Character Symbols scattered about the Island. You will not receive anything for this, however it may take the boredom out of these long runs! Remember, keep a steady pace going throughout, pay attention to the writing at the bottom of the screen indicating whether you're running 'Too Slow', 'Too Fast', or that your speed is 'Uneven', and alter your movement accordingly; and then simply continue to Jog for the required amount of time, to complete the session. Remember, this is the best Cardio workout that you do, so get sweating, and feel the burn!!

your pace and distance guide, and judge your speed accordingly to them! Remember, speed isn't everything here, instead it's all about a steady Jog to keep your heart-rate and Burn Rate at a continuous steady rise throughout the entire Lap.

2P Jogging is exactly the same as Jogging, however this time round, a friend can join the session also. You'll require two Wii Remotes for this session for each player, as you Jog side by side with a friend! Spur each other on if

either person is struggling; and stay close together as you Jog the Lap in unison. This exercise can make the single player Jog a little more entertaining!

Wii Fit balance games

This is the perfect way to increase your Balance even more, especially when combining and incorporating it with your Yoga training skills.

b alance Games are light exercises that bring a little bit of fun and excitement to your training, whilst developing your body's Left-Right Balance also, to ultimately help improve your overall Athletic Ability and Balance!

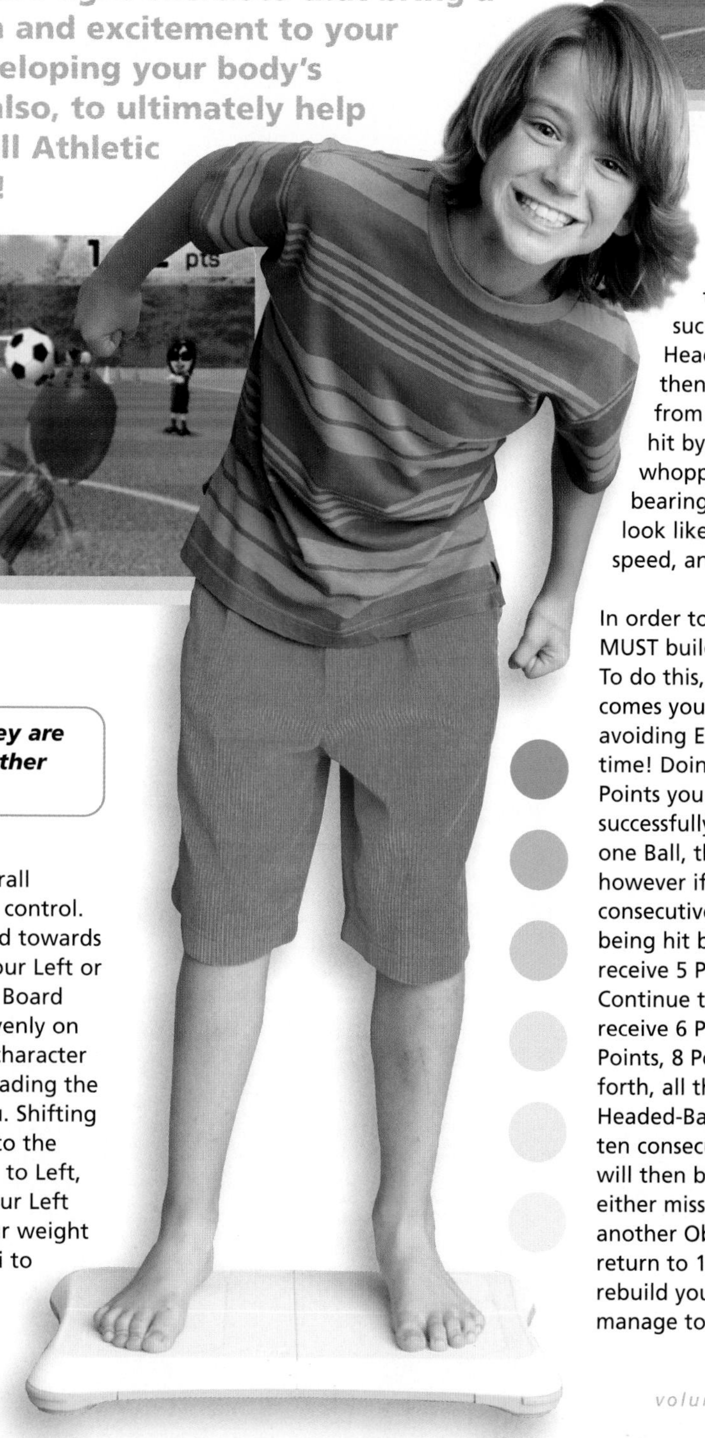

Heading

> **INFO:** *Head the Balls as they are kicked at you, but avoid other flying Objects!*

■ How to Execute:

This game is all about your overall Balance and Left-to-Right Body control. Numerous Objects will be kicked towards you, either Straight on, or to your Left or Right. Standing on the Balance Board with your weight distributed evenly on both sides, will cause your Mii character on screen to stand still, thus Heading the Objects coming Straight for you. Shifting your Body weight and leaning to the Left, will cause your Mii to lean to Left, thus Heading the Objects on your Left hand side; whereas shifting your weight to the Right, will cause your Mii to lean to the Right, thus Heading the oncoming Objects on your

Right hand side. Sounds easy enough, however simply Heading the Footballs isn't enough – you also need to lean from side to side to avoid the other oncoming Objects, such as the Boots, and the Panda Heads! If you get hit by a Boot, then you'll have 1 Point deducted from your Score; whereas if you get hit by a Panda Head, you'll have a whopping 3 Points deducted! And bearing in mind that the Panda Heads look like Footballs; concentration, speed, and control is everything here.

In order to Score massive Points, you MUST build up your Combo-Multiplier! To do this, you need to hit EVER Ball that comes your way, whilst successfully avoiding EVERY other Object at the same time! Doing this increases the amount of Points you get from each Ball that you successfully Head. For example, if you hit one Ball, then you'll receive 1 Point; however if you successfully hit 5 Balls consecutively, without missing any, or being hit by other Objects, then you'll receive 5 Points for the that Ball instead. Continue to do this, and you'll then receive 6 Points for the next; then 7 Points, 8 Points etc and so on and so forth, all the way up to 10 Points per Headed-Ball. Once you successfully Head ten consecutive Balls, every Ball after this will then be worth 10 Points until you either miss a Ball or get struck by another Object, at which point you'll return to 1 Point again, and have to rebuild your Multiplier. So basically if you manage to increase your Multiplier to x10, and successfully manage to hit another ten Balls, then you'll receive 100 Points!! This is the Only way to score Big Points, so you must perfect your Balance and Left / Right Body control if you want to master this game with the 'Perfect' rating!

If you're having trouble with this, then try holding onto a Chair in front of you for support for the first few attempts, as this will help with your Balance and Body control significantly. However, this can make things a little too easy sometimes; so perfect and master your Balance and advanced Yoga skills, and then remove the Chair for a more accurate result!

Ski Jump

> **INFO:** *Straighten your Knees at the right moment to do a Ski Jump.*

■ How to Execute:

This game is all about good Posture, Balance, and perfect Straightness at the top of the Jump! The idea is to speed down the slope towards the Ramp at the end, and then jump off at the precise moment, in order to get maximum height and distance before you land. The further you Jump, the higher your Score! Your overall Distance scored is tallied up over 2 Rounds (2 Jumps).

Just like the Ski Slalom game explained above, Ski Jump also has the speed-boost Box in the top right hand corner of the screen; however this one is slightly different. Instead of having the large Blue Bar in the upper half of the Box, this time you only have a small Blue Circle, the same size as your COG Red Dot, making it rather tricky to maintain

Ski Slalom >>>

> **INFO:** *Lean Left and Right to Ski down the Slalom course.*

■ How to Execute:

Again, this game is all about your overall Balance, and Left-to-Right Body control. The idea is Ski down the Slalom Course at speed, whilst successfully navigating yourself from Left to Right through the numerous Red and Blue Checkpoints, by shifting your Body weight left to right on the Balance Board.

As you can probably guess, the slower your travel, the easier it is to Ski from left to right, however without manually speeding up, you'll be unable to receive the highest Score rating! When you begin, you'll notice in the top right hand corner of the screen, a small Box with a Blue Bar in the upper half, and your Centre of Gravity (COG) Red Dot marker in the centre. In order to pick up tremendous speeds to ultimately get the highest of Scores, you must manually shift your Body weight to the front of the Balance Board so that the Red Dot remains inside the Blue Bar! Once the Red Dot is inside the Blue Bar, you'll start to speed up quickly. Now, for the initial part of the Course where the Checkpoints are positioned far apart from one

another, this speed-boost ability can be used, and you can still navigate from left to right through the Checkpoints quite easily. However, as

you advance down the Course, the Checkpoints start to get smaller and much closer together, and the Course begins to slope downwards significantly, meaning that you will not be able to use full-speed and still navigate through the Checkpoints, as you'll be travelling too fast, and will be unable to turn in time! Therefore you will have to judge when to use your speed-boost, and when to shift your Body weight backwards to slow down.

Start by leaning forwards on the Balance Board and keep an eye on the Red Dot to receive your boost. The Checkpoints usually appear from left to right, therefore if the first Checkpoint is on the Right, then the next one will be on the Left, and vice versa if the first Checkpoint is on the Left; the next will be on the Right. Therefore for the entire Course, you must zigzag from Left to Right in order to pass through EVERY Checkpoint. If you miss a Checkpoint, then you'll be penalized by 7 seconds!! Miss any more than two or three Checkpoints (21 seconds), and it's impossible to receive your 4 Stars! At the very end of the Course, the Checkpoints are almost in line with one another, enabling you to speed through the last few Checkpoints at top speed, to save those all-important seconds! Basically the Course requires you to use full speed boost for the first part; then slow down slightly for the middle part, and end with full speed on the final straight. Just remember to exert added pressure on the Front to speed up; added pressure on the Back to slow down; and added pressure on either the Left or Right side to turn sharply, and you'll master this game in no time!

If you're having trouble with this, then try holding onto a Chair in front of you for support, for the first few attempts, as this will help with your Balance and Body control significantly. However, this can make things a little too easy sometimes; so perfect and master your Balance and advanced Yoga skills, and then remove the Chair for a more accurate result!

inside! With enough practice, control and Balance however, you can keep the Red Dot within the Blue Circle for the entire slope, and reach the maximum speed of 60mph!!

In order to perfect your Jump, there is a precise technique and stance that you must use and abide to if you want to gain enough Distance for a high Score, so listen closely. At the beginning of the Round, stand with your Legs evenly apart, lean forwards exerting more pressure onto the front of the Balance Board so that the Red Dot is inside the Blue Circle, and then bend your Knees and crouch down into the full-Squat position. The lower you Squat down, the higher you will be able to Jump when you come to the ramp. As you speed down the slope, keep a close eye on the speed-boost Box in the corner and

remain perfectly still and perfectly Balance in order to reach the 60mph max speed. As you approach the Ramp, the word 'Extend' will appear on screen. Immediately when this appears, extend your Legs fully into the standing position to Jump off of the Ramp; but make sure that you alter your positioning slightly in midair, so that the Red Dot remains where the previous Blue Circle was, as this will increase your Jump Distance! Do this quickly, and then remain as still as you possibly can to maintain Balance as you fly through the air. If you move too much, then you'll lose height and Distance! Also, if you wobble around too much upon landing, then you'll Fail the Landing and receive no Points! To gain maximum distance, you need to extend your Legs fully as quickly as you can, then keep your entire Body (Legs and Back) as straight as you

possibly can, and hold your steady Balance throughout, until you land. If done correctly and with enough practice, you should be able to land beyond the Finish Line!!

Tightrope Tension

> **INFO: *Walk in place to cross the Tightrope. Bend and Straighten your Knees to Jump.***

■ How to Execute:
This game is all about your Left-to-Right Balance control, and how successfully you can shift your Body weight from Left to Right whist Walking! The idea here is to Walk in place on the Balance Board, causing your Mii character on screen to Walk forwards along the Tightrope. Sounds easy enough; well it's not!

Table Tilt >>>

> **INFO: *Lean your Body Left, Right, Forwards and Backwards to Tilt the Balls into the Holes.***

■ How to Execute:
This game involves a lot of skill, patients, and total Body Balance Control and movement in all directions! There are 8 Levels in each Difficulty, and each Level gets progressively harder as you go along.

On screen you'll notice a moveable Platform (Table) with a few Mii Balls rolling around; and each Table contains one or two Holes. The idea is to shift your Body weight around in all direction, from Right to Left, Front and Back, in order to Tilt the Table, and guide the Balls into the available Holes. The first few Levels are pretty simple, involving only one or two Balls, a pretty basic Table platform, and usually containing slightly raised Side-Lips around the entire outer edge, which will keep the Balls on the Table if you're gentle enough with your movements, and not too forceful. However, as you advance through the Levels, they become much more complicated, incorporating more Balls, removing the outer edge Side-Lips, and adding more levels to each

Platform, as well as more intricate routes to the Holes! These Levels require much more patience and Body Balance skills.

If the Table has numerous Balls on it, yet there is an outer raised edge, then the idea is to stick to one Ball at any one time, and focus on Only guiding this Ball into a Hole. The outer raised Lips should keep the other Balls on the

Table without falling off, only if you're gentle enough with your movements of course. Once you've successfully sunk one Ball, move onto the next and do the same again. The softer your movements, the easier it will be!

If the Table has no outer edge, then things are slightly more difficult. This time you need to be aware of all the Balls on the Table at the same time, and try your very best to Tilt the Table in order to get all the Balls in the same area, close together. Once there all in

close proximity to one another, you can then guide them towards the same Hole simultaneously. Sometime however, it might be beneficial to sacrifice a few other Balls in order to get one or two Balls into the Holes. After dropping a Ball however, the Table will jolt violently and rotate around, causing the other Balls on the Table to shift around. Find your bearings after this, and continue.

After completing each Level, you'll receive added Bonus Time for the next stage. The idea is to complete all 8 Levels before your Time Limit runs out at the top of the screen! To do this quickly, you need to remember that speed isn't actually the answer here; you need to be soft and slow with your movements and actually take your time with each Level. If you rush through the stages, then you will fail! Forget about the time, take it easy, and you'll dominate this game.

If you're having trouble with this, then try holding onto a Chair in front of you for support, for the first few attempts, as this will help with your Balance and Body control significantly. However, this can make things a little too easy sometimes; so perfect and master your Balance and advanced Yoga skills, and then remove the Chair for a more accurate result!

Each time you take a Step, you naturally place more weight onto one side of your Body, and therefore more weight onto one side of the Balance Board. For example, if you take your Left Foot off of the Board, then your Right side is exerting the most pressure; and vice versa. This will obviously cause your Mii to lean and tilt to one side. Lean too far without realigning yourself, and you'll fall off the Tightrope and fail the game! In order to counteract this leaning motion when you Walk, you yourself must to lean back in the opposite direction, by placing more pressure on the other side, to straighten yourself out again. There is an easy way to master this game however, and counteract the leaning easily; so listen up.

Most people Walk slowly across the Tightrope worrying too much about when they're going to lean, however this isn't the answer. The slower you Walk, the longer you remain standing on one foot, which ultimately means the further you're going to lean! This then takes time to realign yourself before continuing. The most effective way to get to the other side quickly and easily is to almost Run or Jog on the spot! The less time your feet are off the Board, the less you're going to lean; and ultimately the faster you're going to reach the other side! There will probably still be times when you need to realign yourself however – so to do this quickly, stop Walking, and manually lean to the other side, by exerting more pressure on one side of the Balance Board.

Balance Bubble >>>

INFO: **Guide your Mii safely down the River by leaning to the Left, Right, Front and Back.**

■ How to Execute:

This game is pretty simple and shouldn't cause too many problems at all. All you have to do here is navigate your Mii Bubble through the narrow River, without touching the Sidewalls or any other Hazard, by shifting your Body weight Forwards, and to the Left and Right!

To start moving down the River, lean forwards, and exert more pressure onto the Front part of the Balance Board. To increase your speed and gain more control over your Bubble, try standing on the Front half of the Board on only your Heels, so that your Toes are hanging over the edge. Doing this will allow you to place all of your Body weight on the front half of the Board, thus speeding up your Bubble movement significantly; whilst also giving you more control over the Bubble's movement as you go! Now simply continue to move forwards, whilst placing more pressure on either the Right or Left hand side of the Board, to maneuver the Bubble in that direction, in order to avoid the Sidewalls. Navigate through the entire Course and try to stay as central as you possibly can to reach the Finishing Line at the opposite end. Once you've mastered your Balance, and become more familiar with the Course, try sticking close to the inside walls as you turn a corner, as this will shave a few seconds off of your overall time come the end!

To save a little extra time also, you can actually pass through the extremely narrow canyon at the end of the River on the left hand side, if however you are careful, steady, and controlled enough with your movements! This will save you having to go around to the right, which will obviously waste a few valuable seconds.

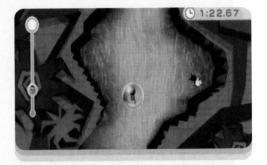

In the Advanced difficulty, you'll have to avoid the Wasps also! These will constantly fly around the screen and sometime block your current path. If you touch these, then your Bubble will pop, and you'll fail the game also! Just be on the ready at all times for their quick sharp movements across the screen, and get ready to move to the side if needs be!

If you're having trouble with this, then try holding onto a Chair in front of you for support, for the first few attempts, as this will help with your Balance and Body control significantly. However, this can make things a little too easy sometimes; so perfect and master your Balance and advanced Yoga skills, and then remove the Chair for a more accurate result!

In all three Difficulties, you'll have to avoid the oncoming Bear Traps! As you approach the Bear Traps, stop Walking, remain still, and wait for the Traps to almost reach you. When they're directly in front of you, Bend your Knees slightly, and then extend them fully back to the Standing position just like the Ski Jump game explained above, to Jump over them! If done correctly, you'll land back on the Tightrope beyond them. You can ONLY do this however, if your Mii is perfectly straight. If your Mii is leaning to one side and you Jump, then you'll Jump to side, and fall off! Realign yourself perfectly straight, and then Jump, to Jump straight up, and not to the side.

On the Advance difficulty, floating Feathers will be introduced as well. These will flutter across the screen over the Tightrope, and block your view for a short period of time. Either wait for them to pass, or continue to Jog on the spot. As you do this however, keep a close eye on your Mii through the Feathers, and alter your Balance accordingly.   On the Super Advanced difficulty, Strong Winds will also be introduced! These are tricky to counteract. Every now and then a strong gust of Wind will blow from the Left or

Right, and will cause your Mii to lean dramatically to the side! STOP Walking altogether here, and simply lean back in the opposite direction to remain on the Tightrope. Once the Wind has passed, continue to Walk. Remember, unlike Table Tilt, speed IS actually everything for this game!!

Penguin Slide

> **INFO:** *Shift your Body rapidly to the Left and Right to Tilt the Iceberg and feed the Penguin.*

■ How to Execute:

Again, this is another easy game that shouldn't cause too many problems at all, if however you can perfect the 'Flip'! On screen is a moveable Iceberg with a Penguin on top. The idea is to shift your Body weight from Left to Right on the Balance Board in order to Tilt the Iceberg in that direction, thus causing the Penguin to slide that way, and ultimately catch the numerous Fish that jump out of the water and flop about of the Iceberg surface! The more Fish you catch, the more Points you'll receive.

The Blue Fish are the most common, and each one is worth 1 Point. These simply flop around on the surface and are very easy to catch. The Green Fish appear regularly also, and are worth 2 Points; however these Fish Bounce across the surface, meaning that you can only catch them when they land for another bounce. Therefore you will have to judge their jump-distance in order to catch them on the drop. And finally the large Red Fish, which only appear a few times at certain points in the game. These are rare and difficult to get, yet are worth a whopping 10 Points each! If you want to receive the highest of Scores, then you MUST catch these EVERY time thy appear, otherwise you'll be unable to rack up enough Points.

The Red Fish do not reach the Iceberg, but instead swim around in the water beneath. When you notice a Red Fish swimming from left to right below, be on the ready, as it's about to jump. There's no telling which side it will jump up to, so you'll have to be quick. When it jumps up out of the water on either the left or right side, it will remain in midair for a second or two before dropping back into the water again. In this short time, you need to slide down the Iceberg towards the end where the Red Fish is located, and then quickly Step on the opposite side of the Balance Board, to cause the Iceberg to Flip the Penguin up high, thus catching the Fish! For example, if the Fish on the Left hand side, then exert more pressure onto the Left side of the Board to begin with, to cause the Penguin to slide in that direction; and then quickly remove your Left Leg, and place added pressure on Only your Right Leg, in order to flip the Penguin up and catch the Fish; and vice versa if it's on the Right hand side – exert more pressure with your Left Leg to flip up. This can be tricky, and will definitely take some practice to master every time! The most common mistake is leaving the flip too late and over-sliding into the water. Avoid this, as you'll waste time, and lose the 10 Points!

Remember to control your Left-to-Right movements and Balance control throughout the entire game, and make sure that you master the 'Flip' to receive those all important 10 Point Fish! Continue to slide from left to right across the Iceberg , and catch every Fish that appears before the time limit runs out, to score Big Points!

Misses   0   0:10,76

Snowboard Slalom

> **INFO: Lean to the Left, Right, Front and Back to Snowboard down the Slalom Course.**

■ How to Execute:

This game is pretty much the exact same as Ski Slalom explained above, and requires almost the exact same techniques and tactics as before. Snowboard Slalom is all about your overall Balance, and Left-to-Right Body control.

Before we begin, position the Balance Board to the side just like a Snowboard, as shown in the Image on screen. This will now require you to shift your Body weight from Front to Back instead of Left to Right, to navigate in those directions; and exerting pressure on the Left hand side of the Board instead of the Front, will cause you to speed up this time. Again, just like Ski Slalom, Snowboard Slalom has the speed-boost Box in the top right hand corner also, with the Blue Bar in the upper half, and your COG Red Dot marker in the centre. To get the Red Dot in the Blue Bar, exert pressure onto the Left hand side of the Board instead.

Instead of navigating Through the Checkpoints like before, this time you'll have to navigate Around the Checkpoints instead. When you approach each Checkpoint, pay attention to the Arrow Directions on each one, indicating which side you have to go around. The

Misses: 0   0:08.16

exact same rules and techniques apply however, such as the zigzagging motion. If you begin by going around the first Checkpoint on the Left hand side, then the following Checkpoint will require

Zazen >>>

> **INFO: Find your Inner Peace through this Ancient Zen practice.**

■ How to Execute:

This challenge is solely about Stillness! The only thing you have to do is sit on the Balance Board and remain as still as you possibly can, in order to keep the Candle Flame alight. The slightest of movements and the Flame will go out, ending the game there and then. Sit on the Balance Board cross-legged if you can, and do not move a muscle. If you can't sit perfectly cross-legged, then sit on the Board with your legs crossed in front of you instead. Breathe deeply and slowly, and remain perfectly still for the entire session

you to pass it on the Right hand side. Continue to zigzag around them from left to right for the entire Course.

Just like before, if you miss a Checkpoint, then you'll be penalized by 7 Seconds! Miss any more than two or three Checkpoints, and you'll be unable to receive the highest of scores. Also, at the beginning of the Course when the Checkpoints are positioned far apart, you can use your full-speed boost ability! However, as you advance down the Course and the Checkpoints start to get closer together, you MUST centre yourself on the Balance Board and refrain from using the boost if you want to successfully hit the Checkpoints. Too much speed and you'll be unable to do so. For more information on Slalom, read the Ski Slalom game explained in full detail above!!

If you're having trouble with this, then try holding onto a Chair in front of you for support, for the first few attempts, as this will help with your Balance and Body control significantly. However, this can make things a little too easy sometimes; so perfect and master your Balance and advanced Yoga skills, and then remove the Chair for a more accurate result!

A lack of focus will cause the flame to shake. Try to keep your body still.

until the Candle burns all the way down. If you see the Flame flickering, then you're moving too much, most times subconsciously without even knowing! With enough practice however, you can actually control your inner muscles.

The Flame should remain still at all times if you want to succeed at this Ancient Zazen Inner Peace challenge! This one is all down to you I'm afraid, so Good Luck.

Wii Fit Workout

We love Wii Fit and alas we didn't like being so chubby around the middle, so we sat down and devised our very own work out routine for Wii Fit to help us get warmed up and ready for some serious sweating. So with great care with your diet and a pile of willpower you could see your waistband tumble.

YOGA

HALF MOON

1

Stand upright with your Legs pinned together, and raise both Arms up above your Head. Straighten them fully, and interlock your Fingers. Keep your Legs and Lower Body completely still; and Bend over to the Right, by leaning with only your Upper Body at Waist / Hip area. Hold for the required time. *Return.*

2

REVERSE SIDE. Return to the original starting position; then Bend and lean in the opposite direction, to the Left now; and hold for the required time. *Return.*

WARRIOR

1

Take one large Step back with your Left Leg, and keep your Right Leg in place. Turn and look forward, and extend both Arms out; one in front, the other behind. Bend your front Right Leg at the Knee, and lean forwards, exerting pressure on your front Leg. Stretch and Straighten your rear Left Leg; and hold for the required time. *Return.*

2

REVERSE SIDE. Return to the original starting position; remove your Right Leg this time; and bend your Left Leg at the Knee. Lean forwards; stretch your Right Leg, and hold for the required time. *Return.*

1

Stand upright with your Legs close together, and raise both Arms up above your Head. Bend your Spine, and arch your Back backwards; keeping your Legs firmly in place.

SUN SALUTATION

2

Bend over, lean forwards; and touch your Toes with your Hands. Look up and to the front; and keep your Back Straight – not hunched. Hold for the required amount of time.

3

Finally, return to the Standing position, and raise both Arms up above your Head in one fluid motion to finish the Pose. *Return.*

1

Stand upright on your Right Leg; then lift and Raise your Left Leg up, and hold your Left Knee with both Hands at Waist / Hip height. Find your balance.

STANDING KNEE

2

Keep your Back and Right Leg Straight, and pull your Left Knee up, and in tight to your Chest using your Hands. Hold briefly; then lower – but do not drop your Leg completely. Repeat this Up-Down pulling-motion for the required Repetitions'. *Return.*

3

REVERSE SIDE. Stand on your Left Leg now; raise your Right Leg, and hold your Right Knee with both Hands. Pull your Right Knee in tight to your Chest; hold, and then lower. Repeat this for required amount of Reps'. *Return.*

1

Stand upright with your Legs evenly apart; and raise both Arms up above your Head. Extend / spread your Fingertips; and rise up onto your Tiptoes.

PALM TREE

2

In one fluid motion, lower both Arms Down in front of you; and then Rotate them Down, and around Behind you, so that the Palms of your Hands are pointing Upwards. Keep your Arms straight; and hold them behind you for the required time. *Return.*

DOWNWARD FACING DOG

Get down onto all fours (your Hands and Knees); and then raise your Buttocks up into the air, to form a V-Shape with your Body. Keep your Arms, Back and Legs straight; lower your Head, and focus on your Legs; then hold for the required time. *Return.*

1

Take one large Step back with your Left Leg, and keep your Right Leg in place. Look ahead in the direction you're facing; and extend both Arms out; one in front, the other behind.

TRIANGLE

2

Bend over to the side, and hold your Right Ankle with your Left Hand; then raise your Right Arms upwards, and extend it fully. Look up, and focus on your Right Hand; then hold for the required time. *Return.*

3

REVERSE SIDE. Return to the original starting position; remove your Left Leg this time; and then bend over to the other side, and hold your Left Ankle with your Right Hand. Raise your Left Arm upwards; look up, focus on your Left Hand; and hold for the required time. *Return.*

KING OF THE DANCE

1

Stand upright on your Right Leg; Bend your Left Leg back behind you, and hold your Left Foot with your Left Hand, with your Thumb on the Sole. Raise your Right Arm up above your Head, extend it fully; and look ahead. Lean over to the front so your Right Arm is pointing forwards; and then pull your Left Leg up even higher, so the Sole of your Foot is pointing upwards. All of your Limbs should be at a 90-degree angle to one another. Focus on your Right Hand; and hold for the required time. *Return.*

2

REVERSE SIDE. Return to the original starting position, and Bend your Right Leg backwards this time. Hold your Right Foot; and raise your Left Arm upwards. Lean over so that your Left Arm is pointing forwards, and pull your Right Leg up and behind you. Focus on your Left Hand; and hold for the required time. *Return.*

COBRA

Lay Face Down on the floor; and tuck your Elbows in tight to your Body. Push up with your Hands, and completely Straighten your Arms to curve your Spine upwards. Expand your Chest; keep your Legs in place; and hold for the required time. *Return.*

BRIDGE

Lay on your Back facing upwards, with your Legs close; Bend your Knees up; and hold your Ankles with your Hands. Now raise your Buttocks and Hips / Waist off of the floor so that there is an opening between your Arms and Back; and support yourself with your Shoulders and Head. Hold for the required time. *Return.*

CROCODILE TWIST

1

Lay on your Back, facing upwards; and extend both Arms outwards to the side. Hold your Right Knee now your Left Hand; and manually pull your Right Leg across your Body to the Left; then hold it down. Twist your Body to the Right as you do this; and look away, to your Right side. Hold for the required time. *Return.*

2

REVERSE SIDE. Hold your Left Knee this time with you Right Hand; and pull your Left Leg across your Body to the Right; then pin it down. Twist your Body, and look away to the Left as you do this. Hold for the required time. *Return.*

SHOULDERSTAND

Lay on your Back facing upwards with your Legs close together; and rest you're the Palms of your Hands on the floor. Raise your Legs and Buttocks off of the floor slowly; and hold them behind your Head for the first stage of this Pose. Now raise and extend your Legs upwards, fully; and support your Back using your Hands. Bring your Head in to your Chest; and hold for the require time. *Return.*

MUSCLE WORKOUTS

1

Stand on your Right Leg; and raise your Left Knee up to Hip / Waist height. Hold your Left Arm at a 90-degree angle 'Down' behind you; and hold your Right Arm at a 90-degree angle 'Up' in front of you.

SINGLE LEG EXTENSION

2

Now swing your Left Leg backwards; your Left Arm upwards; and your Right Arm backwards simultaneously in one fluid motion; and extend all Limbs fully. Repeat this back-forth motion, as if you are 'Running' on the spot in slow-motion, for the required Repetitions. *Return.*

3

REVERSE SIDE. Stand on your Left Leg this time; raise your Right Knee up to Hip / Waist height; and hold your Right Arm at a 90-degree angle 'Down' behind you; and your Left Arm at a 90-degree angle 'Up' in front of you. Now swing your Right Leg backwards; your Right Arm upwards; and your Left Arm backwards together in one fluid motion. Repeat this back-forth motion for the required Reps'. *Return.*

PRESS-UP & SIDE STAND

1

Press-Up. Get down on all fours; and then get into the Press-Up position. Start by completing one Press-Up by lowering yourself down to the floor, and then pushing back up again using your Arms.

2

Side Stand. Cross your Right Leg over your Left Leg; and then raise your Right Arm out to the side, and up above your Head. Look up and focus on your raised Hand; then hold this position for the required time. Uncross your Legs now, and return to the Press-Up position.

3

REVERSE SIDE. Complete another Press-Up in the same fluid motion; and then move onto the reverse side, Side Stand. Cross your Left Leg over your Right Leg this time; and raise your Left Arm out to the side, and up above your Head. Focus on your raised Hand; hold this position for the required time. Uncross your Legs, and return to the Press-Up position. Continue to do this two-part exercise for the required Repetitions.

JACKKNIFE

Lay on your Back facing upwards; Bend your Knees slightly; and extend both Arms back behind your Head. Now raise your Upper Body and Lower Body simultaneously, so that your Arms and Knees meet one another. Support yourself on your Buttocks; and hold for the required time. *Return.*

ROWING SQUAT

Stand upright with your Legs Shoulder-width apart; and hold both Arms out in front of you. Bend your Knees; Squat down into an almost Sitting-position; and pull your Arms in tight to your Body, by bending your Elbows. Arch your Back; and manually contract your Back muscles as you pull your Arms in. *Return.*

TORSO & WAIST TWIST

1

Torso Twist. Stand upright with your Legs spread evenly apart; and extend both Arms out fully to your sides. Keep your Legs in place; and only Rotate (Twist) your Upper Body around – to the Right first; and then the Left. Repeat this Right-Left rotational movement for the required Repetitions. *Return.*

2

Waist Twist. Extend both Arms out to your sides again; and then Twist your Upper Body down to the Right, so that your Left Hand is now down by the Right hand side of your Body, and your Right Arm is pointing upwards.

3

REVERSE SIDE. Twist back to the original standing position; and then Twist down to the Left this time, so that your Right Hand is now down by your Left hand side, and your Left Arm is pointing upwards. Repeat this Right-Left twisting movement for the required Reps'. *Return.*

LUNGE

1

Take one large Step back with your Left Leg; and keep your Right Leg in place. Hold your Hands behind your Head; interlock your Fingertips; and look forwards. Bend your Right Leg Forwards at a 90-degree angle at the Knee; and Bend your Left Leg Backwards at a 90-degree angle. Keep your Back straight; and hold for a second. Lunge back; and repeat for the required Repetitions. *Return.*

2

REVERSE SIDE. Take one large Step back with your Right Leg this time; and keep your Left Leg in place. Interlock your Fingers behind your Head; and then Bend your Left Leg at a 90-degree angle; and your Right Leg 90-degrees also. Hold; Lunge back; and repeat for the required Reps'. *Return.*

SINGLE LEG TWIST

1

Stand on your Right Leg; and raise your Left Leg out to the Side. Raise and extend your Right Arm up and out to Side; and hold your Hip with your Left Hand.

2

Raise your Left Knee up to your Waist / Hip area, and bring your Right Arm down across your body, touching your Left Knee with your Right Hand. Raise your Arm back up, and lower your Leg again; then repeat for the required Repetitions. *Return.*

3

REVERSE SIDE. Stand on your Left Leg this time; and raise your Right Leg out to the Side. Raise your Left Arm up; and hold your Hip with your Right Hand. Raise your Right Knee up to your Waist, and bring your Left Arm down across your body, touching your Right Knee with your Left Hand. Raise your Arm back up, and lower your Leg; then repeat for the required Reps'. *Return.*

PARALLEL STRETCH

Get down onto all fours; straighten your Back and Legs completely; and raise your Body off of the floor. Support yourself with only your Forearms and Elbows; and hold for the required time. *Return.*

1

Stand on your Right Leg; lean slightly to the side; and lift your Left Leg off the floor about an Inch. Hold your Waist / Hip with your Left Hand; and keep your Right Arm down by your side.

SIDEWAYS LEG LIFT

2

Raise your Left Leg out to the Side; and raise your Right Arm out to the side and then Upwards simultaneously. Lower your Arm and Leg again; and repeat for the required Repetitions. *Return.*

3

REVERSE SIDE. Stand on your Left Leg this time; lean to the side; and lift your Right Leg up about an Inch. Hold your Waist with your Right Hand; and keep your Left Arm down by your side. Raise your Right Leg out to the Side; and your Right Arm out to the side and Upwards. Lower your Arm and Leg; and repeat for the required Reps'. *Return.*

1

Stand upright with your Legs close together; raise your Right Arm upwards above your Head; and bring your Left Arm across your Body, and hold your Right Elbow with your Left Hand.

TRICEP EXTENSIONS

2

Bend your Right Elbow downwards Behind your Head; and keep your Upper Arm perfectly still. Only move your Elbow and Forearm! Extend your Arm back up above your Head; and manually contract your Tricep muscle. Repeat this Up-Down motion for the required Repetitions. *Return.*

3

REVERSE SIDE. Raise your Left Arm this time; and hold your Left Elbow with your Right Hand. Bend your Right Elbow downwards Behind your Head; and keep your Upper Arm still. Extend your Arm back up above your Head; manually contract your Tricep; and repeat this Up-Down motion for the required Reps'. *Return.*

ea sports active

>>>

personal trainer

>>>

The amazing Electronic Arts know their sporting games, from the makers of the FIFA and Madden series comes a whole new way to work out. With intensive exercise routines, EA Active can become your very own personal trainer and with our help we are positive that you will shed those pounds and have a blast doing it!

guide >>> contents

Setting-Up & Getting Started

With purchase of the 'Active' package, you'll also receive the Resistance Band and Leg Strap for increased effectiveness of your Exercises. Both require precise assembling in order to be 100% successful and accurate of your movements.

Assembling Resistance Band

INCLUDES:
Red Resistance Band
2 Black Straps

■ How to Assemble:

Straighten out the Red Resistance Band, and lay it flat on the floor or any other large flat surface.

Place the smaller Loop of the Black Strap beneath the Red Band about 2 or 3 inches from the end, and then fold the larger Loop over the top of the Band, so that the larger Loop is facing you. The smaller Loop should now be beneath, and the larger Loop should now be on top.

Now pull the larger Loop through the smaller Loop of the back Strap, and continue to pull the larger Loop through to tighten the knot.

Repeat this a few times until the Band is locked in position and is secure! Repeat the same procedure on the other side with the second Black Strap, and once both are secured in position, they will act as Handles for your exercise.

■ How to use Effectively:

Lay the Red Band on the floor and place both feet on the middle of it.

Grab both Black Strap Handles in your right and left hand and grip them tightly. Raise your Arms up and down, and you should feel the resistance of the Band pulling against you. This is perfect!

If not and the Band is too loose, then fold the middle of the Band back over itself once of twice, and tie it up. This will reduce the length of the Band, increasing the resistance even more. Retry it and get the desired resistance for YOU. Keep tightening it if needs be until you're happy with the resistance.

Assembling Leg Strap

The Leg Strap needs to be in the correct position for maximum effectiveness, and the Nunchuck MUST be placed in the Pocket in the precise way, in order to even work!

■ How to Assemble:

Place the Leg Strap around your RIGHT Leg, and then position it so that the Pocket is at the front, and the opening is facing up.

Position it on your Thigh in the correct position, so that it cannot slip off, and will not interfere with your Exercises. If it's too low, then it will prevent you from bending your knee properly, whereas if it's too high, it may affect your Hip movement. Find the best position for YOU.

Thread the Strap through the Buckle if it isn't already, and then double it up, back on itself to tighten it around your leg.

Keep pulling so that it is secure, and then attach the two Velcro Sides together, to hold the Leg Strap in place. Make sure that it is secure, but not too tight to interfere with your Exercises. Now place the Nunchuck in the front Pocket, but make sure that the Analog Stick is facing down and to the RIGHT. The shape of the Pocket will give you correct angle and position of the Nunchuck. If the Nunchuck is inserted incorrectly, then it will not pick up on your movement, so double check it before finishing!

the journal

your Journal is one of the most important factors of your new healthy living lifestyle and exercise routine, as it helps keep track of your overall Fitness and Health, and offers you a variety of different Exercises and Workouts to keep you in shape depending on your strongest and weakest points of exercise. Your Lifestyle and Nutrition is evaluated also, as are any other Activities that you may take part in outside of the Game.

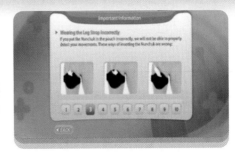

Active Workouts:

The Active Workout option is your current Workouts and Exercises for that particular Day, Week, and Month. Click on this and you'll be taken to your currently set Fitness program based on your Lifestyle & Nutrition Survey and Other Activity Survey results.

Lifestyle & Nutrition Survey:

The Lifestyle and Nutrition Survey requires you to answer a variety of important questions about the way you eat, drink, and live your life. Simply exercising and working out isn't enough to keep you and body healthy - your overall Lifestyle and Nutrition needs to be taken into account, and monitored also! Take the Survey, and answer each question as truthfully as possible in order to gain the most accurate result for YOU. Depending on your answers, the outcome of the Survey will differ, and will affect your Daily Medal goal for

that particular day. For example, if your Lifestyle and Nutrition is healthy, then your Daily Medal goal may be Silver or Gold, giving you an intense fitness workout and an advanced exercise regime; whereas if your Lifestyle and Nutrition is unhealthy, then you'll receive a Bronze Daily Medal goal, making your fitness workout steady and not as strenuous as the Silver or Gold. Therefore you MUST answer correctly in order to receive the most effective workout plan for YOU! You can then check the Graph and see how you are advancing over time – if you're not, then it might be time to change your diet.

Other Activity Survey:

The Other Activity Survey again requires you to answer a few questions about other Activities that you may take part in outside of this Game, and outside of this particular fitness program. Other Activities involve anything from Walking to Running, all the way up to Sports and other Fitness

Activities. Again, answer them as truthfully as possible in order to get the most accurate result for YOU. Again, this will affect your Daily Medal goal, so be truthful, as bending the truth may result in a Workout plan that is too difficult for you. Do not worry if your Lifestyle & Nutrition is unhealthy, or that you lack Other Activities outside of this game...as ultimately the idea is to work on this, increase them, and become healthier over time! It won't happen immediately, but using your Journal and updating these Surveys Daily will of course help keep track of your diet and active lifestyle, and ultimately increase your fitness. The higher your Activity Survey results, the higher your overall Activity Rating will be! You can then check the Graph and see how you are advancing over time – if you're not, then it might be time to add some new Activities to your day.

Daily Medal:

Once you have completed the Surveys, your current Daily Medal for that particular day will be given, depending

on how healthy and active your answers were. This will change the intensity and difficulty of your exercises for that day depending on whether it's Bronze, Silver, or Gold. DO NOT lie about your answers just to get a Gold Medal, as this won't help you in the long run; instead, actually alter your diet and activities, and change them slightly in your every day life slowly, and ultimately you WILL reach your Gold Medal target!

My Goals:

Here you can set yourself your own personal Goals for how many Calories you want to lose, how many Hours you want to work out for, and how many Workouts you want to complete. You can set these Goals and targets for as many days as you want, however setting yourself Daily Goals instead of Weekly Goals will prove more effective, as you can work towards this target each day, and end your exercise routine once it has been completed. A decent Daily workout should have you setting your Goals to:

> ■ **Calories:** 200 - 400 Calories a Day
> ■ **Hours:** 1 - 2 Hours a Day
> ■ **Workouts:** 10 - 12 different Workouts a Day

The more you work out, and the more you keep track of your Lifestyle & Nutrition, the easier exercising will become, and ultimately the higher your Goals can be set! Complete your set Goals each and every day, and if it's too difficult, then reduce the intensity, or if it's too easy, then increase the intensity to best suit YOU – work to *your own* limits.

Calendar:

The Calendar helps keep track of your exercises and workouts over the previous days, weeks, and months. Check this regularly and try to increase your workouts over time. Some days you should Rest, however most days, the Calendar days should have a workout plan assigned to them.

Profile:

Checking your Profile allows you to View your Trophies, Edit your Fitness Profile, and Delete your Fitness Profile. Setting targets to complete the requirements for earning Trophies is a great way to keep in shape as well, whilst receiving an Award at the same time also. Check the 'My Trophies' section further

on in the guide and work your way through every single one. Trophies' are a great sign of Fitness!

Trainer Feedback:

Each and ever day, you'll be given new Trainer Feedback, which is consists of interesting facts about healthy living, and a variety of the most effective ways to keep fit, active, and in shape. Read these daily, and try to put these easy-to-follow healthy living hints and tips into your daily routine.

>>>

ALL exercises mastered & perfected!

mastering and perfecting each and every exercise is key to getting in shape and keeping fit, and that's why we've compiled this easy to follow guide of ALL the precise techniques and positions for EVERY exercise, and how to execute each one correctly, so that you can get the most out of your workouts! Remember, technique is everything – it's not about speed or power, but instead precise movement and control; therefore following this guide exactly will enable you to perfect each exercise quickly and easily, getting the most out of your new Active routine, and working the muscles that NEED to be worked for each exercise!

upper body exercises >>>

Bicep Curls

> **INFO: This exercise works the Bicep muscles in the front of both Upper Arms.**

■ How to Execute:

To execute the perfect Bicep Curl, follow the Trainer Picture on the right hand side of the screen. Mimic his / her movements exactly and listen out for the 'Ding' sound, indicating when to Raise and Lower your Arms with perfect timing. Stand on the Resistance Band also for increased resistance and added effectiveness!

Stand with your Legs Shoulder-width apart and your Arms down by your sides. When told to do so, keep the upper part of your Arm still, and raise your Forearm up slowly 180 degrees so that your hand is now up

by your shoulder, but make sure that you keep your Elbows tucked in tight to your body as you do so. As you raise your Forearm, tense and contract your Bicep muscle manually for added effectiveness! With the Resistance Band, you will feel the resistance and strain pulling against your muscle – this is good, as the resistance is what will increase your muscle size! Hold your Arm up at shoulder height for a second or two, and then slowly lower your Hand back down to the original starting position by your side to complete the perfect the Bicep Curl. Once you've done this, alternate Arms and repeat the exact same procedure and motions as before. For maximum intensity, actively contract your Bicep muscle at the top of the Bicep Curl. Remember, speed isn't the answer here; instead, it's all about technique, and slow and steady contractions to isolate your Bicep muscles.

Triceps Kickbacks

> **INFO: This exercise works the Tricep muscles in the back of both Upper Arms.**

■ How to Execute:

To execute the perfect Tricep Kickback, follow the Trainer Picture on the right hand side of the screen. Mimic his / her movements exactly and listen out for the 'Ding' sound, indicating when to Raise and Lower your Arms with perfect timing. Stand on the Resistance Band also for increased resistance and added effectiveness!

Stand with your Legs shoulder-width apart, and arch your Back upwards at a 45-degree angle. This precise technique and posture is vital for this exercise so make sure that you master it correctly before continuing. The Triceps Kickback starting position should now resemble the starting position for the Bent Over Rows. Keep your head up and look forwards as you arch your Back to maintain this position and the 45-degree angle throughout! Now tuck both of your Arms in tight to your Body (Rib Cage area) so that the Palms of both Hands are facing each other, and then bend your Arms at a 90-degree angle so that both the Wii Remote and Nunchuck and facing forwards. Keep your Elbows in tight at all times!! Now, keep your Elbows in place, and straighten one Arm backwards behind you and fully extend it so that the Wii Remote / Nunchuck is now pointing towards the floor. Manually contract your Tricep muscle at this point, and hold it for a second or two before bending back and returning to the starting position to complete the perfect Tricep Kickback! Alternate Arms now and repeat the same procedure as before. For increased intensity and effectiveness, manually contract your Abdominal muscles also! Remember, technique is everything here.

Shoulder Presses

INFO: *This exercise primarily works the Deltoid muscles in your Shoulders, and as you're standing, works your Core muscles also.*

■ How to Execute:

To execute the perfect Shoulder Press, follow the Trainer Picture on the right hand side of the screen. Mimic his / her movements exactly and listen out for the 'Ding' sound, indicating when to Raise and Lower your Arms with perfect timing. Stand on the Resistance Band also for increased resistance and added effectiveness!

Stand upright with your Legs shoulder-width apart, bend both Arms, and hold them up at your sides so that both Hands are at Ear-height, either side of your Head. Do not allow your Hands to drop

Bicep Curl with Shoulder Press >>>

INFO: *This exercise is a combination workout for the Upper Body, and works both the Deltoid and Bicep muscles simultaneously.*

■ How to Execute:

To execute the perfect Bicep Curl with Shoulder Press, follow the Trainer Picture on the right hand side of the screen. Mimic his / her movements exactly and listen out for the 'Ding' sound, indicating when to Raise and Lower your Arms, and Push, with perfect timing. Stand on the Resistance Band also for increased resistance and added effectiveness!

This is an advanced challenging workout that incorporates both the Bicep Curl, and the Shoulder Press simultaneously; and requires precise technique and timing to perfect both consecutive-exercises! Listen closely. Stand with your Legs Shoulder-width apart and your Arms down by your sides. For the first Bicep Curl part of the exercise, the exact

down to shoulder-height and relax completely; instead fight the resistance of the Band, and keep them up at Ear-height – this way you'll constantly be working your Deltoid muscles in your Shoulders, even before Pressing, and pushing upwards! Once you're in this position, raise one Arm upwards slowly, and point the Wii Remote / Nunchuck at

same methods and techniques apply as before, only this time, you'll be raising and lowering both Arms simultaneously, rather than intermittently, Left then Right, like before! Keep your upper Arms still, and raise your Forearms so that your Hands are up by your shoulders. Tense and contract your Bicep muscles manually for added effectiveness as you do this! Hold your Arms up at shoulder height, and keep them in place for a second or two – DO NOT lower your Arms back down to the starting position just yet! Read 'Bicep Curls' above for more details…

Do not complete the Bicep Curl by lowering your Arms like usual; instead you need to get into the Shoulder Press starting position now, by Rotating your Hands around so that both of your Thumbs are now facing your Head at Ear-height. Push upwards with both Arms now, and fully extend them straight up above your head. Hold this for a second or two, and then lower your Arms back down to Ear-height. From here, Rotate your Hands back around into the Bicep Curl position, and then complete the Curl by lowering your Arms back down to the original starting position to complete the exercise! Read 'Shoulder Press' above for more details…

To get the most out of this exercise, try to complete this five-step workout in one fluid motion, from Bicep Curling, to Hand Rotation, to Pushing upwards, then back down to Ear-height, and finally end at your sides! The smoother you can do this, the better.

the ceiling. At the top of the Shoulder Press, your Arm should now be fully extended. Hold this position for a second or two, and then lower your Arm back down to the starting position at your Ears. Repeat the same technique on the other side to complete the perfect the Shoulder Press. To maximise the intensity even more, manually contract your Upper Back muscles as you're lowering your Arms back down, to work the Lateral muscles also, as well as your Deltoids!

Lateral Shoulder Raises >>>

> **INFO:** *This exercise works the Lateral Head of the Deltoid muscle, which ultimately gives your Shoulder shape.*

■ How to Execute:

To execute the perfect Lateral Raise, follow the Trainer Picture on the right hand side of the screen. Mimic his / her movements exactly and listen out for the 'Ding' sound, indicating when to Raise and Lower your Arms with perfect timing. Stand on the Resistance Band also for increased resistance and added effectiveness!

Stand with your Legs shoulder-width apart, and both Arms down by your sides; then bend your Elbows at a 90-degree angle, so that your Arms / Hands are in the Hammer position, with your Palms facing each other. Keep your Elbows tucked in tight to your body as you do this. From this starting position, raise both Arms up and out to the side simultaneously, but make sure that you maintain that 90-degree bend in your Arms at ALL times! If done correctly, then your stance should resemble a 'Chicken'!

Hold both Arms up at shoulder-height for a second or two, and then lower them slowly back to the Hammer starting position to complete the Lateral Shoulder Press. Remember – you MUST keep the 90-degree angle throughout, if you want this exercise to work effectively! And to maximise the effectiveness even more, arch your Back, and manually contract your Upper Back muscles also.

Front Shoulder Raises

> **INFO:** *This exercise works the front Deltoid muscles in your Shoulders.*

■ How to Execute:

To execute the perfect Shoulder Raise, follow the Trainer Picture on the right hand side of the screen. Mimic his / her movements exactly and listen out for the 'Ding' sound, indicating when to Raise and Lower your Arms with perfect timing. Stand on the Resistance Band also for increase resistanced and added effectiveness!

Stand with your Legs shoulders-width apart, and hold both Arms down by your sides so that the Wii Remote and Nunchuck are pointing forwards. When told to do so, raise both Arms up in front of you simultaneously to shoulder-height. As you do this however, bend your arms at the Elbows ever so slightly, and pull your Shoulders back, to execute the perfect technique. Raise them up to shoulder-height so that the Wii Remote and Nunchuck are now pointing towards the ceiling, and then hold this position for a second or two to feel the resistance on your Deltoid muscles – the front part of your Shoulders. Wait for the 'Ding' sound, and then lower your Arms back down to the starting position slowly to complete the exercise. Repeat this and feel the burn!

Cross Knee Punches

> **INFO:** *This exercise trains your Upper and Lower Body simultaneously, and ultimately works on your Dynamic Balance.*

■ How to Execute:

To execute the perfect Cross Knee Punch, follow the Trainer Picture on the right

hand side of the screen. Mimic his / her movements exactly and listen out for the 'Ding' sound, indicating when to Cross and Thrust with perfect timing.

Stand upright with your Legs shoulder-width apart, extend both Arms straight out in front of you, and hold them up at shoulder-height. This is now your starting position. From here, bring your Left Knee up across your body, and end the Cross Knee Punch up at the Right hand side of your Hip. When you're Crossing your Right Knee, bring it up across your body to the Left – simply raising your Knee up straight isn't enough; you MUST bring the Knee ACROSS the body! As you bring your Knee up across the body, pull both of your Arms down at the exact time, simultaneously to either side of your Knee. To get the most out this workout, put added force into your Knee crunches, and forcefully thrust your Arms down to your sides, and back up again quickly. The more aggressive you are with this exercise, the better! Immediately after Crossing the Knee and thrusting your Arms down to your sides, return to the starting position, and repeat the same procedure again on the opposite Leg. For maximum effectiveness, manually Tense and Contract your Abdominal muscles in your Stomach as you Cross and crunch your Knee, as this will strengthen your Abs also!

Bent Over Rows with Triceps Kickbacks

> **INFO:** *This exercise combines the Bent Over Row with Triceps Kickbacks to work on your Upper Back and Arms.*

■ How to Execute:

To execute the perfect Bent Over Row with Tricep Kickback, follow the Trainer Picture on the right hand side of the screen. Mimic his / her movements exactly and listen out for the 'Ding' sound, indicating when to Contract and Relax your muscles, and Raise and Lower your Arms, with perfect timing. Stand on the Resistance Band also for increased resistance and added effectiveness!

Bent Over Rows

> **INFO:** *This exercise works on the Rhomboid and Lateral muscles in your Back, whilst targeting your Core Musculature also.*

■ How to Execute:

To execute the perfect Bent Over Row, follow the Trainer Picture on the right hand side of the screen. Mimic his / her movements exactly and listen out for the 'Ding' sound, indicating when to Contract and Relax your muscles with perfect timing. Stand on the Resistance Band also for increased resistance and added effectiveness!

Stand with your Legs Shoulder-width apart, and slightly bend your knees. Keep your Legs in place, and lean forwards, but make sure that you arch your lower back at a 45 degree angle. This technique is vital if you want to benefit from this exercise properly!! To help maintain this precise technique and correct posture, raise your head as you're leaning forwards, and look straight ahead. Stick your

This is an advanced challenging workout that incorporates both the Bent Over Rows, and the Triceps Kickbacks simultaneously; and requires precise technique and timing to perfect both consecutive-exercises! Listen closely. Firstly, get yourself into the starting position for the Bent Over Rows – which is also the same stance for the Triceps Kickbacks. Stand with your Legs Shoulder-width apart, and slightly bend your knees. Lean forwards and arch your lower back at a 45-degree angle. To maintain this precise technique, raise your head and look forwards; then stick your buttocks out behind in order to keep your upper back straight throughout. Perfect this technique and then drop your Arms

buttocks out behind you as well whilst arching your lower back, and this will help keep your upper back straight also. If you're back is arched downwards, then you're doing it wrong - it MUST be arched upwards at all times - not just for maximum effectiveness, but for safety also! The lower you lean and the more arched your lower back is, the more effective this exercise will be.

Once you have this position mastered, drop your Arms down by your side and point the Wii Remote and Nunchuck at the floor. Now, keep your Elbows tucked in tight to your body, and raise your hands up, close to your Rib Cage. At this point, contract your Upper Back muscles and feel the strain! You should feel the strain on all of your upper back muscles now; if you feel it on your arms or anywhere else, then you're doing it wrong. Master this technique and once you feel the workout of your Rhomboids and Lateral muscles in the upper and middle part of your back, hold your Arms in place and contract these muscles for a second or two, before lowering your Arms back down to the starting position again. When you lower your arms back down, point the Wii Remote and Nunchuck to the floor again to complete the perfect Bent Over Row. Remember, technique and precise contractions are everything here! Repeat this procedure and maintain the correct stance at all times for maximum effectiveness and intensity.

down by your side and point the Wii Remote / Nunchuck at the floor. Keep your Elbows tucked in tight to your body, and then raise your Hands up, close to your Rib Cage so that your Arms are at a 90-degree angle now. At this point, manually contract your Upper Back muscles! Hold your Arms in place and contract your Rhomboids and Lateral muscles for a second or two before moving onto the Tricep Kickback. DO NOT lower your Arms back down to complete the Bent Over Row like before – instead the Tricep Kickback comes at the top of the Bent Over Row contraction. Read 'Bent Over Rows' above for more details…

Hold your Arms at the top of the contraction, and then move smoothly into the Tricep Kickback with one of your Arms. To perfect this, keep your Arms tucked in tight to your Body (Rib Cage) with your Palms facing each other, and then straighten one Arm backwards behind you and fully extend it so that the Wii Remote / Nunchuck is now pointing towards the floor. Manually contract your Tricep muscle at this point, and hold it for a second or two before bending back and returning to the Tricep starting position! From here, lower both Arms back down to complete the Bent Over Row now, and return to the original starting position for this entire exercise. Now execute another Bent Over Row just like before, but this time, follow it up with a Tricep Kickback using the other Arm! Return to the starting position and repeat this method by alternating your Tricep Kick Arms from Left to Right throughout. Read 'Triceps Kickbacks' above for more details…

Remember, the smoother the transaction of the two exercises, the better! These two workouts should be completed in one fluid motion for maximum effectiveness.

Bicep Curls with Uprights Rows

> **INFO: This exercise works on both your Biceps and Deltoid muscles simultaneously, and over time the increase of these muscles will give your Upper Body great shape and tone.**

Upright Rows >>>

> **INFO: This exercise works the Deltoids and Bicep muscles simultaneously, and as you're standing, your Core muscles and Stabilisers are triggered also, increasing an overall good posture.**

■ How to Execute:
To execute the perfect Bicep Curl with Upright Row, follow the Trainer Picture on the right hand side of the screen. Mimic his / her movements exactly and listen out for the 'Ding'

■ How to Execute:
To execute the perfect Bicep Curl with Upright Row, follow the Trainer Picture on the right hand side of the screen. Mimic his / her movements exactly and listen out for the 'Ding' sound, indicating when to Raise and Lower your Arms, with perfect timing, both times. Stand on the Resistance Band also for increased resistance and added effectiveness!

This is an advanced challenging workout that incorporates both the Bicep Curl, and the Upright Row simultaneously; and requires precise technique and timing to perfect both consecutive-exercises! Listen closely. Stand with your feet Shoulder-width apart and your Arms by your sides. For the first Bicep Curl part of the exercise, the exact same techniques apply as usual, only this time, you'll be raising and

sound, indicating when to Raise and Lower your Arms, with perfect timing, both times. Stand on the Resistance Band also for increase resistanced and added effectiveness!

Stand upright on the spot with your Legs shoulder-width apart, and hold both Arms down in front of your Body at Crotch-level. Stick your Chest out and pull your Shoulders back for maximum effectiveness for the following Upright Row, and then rotate your Hands around so that both Palms are facing your Thighs, and the Back of your Hands are pointing away from you. From this starting position, bend both Arms at the Elbows, and then raise your Arms up to shoulder-height. For the perfect Upright Row, your Elbows should be bent inwards, and your Hands should almost be in front of your Face. Hold this for a second or two, and then lower and straighten your Arms back down to the starting position to complete the perfect Upright Row.

lowering your Arms simultaneously, rather than intermittently! Keep your upper Arms still, and raise your Forearms. Tense and contract your Bicep muscles manually for added effectiveness! Hold briefly, and then lower your Hands back down to the original starting position. Read 'Bicep Curls' above for more details…

Once you've lowered your Arms and have returned to the starting position, rotate your Hands around and get into the Upright Row starting position, so that the Palms of your Hands are now facing your Thighs, and the Back of your Hands are pointing away from you! From this position, bend both Arms at the Elbows, and then raise your Arms up to shoulder-height. For the perfect Upright Row, your Elbows should be bent inwards, and your Hands should almost be in front of your Face. Again, hold this for a second or two, and then lower and straighten your Arms back down to the starting position. Read 'Upright Rows' above for more details…

Finally, rotate your Hands back around again, ready for the following Bicep Curl. To maximise the effective of this workout, you'll want to perform these two exercises in one fluid motion - like always, the smoother the transaction, the better!

lower body exercises

Lunges

> **INFO: This exercise works the Quadriceps, Hamstrings, Glutes, and Adductors (inner Thighs); and is a perfect workout for overall Leg Strength.**

■ How to Execute:

To execute the perfect Lunge, follow the Trainer Picture on the right hand side of the screen. Mimic his / her movements exactly and listen out for the 'Ding' sound, indicating when to Lunge out and back in again with perfect timing.

Stand on the spot with your Legs close together, and your Arms on your Hips for added balance and easy movement when Lunging. When told to do so, take one large extended-Step forwards with your Left Leg and place it back down on the floor in front of you. Make sure that your rear Right Leg remains in place at this point, and keep it firmly pinned to the floor! After taking the Step and Lunging forwards, bend both your Right and Left Leg at a 90- degree angle at the Knee, so that ONLY the Toes on your Right Leg are touching the floor behind you, and the sole of your Foot is pointing backwards. Your Left Leg should still be flat on the floor in front of you here! If both of your Thighs are almost parallel to the floor, and your stance resembles the 'Wedding Proposal' position – then you're doing it right! Lunge forwards even more and feel the strain on your entire Leg; Quads, Hamstrings, Glutes, and Inner Thighs! Lunge forwards to the floor until both Knees are at a 90 degree angle, and then hold it for a second or two before pushing back up and returning to the starting position to complete the perfect Lunge. Repeat this same procedure and technique on the Right Leg and work those muscles!

Side Lunges

> **INFO: This exercise works on your Gluteus Medius (outer Thighs & Hip area) and your overall Hip Mobility.**

■ How to Execute:

To execute the perfect Side Lunge, follow the Trainer Picture on the right hand side of the screen. Mimic his / her movements exactly and listen out for the 'Ding' sound, indicating when to Lunge out and back in again with perfect timing.

Start by standing upright on the spot, and make sure that you've got enough full-leg space to your left and right. Lunge outwards to the

Left now with your Left Leg so that it's almost fully outstretched, and then place it flat on the floor away from your body. Keep your Right Leg firmly in place at this point and do not remove it from the floor. Now bend your Left Lunging-Leg, so that your Right Leg is now the outstretched Leg, and then push down and Lunge even further Left to feel the strain on your the inside of your Right Leg (Thigh area)! For increased effectiveness, stick your buttocks out behind you at this point, and feel the burn in your Glutes as well. Hold this position briefly, and then return to the starting position to complete the Side Lunge. Once you've completed the Left Lunge, switch sides, Lunge out to the Right, and repeat the same procedure and technique again to work the other Leg. Remember, the further you Lunge and the lower you drop, the more effective this exercise will be!

Side Lunges with Toe Touches

INFO: *This exercise combines Side Lunges with Toe Touches to work the Gluteus Medius, and to increase your overall Hip and Trunk Mobility.*

■ How to Execute:

To execute the perfect Side Lunge with Toe Touch, follow the Trainer Picture on the right hand side of the screen. Mimic his / her movements exactly and listen out for the 'Ding' sound, indicating when to Lunge out and back in again with perfect timing.

This exercise incorporates almost the exact same techniques as Side Lunges mentioned above, only this time round, you'll have to end with a Toe Touch once you've completed the Lunge, for increased intensity! Unlike the standard Side Lunges, this exercise requires you to hold your Arms out in front of you as you Lunge, so that the Wii Remote is facing the ceiling! If the Wii Remote is not pointing at the ceiling, then the Sensor wont pick up on your movements and Toe Touches properly, so make sure your Hands are out in front of your body, with the Wii Remote pointing upwards at the beginning of the exercise.

Stand upright on the spot with enough leg space to your left and right, and then Lunge outwards to the side so that your Lunging-Leg is almost fully outstretched. Place it flat on the floor away from your body, and keep your non-Lunging Leg firmly in place. Now bend your Lunging-Leg, so that your other Leg is now the outstretched one, and then push down and Lunge even further to feel the strain

on the inside of your non-Lunging Leg! For increased effectiveness, stick your buttocks out behind you, and feel the burn in your Glutes! ...Read 'Side Lunges' above for more details.

Once you're in the completed Lunge position, follow the Trainer, and bend down to touch the Toes of your Lunging Leg! Like we mentioned previously, for the Sensor to pick up your movement and Toe Touches, you must go from pointing the Wii Remote at the ceiling, to pointing it down at the Floor. Hold the Toe Touch for a second or two with the Wii Remote pointing towards the floor, and then return to the upright starting position to complete the exercise. Keep your Back straight as you bend down to touch the Toes, and arch

your Lower Back upwards like the Bent Over Rows for perfect technique and added effectiveness! To get the most out of this workout, try to complete this two-part exercise in one fluid motion, going from Side Lunge to Toe Touches with no hesitations. The smoother the motion, the more effective it will be!

Jump Lunges

INFO: *This exercise is an intense workout that trains the Glutes, Quadriceps, and Adductors (inner Thighs).*

■ How to Execute:

To execute the perfect Lunge, follow the Trainer Picture on the right hand side of

High Knee Reverse Lunges >>>

INFO: *This exercise works predominantly on the Glutes, but also trains the Quadriceps and Hamstrings also, whilst increasing your overall Coordination as well.*

■ How to Execute:

To execute the perfect High Knee Reverse Lunge, follow the Trainer Picture on the right hand side of the screen. Mimic his / her movements exactly and listen out for the 'Ding' sound, indicating when to Lunge out and back in again with perfect timing.

Stand upright with your Legs close together, and hold both Hands on your Hips for the perfect posture. Keep your Back arched upwards as you perform the following High Knee Reverse Lunges to maintain the correct technique throughout. When told do so, Lunge Backwards this time with your Left Leg, and bend it at a 90-degree angle at the Knee so that the Toes on your Left Leg are touching the

floor behind you, and the sole of your Foot is pointing backwards. Bend your Right Leg also at this point, but keep it firmly planted on the floor so that both your Thighs are almost parallel to the floor. Your stance should now resemble the 'Wedding Proposal' position (in reverse to the standard Lunges) – if so, then you're doing it right!

Lunge as far back as you can and hold this position briefly, before raising your Left Lunging Leg up to your Hip for the High Knee part of the Reverse Lunge. Your Front Right Leg should now be straight so that you're standing and balancing on one Foot. To perfect this, push off with both Feet back up to the standing position, and then follow through with your Lunging Leg, so your Knee is up high at your Hip. Contract your buttocks at this point for maximum intensity, and maintain your balance at all times on one foot! To complete the perfect High Knee Reverse Lunge, you'll want to execute this three-part exercise in one fluid motion, from Lunging backwards, to standing up, then raising the Knee. The smoother the motion, the more successful this exercise will be! Once you've held the High Knee for a second or two, lower it back down to the original starting position, and then repeat the same procedure again on the opposite Right Leg.

position briefly, before Jumping and reversing once again. Repeatedly Jump and switch your Legs in midair to perform perfect Jump Lunges. This technique may take a while to master - but remember, practice makes perfect!

Squats

> **INFO: This exercise works the Quadriceps, Hamstrings, and Glutes. It is the most functional exercise for daily life, and will increase your Leg Strength dramatically.**

■ How to Execute:

To help execute the perfect Squat, follow the Trainer Picture on the right hand side of the screen. Mimic his / her movements exactly and listen out for the 'Ding' sound, indicating when to Squat down and back up, with perfect timing.

Stand upright with your Legs shoulder-width apart, and hold your Arms out in front of you. Arch the lower part of your

action before landing again. For increased height, thrust your Arms up in the air also and forcefully push yourself off from the floor. Upon landing, you'll want to land back in the Lunge position – only this time, in reverse. The softer and smoother you land, the more effective this workout will be! Once you've performed the reverse Leg switch in midair, hold the landing-Lunge

the screen. Mimic his / her movements exactly and listen out for the 'Ding' sound, indicating when to Lunge out and back in again with perfect timing.

To perfect this exercise, you must first master the Lunge staring position! Take one large extended-Step forwards and keep your other Leg firmly in place behind you. After taking the Step and Lunging forwards, bend both of your Legs at a 90- degree angle at the Knee, and Lunge forwards so that both of your Thighs are almost parallel to the floor, and your stance resembles the 'Wedding Proposal' position! DO NOT return to standing position this time; instead, hold this crouched-Lunge stance. This is now the starting position for the following Jump Lunges. Read 'Lunges' above for more details…

From this Lunge position, push off with both Feet and Jump up high into the air. At the top of the Jump, you must quickly switch and reverse your Legs in midair from Back to Front and Front to Back, so that your Front Leg is now your Rear Leg, and your Rear Leg is now your Front Leg! To perfect this, you MUST be quick in the transaction, and you'll need to generate a decent amount of height in order to complete the 'Scissor-Kick'

Standing Knee Crunches > > >

> **INFO: This exercise increases your Balance on one foot. Balance is the foundation of Strength and Power!**

■ How to Execute:

To execute the perfect Standing Knee Crunch, follow the Trainer Picture on the right hand side of the screen. Mimic his / her movements exactly and listen out for the 'Ding' sound, indicating when to Crunch up and down with perfect timing. Stand on the Resistance Band also for increased resistance and added effectiveness!

This exercise focuses predominantly on your overall Balance - however if executed correctly, it can also work on

your Leg muscles, and Abdominal muscles as well! Stand upright on the spot with your Legs pinned together. Hold your Arms close to your body, tuck your Elbows in tight, and hold your Hands out in front of you slightly. Once you have this position mastered, raise your Knee up to your Hip / Stomach, and bow forwards slightly, to meet your rising-Knee. Hold your Knee up at Stomach-height, and keep the bow held for a second or two, before dropping your Leg back to the floor, and returning to the starting position to complete the perfect Standing Knee Crunch! Alternate Legs at this point and repeat the same techniques as before. The Trainer pic in the bottom corner will perform these Knee Crunches too fast – so remember, the longer you hold the Crunch for, the more effective this exercise will be. Therefore your best bet is to manually hold the Crunch for a second or two longer than the Trainer, to really feel the burn in your Legs and Abs; otherwise you'll just be focusing on your Balance and nothing else!

Back so that when you Squat down, your Back remains completely straight. Once you have this technique mastered, Squat down into an almost-sitting position so that your Thighs are parallel to the floor. Your Calves and Thighs should now be at a 90 degree angle to one another. The lower you Squat, the more effective this exercise will be! However DO NOT allow yourself to sit down onto your and rest on your Calves, as this will take the strain away from your Quads! Once you're in the full Squat position, push away from the floor now using your feet, and rise back up to the standing position to contract your Glutes, and complete the Squat. Keep an eye on the Bar on the left hand side of the screen, and Squat down until the Bar drops into the Yellow section. Once you reach halfway into the Yellow section, stand back up again slowly to the starting position, to execute the 'Perfect' Squat. Remember, technique is key here, and following the Trainer will help you master this exercise quickly.

Squat & Hold

> **INFO: This exercise works on your Lower Body muscle Endurance.**

■ How to Execute:

To help execute the perfect Squat, follow the Trainer Picture on the right hand side of the screen. Mimic his / her movements exactly and listen out for the 'Ding' sound, indicating when to Squat down and back up, with perfect timing.

This exercise requires the exact same posture and precise

Jump Squats >>>

> **INFO: This exercise works the Glutes, Quadriceps, Hamstrings, Spinal Erectors and Calves. The higher you jump, the more your muscles and Cardiovascular System will be worked.**

■ How to Execute:

To help execute the perfect Squat, follow the Trainer Picture on the right hand side of the screen. Mimic his / her movements exactly and listen out for the 'Ding' sound, indicating when to Squat down and back up, with perfect timing.

Start by crouching down into the full-Squat position so that your Thighs are parallel to the floor, and keep the lower part of your Back arched so that you can maintain the perfect technique

techniques as the 'Squats' mentioned above, only this time round, you only have to complete 1 elongated Rep. Squat down into the full-Squat position so that the Bar on the Left hand side of the screen is in the Yellow Section, and then hold it! Read 'Squats' above for more details...

Remain in this almost-sitting Squat position for the required amount of time, and seriously feel the burn on your Legs! Stay strong at this point as the Lactic

throughout. The lower you Squat, the more effective this exercise will be! However DO NOT allow yourself to sit down and rest on your Calves, as this will take the strain away from your Quads! DO NOT stand back up at this point like before, instead, hold it, and prepare for part two of the exercise. Read 'Squats' above for more details...

Once you're in the full-Squat position, Jump upwards with both Legs, and thrust your Arms up also for added height and intensity! The higher you Jump, the more effective this exercise will be. As you land, you'll want to land lightly on your Toes to cushion your fall, and land perfectly back into the Squat position, ready for the next Jump. All of this should be executed in one fluid motion, with no hesitations. Upon landing, hold the Squat for a split second, and then Jump up once again. Repeat this procedure to complete the exercise.

Acid builds up, and DO NOT move. If you wiggle around, then you'll take the strain off of your Legs – stay still for it's entirety and hold the Squat until the time reaches 0; at which point, stand back up to complete the Squat Hold. This is an intense workout and will really take its toll on your overall Endurance as the Lactic Acid increases!!

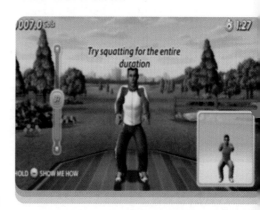

Squats with Calf Raises

INFO: This exercise combines Squats with Calf Raises to train all of your Lower Body muscles simultaneously, whilst increasing your overall Balance also.

■ How to Execute:

To help execute the perfect Side to Side Jump, follow the Trainer Picture on the right hand side of the screen. Mimic his / her movements exactly and listen out for the 'Ding' sound, indicating when to Jump, with perfect timing.

This exercise incorporates almost the exact same techniques as Squats, only this time round, you'll have to end with a challenging Calf Raise, for increased intensity! Stand with your Legs shoulder-width apart, crouch down into the Squat position to begin with, and keep the lower part of your Back arched throughout, as this will make the Calf Raises easier. Read 'Squats' above for more details...

DO NOT rise back up just yet – instead it's time for the Calf Raises whilst you're still Squatting! Whilst you're in the full-Squat position and your Thighs are parallel to the floor, lift your Heels off of the floor and rise up onto the tip of your Toes to enter the Calf Raise position. Remain in the Squat position as you do this, and hold the Calf Raise up on your Toes for a second or two, before dropping back down onto the full base of your Feet, and then rising back up to the original standing position! To make the Calf Raises easier, hold your Arms out in front of you for support, and keep your eyes on a single object ahead to maintain balance and steadiness throughout! For increased effectiveness, manually contract your Abdominal muscles also as you're executing the Calf Raise!

Side to Side Jumps

INFO: This exercise works on your Lower Body muscle groups, and your Cardiovascular System.

■ How to Execute:

To help execute the perfect Side to Side Jump, follow the Trainer Picture on the right hand side of the screen. Mimic his / her movements exactly and listen out for the 'Ding' sound, indicating when to Jump, with perfect timing.

First off, make absolute certain that you have enough Jump-space to your Left and Right before beginning! ...Start by standing upright with your Legs shoulder-width apart, and then bend your Knees, and Squat down into the Half-Squat position. Your stance should be halfway between Crouching and Standing, but not as low as the Full-Squat! Once you have your starting position ready, Jump up and to the Side. The further you Jump, the better! As you Jump, make sure that you're light on your Feet, and that you Jump up off of your Toes and not the flat base of your Feet, as this will give you added height and agility. Jumping with your Feet flat on the floor will seem heavy and uncontrollable, whereas Jumping and pushing off with your Toes will

make your movement light and smooth. As you're in midair, thrust your Arms up also to increase the height of your Jump and maintain balance. When landing, you'll want to land evenly with both Feet simultaneously, not one then other – as again, this will result in a heavy landing, when you want it to be light. DO NOT stand back up when you land; instead, remain in the Half-Squat position for this entire exercise and feel the burn on your Quads constantly throughout! Hold this position briefly, and then Jump up and back to the other

Side; and repeat the same procedure again. This exercise is all about control, and light-footwork. The more controlled your Jumps and Landing are, the more effective this workout will be! Remember, light-Landings are key.

Standing Twists >>>

INFO: This exercise increases Movement in the Transverse Plane, to enhance overall Trunk Mobility. This should also be used to warm-up and warm-down in between Sport drills and more intense exercises.

■ How to Execute:
This exercise is by far the easiest one

of them all, as it requires no real strength or precise technique. Standing Twists is not a muscle-building exercise, but instead a workout that increases your overall Movement and Mobility in your midsection. Stand with your Legs shoulder-width apart, and slightly bend your Knees. Now hold your Arms out in front of you and fully extend them both. From this position, keep your Legs in place firmly on the floor, and Twist (rotate) your Torso around from Left to Right. As you Twist around, forcefully swing your Body to generate more momentum, and then stop briefly when you're facing to the side. Switch sides now, and rotate back around in the other direction. Hold it again, and then Twist back. Repeatedly do this, and contract your Abdominal muscles as you do so for added intensity!

cardio exercises

Cardio Boxing: Punching Targets

INFO: This exercise requires you to hit the Targets that appear by performing Straight jabs and Cross punch combinations.

■ How to Execute:

For this exercise you'll be performing different Punch combos to hit the Targets that appear on the apparatus in front. There are four Targets that you must successfully hit in order to complete the workout – the first two Red Targets appear on the inner half of the apparatus, and require you to perform Straight Jabs using either your Right or Left hand depending on what side the Target is currently on. To hit the Right Red Target, simply Punch straight ahead using your Right Wii Remote hand, and to hit the Left Red Target, Punch straight ahead using your Left Nunchuck hand.

Shortly into the workout, two Blue Targets will pop up on the outer sides of the apparatus, to the Right and Left. In order to successfully

Cardio Boxing: Heavy Bag >>>

INFO: This exercise requires you to repeatedly hit the Heavy Bag for a period of time, for an intense Speed-Endurance Cardio workout.

■ How to Execute:

This exercise is all about pure Cardio work, and requires no real skill or technique. Simply unleash a continuous combination of Right-Left Punches to hit the Heavy Bag in front! Repeatedly Punch Left, Right, Left, Right for the required amount of Punches until you move on. After a few rounds, the Bag will fall and the workout will be complete! Each Punch should be a straight Jab, just like

Punching the Red Targets in the previous exercise mentioned above. To get the most out of this workout, put added force into each Punch and snap your Elbows back to really get your heart going. DO NOT stop Punching throughout this entire exercise – keep going, and sweat it out!

hit these, you must perform Cross Punches using the opposite hand. For example, if the Blue Target appears on the Left side, then you must bring your Right Wii Remote hand across your body, and Punch out to the Left; and if the Blue Target appears on the Right hand side, then you must bring your Left Nunchuck hand across your body, and Punch out to the Right. You CANNOT Punch a Left Blue Target with your Left hand or a Right Blue Target with your Right hand – it HAS to be a Cross Punch with the opposite hand. Also, the harder you hit the Targets, the better...and you could even shatter them with enough force! Snap your Elbows as you thrust your Arm forwards to exert more force into the Punch! Smash the Targets for better results. Adding increased movement and power to your Punches will also increase the effectiveness and intensity of the workout, and get your Cardiovascular System working even more!

Cardio Dancing

INFO: This exercise requires you to complete multiple Dance moves to work on your Upper and Lower Body, and Cardio-vascular System. Dancing is also a perfect exercise to warm-up and cool-down before and after the more intense workouts.

■ How to Execute:

For this exercise, you must mimic the Arrow Directions on screen using your Wii Remote and Nunchuck Hand to perform different Dance Moves. As the Arrows drop down the screen and enter the Green Section of the Bar, mimic the Arrow Directions exactly. The Left hand side of the Bar requires you to use your Left Nunchuck Hand, whereas the Right hand side of the Bar requires you to use your Right Wii Remote Hand. If the Arrow points Left, then you must thrust your Arm out to the Left. If the Arrow is pointing Right, then thrust your Arm out to the Right. Down for Down, Up for Up, and Diagonally also! Watch closely on screen and copy the exact movements depending on the Arrows shown. After completing each Dance Move, return to starting position with your Arms in front of you ready for the next direction.

Every now and then you'll have to complete a Special Dance Move! These come in a few forms (i.e. Wave Arms from Side to Side, Shopping Cart etc). Listen to what is said and the requirements for each Move, and then follow the other characters on screen to complete move on. To get the most out of this exercise routine, jig on the spot and put added movement into your Dance Moves for increased intensity!

Track: Walking & Running

> **INFO: This exercise requires you to Walk around the Track over a set distance. This is also a perfect exercise for warming-up and cooling-down.**

■ How to Execute:

Walking: …To begin Walking, you yourself must Walk on the spot. To execute this correctly, alternate raising and lowering both Legs one after the other at about a 45 degree angle in the air, as if you were actually walking; and then make the 90 degree 'Up-Down' Hammer-motion with your Arms also, so that the Wii Remote sensor can pick up your Arm movement. Slowly Walk in place, perform small steps and in-time Arm movements, and maintain a steady pace throughout, to Walk along the track. If done correctly, your character on screen

will begin to Walk, and the word 'Perfect' will appear. Remember to accentuate your Leg and Arm movements for maximum effectiveness of this Cardio workout.

Running: …Running is much like Walking, although this time the intensity of the exercise is increased of course, as you will actually have to Run on the spot in order to

Track: >>> High Knees

> **INFO: This exercise requires you to bring your Knees up high to your chest as you make your way around the Track, thus increasing the intensity and Cardio workout even more.**

■ How to Execute:

The High Knees exercise is a great intense Cardio workout, even more so than Running! For this exercise, you must repeatedly perform High Knee movements as you advance along the Track. Start jogging in place, but make sure that you remain light on the tip of your Toes with each step, for added bounce and agility. Being on your Toes will make executing the High Knees easier, and your Cardio workout even more effective. To perform High Knee movements, you must bring your Knees up high to your Hips / Stomach with each step. You'll

complete the workout. The same methods apply as Walking, however this time round you'll have to alternate raising and lowering your Legs at a much faster pace, and you must raise your Legs at a 90 degree angle instead of a 45 degree angle now, so that they are parallel to the floor and your knees come up high to your stomach. If done correctly, your character on screen will begin to Run. Maintain this Running motion at all times and keep a steady pace going throughout. If the words 'Too Slow' appear on screen, then you will have to increase your speed, and maybe even accentuate your Leg and Arm movement even more for the sensors' sake, and to get that 'Perfect' rating.

have to accentuate each high step dramatically in order to get the height! Thrust your Knee up to your Hips / Stomach and then drop back down onto your Toes, before thrusting your other Knee up in one fluid motion immediately after. For the perfect High Knee combination, there should be a split second where neither Foot is touching the floor – almost like bouncing. If you're doing it correctly, then your character on screen will begin to jog with High Knees, and the word 'Perfect' will appear! If not, then you may have to accentuate your High Knees even more. Lean backwards slightly also, and perform back-forth Arm motions in perfect timing to your Legs, to maintain your balance and keep a smooth Jog going throughout!

Track: Kick Ups >>>

INFO: *This exercise requires you to perform Kick Ups as you make your way around the Track. Again, this advanced drill increases the intensity even more.*

■ How to Execute:

Much like the High Knees exercise above, Kick Ups are ideal for an intense Cardio workout! For this exercise, you must repeatedly perform Kick Ups as you advance along the Track. To execute this correctly, start Jogging on the spot, but make sure that you remain light on the balls of your feet with every step. Accentuate each step dramatically and drive your Heels back as you jog, so that the Heels of both Feet touch the back of your Legs / Buttocks with each step! If you're doing it correctly, then your character on screen will begin to jog whilst performing Kick Ups, and the word 'Perfect' will appear! If not, then you may have to accentuate your Kick Ups even more, and drive your Heel even further back until it touches your Upper Leg / Buttocks area to get the technique and speed correct. The more motion you put into this exercise, the better! Also, repeatedly thrust your Arms up and down in time with your Leg movement as you run, to maximums the intensity even more, and to maintain balance at all times!

sports exercises

Baseball: >>> Catching & Pitching

INFO: *This exercise Drill requires you to Catch the oncoming Ball, and Pitch the Ball to knock over the Bottles ahead.*

■ How to Execute:

Baseball Explanation: ... This is a fun exercise that should keep you on your toes throughout. To Catch the Ball, you must use your Left Nunchuck Hand, and to Pitch the Ball, you must use your Right Wii Remote Hand. Execute the Catching and Pitching motions to complete the exercises.

Catching: ...To Catch the Ball, you must use your Left Nunchuck Hand, and point it wherever the oncoming Ball is heading. For example, if the Ball is Up high and to the Left, then you must hold your Left Hand Up high and to the Left.

If the Ball is Up high and to the Right, then hold your Left Arm across your Body and Up high to the Right. If the Ball is straight above your head, then simply hold the Nunchuck Up high straight above you. This also applies for low Balls – Down low and to the Left, Down low and to the Right, and straight Down beneath your Legs. Wherever the Ball is heading, simply hold your Nunchcuk Hand in that direction to successfully Catch the Ball!

Once you have successfully caught the Ball, you must Throw it at the Target. To do this, hold your Right Wii Remote Hand up above your Head on your right hand side, and then swing forwards, bringing your Arm down and across your body. The more power and force you exert into the Throw, the more intense this Drill will be, and the more chance you will have in knocking the Target over!

Pitching: ...Pitching is pretty much the exact same as throwing the Ball back after Catching, mentioned above. Hold your Right Wii Remote Hand up high above your Head on your right hand side, and then swing forwards, bringing your Arm down and across your body from Right to Left to Pitch the Ball! For increased intensity, raise your Left Leg up also, as if you were a professional Pitcher.

On screen ahead are a few stacked Bottles. The idea is to Pitch the Ball with power and accuracy, in an attempt to knock down as many Bottles as you can in 3 attempts! Wait until the continuously moving Target-Cursor is aiming at the Bottles, and then unleash your Pitch! The most effective way to knock down every Bottle is to aim for the Bottom Row first and Pitch with tremendous force and increased

Baseball: Batting

> **INFO: This exercise Drill requires you to swing the Bat, to hit the oncoming Ball at the Targets ahead.**

■ How to Execute:
This exercise requires you to Swing the Wii Remote just like a Baseball Bat to smash the oncoming Ball at the Targets ahead. Stand to the side so that your Left Arm is facing forwards, and then hold your Wii Remote hand behind you. Wait for the Ball to approach, and then Swing your Arm forwards, bringing your Wii Remote Hand across your Body, to in front of you, and to the Left. If you Swing early, then you'll hook the Ball and hit the Targets on the Left, whereas if you Swing late, you'll slice the Ball and hit the Targets on the Right. Swing with perfect timing, and you'll hit the Ball straight at the centre Targets. The more power and force that you exert for each swing, the more intense this exercise Drill be. Swinging hard will hit the Higher Targets, whereas swinging lightly will hit the Lower Targets. Repeatedly swing and hit the oncoming Balls to complete the workout.

movement, as this will take down the Higher Rows also! Then you can accurately aim for the ones left on the bottom afterwards.

Basketball: >>> Passing & Shooting

> **INFO: This exercise drill requires you to Pass the Ball to hit the Targets, and shoot the Ball to sink it in the Net.**

■ How to Execute:
Basketball Explanation: … This is a fun exercise that should keep you on your toes throughout. To begin with, you will have to manually pick up the Ball. Stand on the spot, and move both your Wii Remote and Nunchuck Hands simultaneously to the Left, to retrieve the Ball on the left hand side of the screen. Once you have the Ball at hand, hold the Wii Remote and Nunchuck together as if you were actually holding a Basketball, and prepare for the following actions!

Passing: … For this exercise, you'll be Passing the Ball at the Targets ahead by executing the actual Basketball Passing-motions. Once you have the Ball at hand, thrust both of your Hands forwards simultaneously in front of your Body as if you Passing the Ball forwards, and fully extend your Arms outwards as you do so. Snap your Elbows for added power and try to knock down the Targets with enough force! The harder you Pass, the

better! Retrieve a new Ball for each Pass, and knock down EVERY Target!

Shooting: …For this exercise, you'll be 3-Throwing the Ball into the Basket ahead by executing the actual Basketball Throwing-motions. Once you have the Ball at hand, push both of your Hands upwards, extend your Arms fully above your head, and flick the Wii Remote / Nunchuck at the top of the extension, to Throw the Ball at the Basket! Forcefully thrust your Arms upwards and vigorously flick your Hands for added power. The harder and faster you perform this Throwing-motion, the more intense the Drill will be, and ultimately the more Baskets you will sink! You don't have to worry about direction or accuracy, as the Ball will automatically head straight for the Net, however Power is necessary. Not enough force on your Throws will cause the Ball to land short. Retrieve a new Ball for each Throw, and sink EVERY Ball for maximum points!

Tennis: Forehand & Backhand

INFO: *This exercise drill requires you to perform different variations of the Forehand and Backhand shot to hit the Ball.*

■ How to Execute:

Tennis Explanation: ...This is a fun exercise that should keep you on your toes throughout. Hold the Wii Remote as if it were a Tennis Racket, and prepare for the oncoming Balls! Your objective here is to successfully hit the oncoming Balls back across the Court, and direct it at the Target ahead. To do this you'll want to time your Swing correctly. If you've played Tennis on 'Wii Sports', then you'll understand how this concept works – swing too early and you'll Slice the Ball; swing to late, and you'll Hook the Ball; swing at the precise moment when the Ball has reached you, and you'll automatically hit it straight at the Target!

Forehand: ... The Forehand shot must be played when you're on the Right hand side of the Court, and requires you to hold the Wii Remote out to your Right, and swing across your body to the Left. Time your swing correctly, and perform a Forehand sweeping motion from Right to Left to hit the Ball back!

Backhand: ... The Backhand shot must be played when you're on the Left hand side of the Court, and requires you to hold the Wii Remote out to your Left (still in your Right hand however), and swing across your body to the Right. Time your swing correctly, and perform a Backhand sweeping motion with your Right Hand, from Right to Left, to hit the Ball back!

Timing is everything here, and practice makes perfect! To get the most out of this workout, put added force into your Swings, and really get your Cardiovascular System working!

Volleyball: >>> Bumping & Setting

INFO: *This exercise is an offensive drill that requires you to Bump and Set the Ball up to hit the Target. Bend your Knees and put your entire Body into it for maximum effectiveness.*

■ How to Execute:

Volleyball Explanation: ...This is a fun exercise that should keep you on your toes throughout. Hold the Wii Remote / Nunchuck as required and prepare for the oncoming Balls! Your objective here is to successfully hit the oncoming Balls back across the Court, and direct it at the Target ahead. To do this you'll want to time your Arm movements correctly. If you've played Tennis on 'Wii Sports', then you'll understand how this concept works – thrust too early or too late, and the Ball will land short! Swing at the precise moment when the Ball has reached you, and you'll automatically hit it straight at the Target!

Bumping: ...Bumping is used when you're far back on the End Line. To Bump the Ball, stand upright on the spot, and hold both Arms together down in front of you by your Crotch area. When the Ball is launched and it has almost reached you, thrust both Arms upwards above your head simultaneously to Bump the Ball back! Return to the starting position down in front of you, and prepare for the next Ball – then repeat the same procedures again. The more forceful you are with your Arm-thrusting, the more intense this Drill will be! And remember, timing is everything here.

Setting: ... Setting is used when you're in close to the Net. To Set the Ball, hold both Arms up at shoulder-height either side of head, and wait for the Ball to come. Again, when it has nearly reached you, thrust both Arms upwards straight

Tennis: Forehand Volley, Backhand Volley & Overhead Smash

INFO: *This exercise drill requires you to perform different variations of the Forehand Volley, Backhand Volley, and Overhead Smash shot to hit the Ball.*

■ How to Execute:

Forehand Volley: ...The Forehand Volley shot must be played when you're on the Right hand side of the Court, and when you're in close to the Net at Front Court. Hold your Hand high up at head-height on your Right hand side, and when the Ball has almost reached you, swing Down across your Body from Right to Left, and end the swing down low on your Left side to execute the Forehand Volley!

Backhand Volley: ...The Backhand Volley shot must be played when you're on the Left hand side of the Court, and when you're in close to the Net at Front Court.. Using your Right Hand again, hold it up at head-height, but on your Left hand side this time; and when the Ball has

almost reached you, swing Down across your Body from Left to Right, and end the swing down low on your Right side to execute the Backhand Volley! Remember, this is a Backhand shot, so you MUST hold your Right Arm across your face to begin with, and then swing across your Body from Left to Right!!

Overhead Smash: ...The Overhead Smash shot must be played when you're in the Centre at Mid Court. To perform an Overhead Smash, hold your Hand high above your head, and fully extend your Arm upwards. When the Ball has almost reached you, swing straight Down quickly, and end down low. The more motion and force that you exert into each swing – the better!

above your head, and fully extend your Arms for added intensity! This Drill almost resembles the Shoulder Press exercise and is great your Deltoid muscles! Once you've Set the Ball, return to the starting position at shoulder-height and repeat.

Volleyball: Blocking

> *INFO: This exercise is a defensive drill that requires you to Block the Ball. Bend your Knees and put your entire Body into it for maximum effectiveness.*

■ How to Execute:

Blocking is used when you're up close to the Net. To Block, you're going to have to Jump up on the spot, and thrust your Arms up above your head to stop the oncoming Ball reaching your side of the Court. Wait for the Ball to approach, and then Jump up. Whilst you're in midair, forcefully thrust your Arms up above your head and fully extend your Arms to Block the Ball. The quicker you do this and the more force you thrust your Arms with, the harder your Block will be, enabling you to knock over the Target with enough power. Again timing is

Volleyball: Serving

> *INFO: This exercise is an offensive drill that requires you to Serve the Ball. Bend your Knees and put your entire Body into it for maximum effectiveness.*

■ How to Execute:

To Serve the Ball, you must use both your Right and Left Wii Remote and Nunchuck Hand - first to Serve the Ball, and then to hit it! Start by holding your Left Nunchuck Hand down by your Left side at Hip-level, and then hold your Right Wii Remote Hand up high behind you, on your Right hand side. Serve the Ball by lifting your Left hand upwards above your head, and then when the Ball is

coming back down, swing your Right hand down across your Body to smash the Ball at the Target on the other side of the Court! The smoother the motion, the better the workout. And the more force and power that you exert, the better! Repeatedly Serve the Ball up into the air with your Left hand, and follow it up with a swinging motion using your Right hand to complete the routine.

everything here! Once you've Blocked the Ball, return to the starting position and repeat the same Jump-Block motions again to compete the exercise.

Inline Skating

> *INFO: This exercise requires you to navigate through a course by Crouching down to gain speed, and Jumping up to Jump off Ramps. The Lower you Crouch, the faster you will travel, and the higher you Jump, the more effective this exercise will be!*

■ How to Execute:

For this exercise you'll be Skating down a

narrow road consisting of a few Ramps, at which you must successfully Jump off to perform Tricks. To gain speed, literally Crouch down into the Squat position and hold it – the lower you Squat, the faster you'll travel! Keep the Squat position held and your feet planted until you reach the top of the Ramp (the Green section), and then actually Jump up on the spot to leap off and execute the Trick! If you Jump too early or too late, then you'll fail the Jump, and lose speed by stumbling on the landing. Therefore you'll want to successfully hit every Ramp with perfect timing in order to maintain speed and momentum throughout the entire course. Each time you land after successfully completing a Jump, immediately Crouch back down into the Squat position again to maintain maximum speed...and ultimately, for a more-intense workout!

our health & fitness tips for YOU!

■ Diet and Nutrition...

One of the most important factors of training and working out is your Diet and Nutrition. Instead of eating 2 or 3 large meals a day like most people do, you should be eating 5-6 smaller balanced meals throughout the entire day that consist of a healthy combination of Carbohydrates, Proteins, and Fats. This will help maintain your energy and blood sugar levels, whilst regularly filling you up throughout the entire day!

■ Plenty of Veg...

Most of the meals that you consume throughout the day should have at least one portion of Vegetables in them also. Vegetables are full of important Vitamins and Nutrients, and are therefore vital for a healthy balanced diet. Each and every day, you should be eating between 4-5 fist-full servings of Vegetables to keep your Vitamins and Nutrients levels high.

■ Keep Hydrated...

The most important factor of them all when training and working out, is to constantly keep yourself well-hydrated - this is vital! You should be drinking a minimum of 8 glasses of Water a day to keep yourself hydrated and healthy, however the harder you workout, the more water you MUST drink! Lack of water causes dehydration, which can lead to tiredness, lack of energy, an unhealthy body, and ultimately dizziness and sickness. Not just that, but if you do not keep yourself hydrated at all times when you're training, then your energy levels will drop significantly, and you will be unable to workout at your usual pace and intensity!

■ Cut down on those High-sugared drinks...

Fizzy, and high-sugared drinks such as Cokes, Lemonades, sugared-Coffees and Teas etc are bad for your health, so avoid these at all costs, or limit them to one a day if you have a sweet tooth. Too many high-sugared fizzy drinks cause a dangerous increase of sugars into your bloodstream, which seriously affects your blood sugar balance. This then releases Insulin, which is the primary hormone that helps your body store fat! To avoid this fatty build-up, avoid these types of drinks.

■ Eat Healthy food...

The healthiest food that you could possibly eat, is Fresh, non-processed, home-cooked meals. When preparing a healthy meal at home, use a mixture of Carbs, Proteins, Fats, and Vegetables, and add very little or no salts to them at all. Try to avoid restaurant food as much as you can, as you never know exactly what is in them; and avoid fast-food meals such as Burgers etc like the plague. Fast-food is all processed ingredients, and is the Devil when it comes to healthy eating! If you have to go to a restaurant, then make sure that you order healthy – plain Chicken, salad, and a glass of water for example. It may seem boring, but it's the best option.

■ Get Plenty of Exercise...

On top of this Active-workout, you should be finding other ways of keeping yourself active and in shape. Instead of sitting on the sofa watching TV for hours on end, or sat in front of a computer screen, you could be walking, cycling, jogging, swimming, enjoying other leisure or sporty activities; or even simply cleaning the house will burn fat. Also, try walking everywhere at a steady pace, instead taking a car or bus – a 10 minute walk can burn hundreds of calories without even realising! Remember, anything that involves movement is great for increasing your overall calorie-burn.

■ Eight Hours a Night...

Another vital factor of working out...is sleep! You should be getting at least 8 hours of undisturbed, uninterrupted sleep each and every day if you want to maintain your physical and mental health to its full potential! Lack of sleep can lead to tiredness, unenthusiastic behaviour, and will ultimately affect your brain and thoughts dramatically. If you ever feel drained or unenergetic, then you may not be getting enough sleep. If you need to be up early in the mornings, then make sure that you go to bed earlier the night before, and get those all-important 8 hours a night! This is even more essential when training.

■ Stress Busting...

Stress plays a significant role in your overall fitness and well-being, and can come between you and many things in your every day life. If you're feeling stressed, low, unhappy or angry for some reason, then workout!! Try to deflect your attention away from your bad mood and stress, by exercising. Each time you feel like this, take a walk, go for a jog, or pick up Wii Active and sweat it out!

■ Quit Smoking...

And finally, DO NOT smoke! Or drink alcoholic drinks regularly! Smoking producing Oestrogen (the female hormone), which prevents your muscles from working to their full potential, thus decreasing the effectiveness of each workout! Smoking seriously damages your lungs and minimises your overall air intake, thus preventing you from exercising for long periods of time without losing breath. Alcoholic drinks have a negative affect your liver, and binge-drinking will serious affect your overall health in the long run! A glass of red wine every other night is good for your Iron intake, however any more, and you're over the daily-recommended units. If you're drinking alcohol, then remember to drink more water to flush the toxins out of your body.

OUR Daily Workout Routine for YOU!

■ **CARDIO 1:**
Warm-up: Walking, Running, Dancing, and / or Boxing

■ **UPPER BODY:**
Biceps, Triceps, Shoulders, Bent Over Rows, and Sit-Ups

■ **LOWER BODY:**
Lunges, Squats, Calf Raises, Jumps, and Cross Knee Punches

■ **CARDIO 2:**
Warm-down: Walking, Running, and / or Dancing Boxing

■ **CALORIES:**
300 - 500 Calories a Day

■ **HOURS:**
1 - 2 Hours a Day

my trophies

There are 30 Trophies overall, and each one can be unlocked by completing specific requirements; for example, Exercising for a certain amount of time, completing a certain amount of Exercises, or completing a specific amount of Reps etc. The more you Exercise, the more Trophies you will inevitably unlock. Check them out, and try to unlock EVERY Trophy...simply by working out!

■ **Go-Getter**
How to Achieve: Complete Workout 1 of the 30 Day Challenge

■ **Halfway There**
How to Achieve: Complete Workout 10 of the 30 Day Challenge

■ **Fitness Superstar**
How to Achieve: Complete Workout 20 of the 30 Day Challenge

■ **30 Day Champion**
How to Achieve: Complete the 30 Day Challenge in 30 Days or less

■ **Dear Diary**
How to Achieve: Complete 1st Journal Entry receiving all 3 Checkmarks

■ **Trend Setter**
How to Achieve: Complete 7th Journal Entry receiving all 3 Checkmarks

■ **Checking In**
How to Achieve: Complete 30th Journal Entry receiving all 3 Checkmarks

■ **Getting Fresh Air**
How to Achieve: Earn an Activity Level Rating of over 400 in the Other Activity Survey.

■ **Fitness 101**
How to Achieve: Complete 101 Exercises

■ **Tennis Pro**
How to Achieve: Complete 200 Swings in Tennis

■ **Born to Skate**
How to Achieve: Complete 100 Jumps in In-Line Skating

■ **Running in the Mix**
How to Achieve: Run 25 Laps on the Track

■ **Slugger**
How to Achieve: Swing the Bat 200 times in Baseball

■ **Volleyball Champ**
How to Achieve: Complete 200 hits in Volleyball

■ **Fists of Fitness**
How to Achieve: Punch 500 Targets in Boxing

■ **Dance Fever**
How to Achieve: Complete 1000 Steps in Dancing

■ **Slam Dunk**
How to Achieve: Complete 200 Baskets in Basketball

■ **Squat Master**
How to Achieve: Complete 100 Squats

■ **GOAAAAAL!**
How to Achieve: Complete 1 Goal

■ **Goal Achiever**
How to Achieve: Complete One Calorie Goal, One Workout Hour Goal, and One Workout Goal

■ **Workout Buddies**
How to Achieve: Workout with a Friend

■ **Completionist**
How to Achieve: Complete every Exercise at least once

■ **Feel the Burn**
How to Achieve: Burn 100 Calories

■ **Fitness Inferno**
How to Achieve: Burn 1,000 Calories

■ **Fuel For The Fire**
How to Achieve: Burn 10,000 Calories

■ **50 Strong**
How to Achieve: Complete 50 Workouts

■ **Going for Gold**
How to Achieve: Earn a Gold Medal

■ **Making in Mine**
How to Achieve: Create and Complete a Custom Workout

■ **Power Hour**
How to Achieve: Work out for a total of 1 Hour

■ **Ten Out of Ten**
How to Achieve: Work out for a total of 10 Hours

ea sports active
workout

L ooking for a more intensive exercise program to aid you in your goal to drop a dress size or deflate those spare tires, then why not try our work out for EA Active? We have put together what we think is a great way to help you get a few steps closer toward your goal of losing weight and getting healthier.

UPPER BODY

BICEP CURLS

1 Stand with your Legs Shoulder-width apart and your Arms down by your sides, facing the Palms of your Hands forwards.

2 Keep your Upper Arm still; raise your Right Forearm up slowly so that your Hand is now up by your Shoulder; and keep your Elbow tucked in tight. Contract your Bicep muscle manually; hold; and then lower back down to the original position. *Return.*

3 *REVERSE SIDE:* Raise your Left Forearm slowly this time; and manually contract your Bicep as your Hand reaches your Shoulder. Hold; and then lower back down to the original position. Repeat this motion for the required Repetitions. *Return.*

TRICEPS KICKBACKS

1 Stand with your Legs Shoulder-width apart; Bend your Knees slightly; and arch your Back upwards at a 45-degree angle. Tuck both Arms in tight to your Body, so that the Palms of your Hands are facing each other; and then bend your Arms at 90-degree angles into a Hammer-position.

2 Keep your Elbow tucked in; Straighten your Right Arm backwards Behind you; and fully extend it. Manually contract your Tricep muscle; hold it; and then Bend back to the starting position. *Return.*

3 *REVERSE SIDE.* Keep your Elbow tucked in; and fully extend and Straighten your Left Arm this time, back Behind you. Manually contract; hold it; and then the Bend back to the original position. Repeat this motion for the required Repetitions. *Return.*

SHOULDER PRESSES

1 Stand with your Legs Shoulder-width apart; Bend both Arms, and raise them up to Shoulder-height, either side of your Head. Hold them in this position.

2 Raise your Right Arm upwards slowly, and manually contract at the top of the full extension. Hold for a second; and then lower your Arm back down to the starting position at your Shoulders. *Return.*

3 Raise your Left Arm upwards this time; and fully extend it. Hold; and then lower your Arm back down. Repeat this motion for the required Repetitions. *Return.*

BICEP CURL WITH SHOULDER PRESS

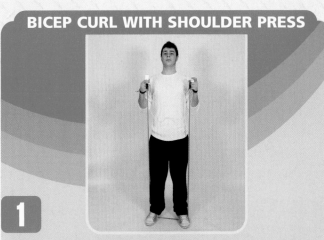

1 **Bicep Curl.** Stand with your Legs Shoulder-width apart; Arms down; and Palms facing forward. Keep your Upper Arms still; and raise both Forearms simultaneously, so that your Hands are now up by your Shoulders. Contract your Biceps muscles manually; and hold your Arms up at shoulder height - DO NOT lower them just yet! …

2 **Shoulder Press.** …At Shoulder-height, enter the Shoulder Press position; by Rotating your Hands around so that your Palms are now facing you.

3 **Shoulder Press.** Now raise both Arms upwards, and extend them fully at the top of the extension. Manually contract; hold for a second; and then lower back down to Shoulder-height. Rotate your Hands back around; and then lower your Arms back down to the original Bicep Curl position. Repeat this five-part motion for the required Repetitions. *Return.*

FRONT SHOULDER RAISES

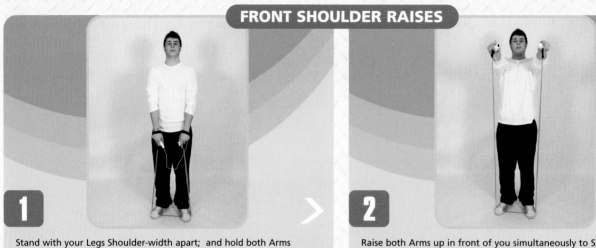

1 Stand with your Legs Shoulder-width apart; and hold both Arms down by your sides.

2 Raise both Arms up in front of you simultaneously to Shoulder-height; and manually pull your Shoulders back. Hold this position; and then lower your Arms back down to your sides. Repeat this motion for the required Repetitions. *Return.*

LATERAL SHOULDER RAISES

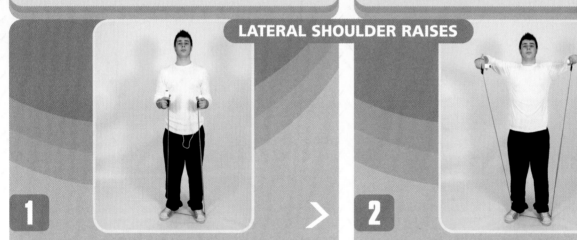

1 Stand with your Legs Shoulder-width apart; hold both Arms down by your sides; and Bend your Elbows at a 90-degree angle, so that your Arms / Hands are now in the Hammer-position. Keep your Elbows tucked in tight; Palms facing each other.

2 Raise both Arms up and out to the Sides simultaneously; but make sure you maintain that 90-degree bend at all times! Hold both Arms up at Shoulder-height; and then lower them back down slowly to the Hammer starting position. Repeat this motion for the required Repetitions. *Return.*

CROSS KNEE PUNCHES

1 Stand upright with your Legs Shoulder-width apart; extend both Arms Straight out in front of you; and hold them up at Shoulder-height.

2 Bring your Left Knee up and across your Body at Waist / Hip height, to your Right hand side; whilst simultaneously pulling both Arms down at the same time, to either side of your Knee. Forcefully thrust your Arms down to your sides, and your Knee up to your Waist; and then quickly raise your Arms again; and drop your Leg back to the original standing position in one fast fluid motion. *Return.*

BENT OVER ROWS

1 Stand with your Legs Shoulder-width apart; slightly Bend your Knees; and lean forwards to arch your Lower Back at a 45 degree angle. Look forwards; stick your Buttocks out; and drop your Arms down in front of you, keeping your Elbows tucked in tight.

2 Slowly pull your Arms in tight to your Stomach, so that your Hands are up by your Rib Cage; and then Bend your Elbows at 90-degrees; and manually contract your Upper Back and Side muscles. Hold for a second; and then lower your Arms slowly back down to the starting position. Repeat this motion for the required Repetitions. *Return.*

3 Thrust your Right Knee up and across your Body this time to your Left; and simultaneously thrust both Arms down at the same time, to either side of your Knee. Quickly raise your Arms again; and drop your Leg back to the original standing position in one fast fluid motion. Repeat this motion for the required Repetitions. *Return.*

BENT OVER ROWS WITH TRICEP KICKBACKS

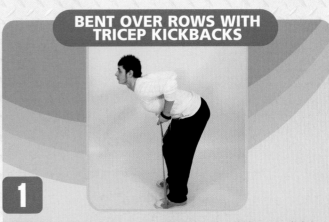

1 **Bent Over Rows.** Stand with your Legs Shoulder-width apart; slightly Bend your Knees; and lean forwards, arching your Lower Back at a 45 degree angle. Look forwards; stick your Buttocks out; and drop your Arms down in front of you, keeping your Elbows tucked in tight. Slowly pull your Arms in tight to your Stomach, so that your Hands are up by your Rib Cage; and then Bend your Elbows at 90-degrees; and manually contract your Upper Back and Side muscles. DO NOT lower your Arms just yet!...

2 **Tricep Kickbacks.** ...Keep your Elbow tucked in; and fully extend and Straighten your Left Arm backwards Behind you. Manually contract your Tricep muscle; hold it; and then Bend back down. Lower your Arms back down to the original starting position; and then complete another Bent Over Row and Return the Tricep Kickback position. *Return.*

3 *REVERSE SIDE.* Keep your Elbow tucked in; and fully extend and Straighten your Right Arm this time, back Behind you. Manually contract; hold it; and then Bend back down. Lower your Arms back down to the original position again; and repeat this four-part motion for the required Repetitions. *Return.*

UPRIGHT ROWS

1 Stand with your Legs Shoulder-width apart; hold both Arms down in front of your Body at Hip-height; and Rotate your Hands around so that both Palms are facing your Thighs. Expand your Chest; and pull your Shoulders back.

2 Bend both Arms at the Elbows now; and raise them up and out to the Sides at Shoulder-height, so that your Elbows are bent Inwards, and your Hands are almost be in front of your Face. Hold this position; then lower and straighten your Arms back down to the starting position. Repeat this motion for the required Repetitions. *Return.*

BICEP CURLS WITH UPRIGHT ROWS

1 **Bicep Curls.** Stand with your Legs Shoulder-width apart; Arms down; and Palms facing forward. Keep your Upper Arms still; and raise both Forearms simultaneously, so that your Hands are now up at Shoulder-height. Contract your Biceps muscles manually; hold; and then lower your Arms back down.

2 **Upright Rows.** Rotate your Hands around now so that your Palms are facing your Thighs

3 Now Bend both Arms at the Elbows; and raise them up and out to the Sides at Shoulder-height, so that your Elbows are be bent Inwards, and your Hands almost in front of your Face. Hold this position; then lower and straighten your Arms back down to the starting position. Rotate your Hands back around; and repeat this motion for the required Repetitions. *Return.*

LOWER BODY

LUNGES

1 Stand with your Legs close together; and hold your Hands on your Hips.

2

REVERSE SIDE. Lunge forwards with your Right Leg now; keep your Left Leg in place; and Lunge so that both Knees are bent at 90-degrees, and your Thighs are parallel. Hold; and Lunge back to the standing position. Repeat this motion for the required Repetitions. *Return.*

2

Lunge outwards to the Left now with your Left Leg so that it's almost fully outstretched; keep your Right Leg in place; and then Bend your Left Lunging-Leg 90-degrees at the Knee, so your Right Leg is now outstretched one. Thrust your Arms up as you do this; hold it; and then Lunge back to standing position. *Return.*

3

Take one large Step forwards with your Left Leg; keep your rear Right Leg firmly in place; and Lunge forwards, by bending both Legs at a 90-degree angle at the Knee. Make sure both Thighs are parallel to the floor. Lunge forwards; hold it; and push back up to the original standing position. *Return.*

3

REVERSE SIDE. Lunge to the Right now with your Right Leg; keep your Left Leg in place; and Bend your Right Lunging-Leg 90-degrees at the Knee. Hold it; and then Lunge back to standing position. Repeat this motion for the required Repetitions. *Return.*

SIDE LUNGES

1

Stand with your Legs close together; and hold your Arms down in front of you; Fists together almost.

SIDE LUNGES WITH TOE TOUCHES

1

Side Lunges. Stand with your Legs close together; and hold your Arms out straight in front of you. Lunge outwards to the Left now with your Left Leg so that it's almost fully outstretched. Keep your Right Leg in place; and Bend your Left Leg 90-degrees. Hold it; and DO NOT Lunge back to the standing position just yet!...

2

Toe Touches. ...Bend down now to the side instead; and touch the Toes of your Left Lunging Leg with both Hands. Hold the Toe Touch; and then Lunge back to the standing position. *Return.*

3

REVERSE SIDE: Lunge outwards to the Right now with your Right Leg; and keep your Left Leg in place. Bend your Right Leg 90-degrees; hold it; and DO NOT Lunge back to the standing position just yet. Bend down to the side instead; and touch the Toes of your Right Lunging Leg with both Hands. Hold it; and then Lunge back to the standing position. Repeat for the required Repetitions. *Return*

HIGH REVERSE LUNGES

1

Stand with your Legs close together; hold both Hands on your Hips; and arch your Back.

2

Lunges. Take a large Lunging Step Backwards with your Left Leg; bend it 90- degrees at the Knee; and Bend your Right Leg also, but keep it firmly in place. Your Thighs should be parallel to the floor.

3

High Knees. Hold the Lunge; then raise your Left Lunging Leg, and follow through up to Hip-height. Your Front Right Leg should be straight; and your Left Knee should be high and Bent at 90 degrees. Hold the High Knee; and then lower it back down to the original standing position. *Return.*

4

REVERSE SIDE. Take a large Lunging Step back with your Right Leg this time; and Bend both Legs 90- degrees at the Knee, keeping your Left Leg in place. Raise your Right Leg now; and follow through up to Hip-height. Hold it; and then lower it back down to the starting position. Repeat this motion for the required Repetitions. *Return.*

JUMP LUNGES

1

Lunge. Take one large Step forwards with your Left Leg; and keep your Right Leg in place. Lunge forwards; Bend both Legs 90- degree angles at the Knee; and hold this Crouched-Lunge position. DO NOT Lunge back just yet!...

2

Jumping. Push off with both Feet now; and Jump up into the air. At the top of the Jump, quickly switch and Reverse your Legs in midair from Back to Front, so your Left Leg is now behind you; and your Right Leg is now in front of you. Thrust your Arms upwards also to generate enough power and height to complete the 'Scissor-Kick' action before landing.

3

REVERSE SIDE. Land back in the Crouched-Lunge position; and then Jump back up; and Reverse your Legs again in midair before landing. Repeat this motion for the required Repetitions. *Return.*

STANDING KNEE CRUNCHES

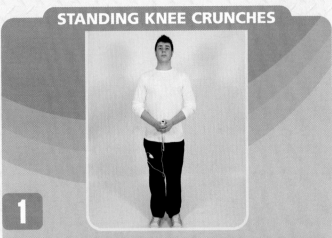

1

Stand with your Legs pinned together; tuck your Elbows in; and hold your Arms down slightly, with your Hands out in front of your Stomach.

2

Raise your Right Knee up to Hip / Waist height; and 'Bow Down' and forwards simultaneously, to meet your rising-Knee. Hold your Knee at Waist-height; keep the Bow held; and manually contract your Abdominal muscles. Then lower your Right Knee and Leg back down to the floor. *Return.*

3

Raise your Left Knee up to Waist height this time; and 'Bow Down' and to meet your rising-Knee. Hold your Knee at Waist-height; keep the Bow held; and manually contract your Stomach. Lower your Left Knee and Leg back down to the floor; and repeat this motion for the required Repetitions. *Return.*

SQUAT

1

Stand with your Legs Shoulder-width apart; hold your Arms out in front of you; and arch your Lower Back, so that it remains completely straight throughout this exercise.

2

Now Squat down into an almost-Sitting position, so your Thighs are almost parallel to the floor. Your Hamstrings and Calves should be 90-degrees to one another. Hold this position; and then push away from the floor using your Legs, to rise back up to the standing position. Repeat this motion for the required Repetitions. *Return.*

SQUAT AND HOLD

1

Stand with your Legs Shoulder-width apart; hold your Arms out in front of you; and arch your Lower Back.

2

Squat down into an almost-Sitting position, so your Thighs are almost parallel to the floor. Your Hamstrings and Calves should be 90-degrees to one another. DO NOT stand back up; but instead, hold this Squat position for the required time! Push away from the floor using your Legs; and rise back up to the standing position. Repeat this motion for the required Repetitions. *Return.*

JUMP SQUATS

1

Squats.   Crouch down into the almost-sitting Full-Squat position; and DO NOT stand back up just yet!...

2

Jumping.   ... Jump upwards now with both Legs now, and thrust your Arms up into the air as you do so to generate mope power and height! The higher you Jump, the more effective this exercise will be.

SQUATS WITH CALF RAISES

1 Stand with your Legs Shoulder-width apart; and hold your Arms out in front of you at Shoulder-height.

2 **Squats.** Crouch down into the almost-sitting Full-Squat position; hold it; but DO NOT stand back up just yet!...

3 **Calf Raises.** ...Whilst still in the Squat position; rise up onto your Tiptoes for the Calf Raise.

4 Drop back down onto the Soles of your Feet; and then stand up and return to the standing position. Return.

3 Land lightly on your Toes to cushion the fall; and land perfectly back into the Full-Squat position, ready for the next Jump. Hold the Squat; and then Jump up again. Repeat this procedure to complete the exercise. *Return*.

SIDE TO SIDE JUMPS

1 Stand with your Legs Shoulder-width apart; and then Bend your Knees, and Squat down into the Half-Squat position, ready to Jump – but do not enter the Full-Squat position!

STANDING TWISTS

1

Stand with your Legs evenly apart; Bend your Knees slightly; and hold both Arms together, straight out in front of you at Shoulder-height.

2

Jump up and to the Right now; and then land perfectly again in the Half-Squat position, ready for the next Jump. The higher and further you Jump; the more effective this exercised will be.

2

Keep your Legs in place, and Twist (Rotate) only your Torso and Upper Body around to the Left. Forcefully swing your Body to generate more momentum; and then hold this position when you're facing to the side.

3

Hold the Squat for a second or two; and then Jump up, and back over to the Left. Land perfectly in the Squat position; and repeat this motion for the required Repetitions. *Return.*

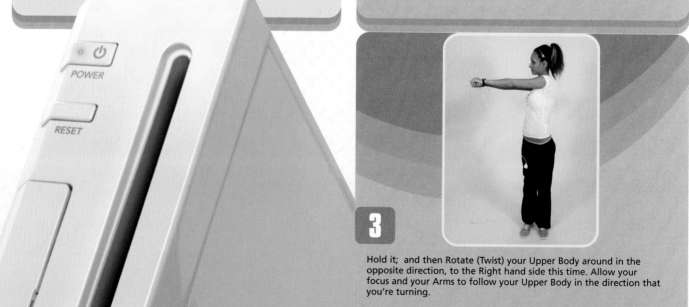

POWER

RESET

3

Hold it; and then Rotate (Twist) your Upper Body around in the opposite direction, to the Right hand side this time. Allow your focus and your Arms to follow your Upper Body in the direction that you're turning.

Wii Fit plus >>>

The long awaited follow up to one of the most beloved and popular Wii games of all time is finally here and we have compiled this Player's Guide for you to bring you all the much know info on the new features that await!

Welcome to the
Wii Fit plus

et ready to raise that workout to a whole new level, with the all new Wii Fit Plus. With more exercises, games and options available to you, doing your daily session of keep-fit will not only become more fun, but more intense. With new additions like the Calorie Counter, you can keep track of what you are actually achieving from all this hard work. Like the original, the Wii Balance Board is used in so many ways to help you lose those extra pounds or tone up your body. Are you ready to work up a sweat? Then let's go...

The Calorie Counter Explained.

There are many new features in Plus, one being the new "Calorie Counter", this tells you just how much you have burned during your workout, as well as how many calories are in specific foods, also it will give you suggestions on what you can eat, so you get a dietitian in this package too.

Do I need to upgrade?

Oh yes, the entire Wii Fitness team would most definitely, highly recommend you purchase this new version of Wii Fit, as it contains all of the original games and exercises as well as a stack of new ones. Also you can transfer your saved data over from the original Wii Fit and carry on from where you were, instead of having to start all over again.

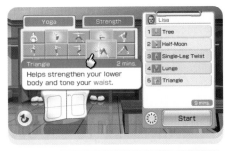

Making The Most From The Routine Scheduler.

But, we think one of the most impressive additions to Plus, is the all new Routine scheduler, you can pick and choose which exercises you want to do then put them in place to fill your desired workout period; be it 10, 20, 30 minutes or even an hour if you so wish. Once you have that pieced together all you

have to do is activate your workout and away you go, your very own personal workout regime based on your specific requirements. But if that wasn't enough Wii Fit Plus also comes with all new balance games to use your Wii Balance Board with. Overall we believe that Wii Fit Plus is a very cost efficient and essential add-on to the original Wii Fit, especially if you already have the balance board.

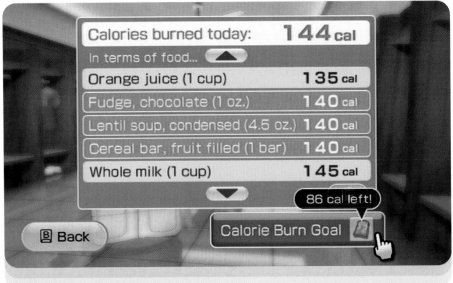

Calories burned today:	144 cal
In terms of food...	
Orange juice (1 cup)	135 cal
Fudge, chocolate (1 oz.)	140 cal
Lentil soup, condensed (4.5 oz.)	140 cal
Cereal bar, fruit filled (1 bar)	140 cal
Whole milk (1 cup)	145 cal

86 cal left!

Back   Calorie Burn Goal

beating the new balance games!

So let's have a closer look at the 15 new Balance games available in Wii Fit Plus, what to expect, how to complete them, what the controls are and most importantly what you are going to get out of each of them!

Basic Run

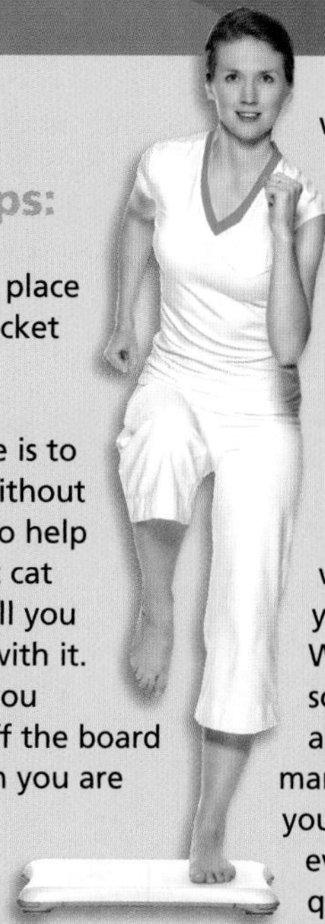

■ Gameplay Tips:

This exercise is a simple running game, you can place the Wiimote in your pocket for this one as it isn't required for motion detection. The objective is to run around the track without burning your Mii out. To help you keep pace your pet cat will run with you and all you need to do is keep up with it. Once the game starts, you have to lift your feet off the board one at a time as though you are walking on the spot, the faster you do this the faster your Mii will run, but do it too fast and you will run out of stamina and your Mii will "burn out". You don't need to control the direction of your Mii as it will do the directions for you, leaving you to concentrate. The reason you need to concentrate is at the end of your run you are asked some questions, varying from obvious things like; Did you fall down? To questions that will need you to pay attention on your circuit, these are things like; Who did you pass? Then show you some pictures, these could be Mario, a Kuppa Trooper or a star. Also how many dogs you passed. So make sure you look for characters and count everything as you go, as the questions could be anything.

Balance Bubble

■ Gameplay Tips:

The objective to this game is to maneuver yourself inside a Mii sized bubble down a meandering river littered with obstacles for you to avoid. In order to control your Mii, you have to lean forward on the balance board, this will make you go forward. By leaning back it will slow you down and eventually make you go backwards. In order to get around the objects in your path you can lean left and right to strafe from side to side. All of these controls must be used to successfully traverse the river without hitting a single thing, even the river banks. If you do, the bubble will pop and you will have to start again. There are different sections to the river including a darkened area that reduces your visibility to a small arc around your Mii, so you will need to move slower and very carefully. You only have a certain time limit and depending on how far you get will determine your overall score and rank. In conclusion a very good game which requires you to be very accurate and have great inner core stability.

Juggling

■ Gameplay Tips:

You are really going to be tested by this exercise, not only do you have to keep your balance on a circus ball, you also have to juggle balls thrown at you. Using the Wii Balance Board, Wiimote and nunchuck you will accomplish all these things at once. Shift your weight left to right on the Wii Balance Board to help you keep your Mii balanced on the ball, when one of the characters throws a ball at you wait for it to reach your Mii's hand, now depending on which hand it reaches you need to strike either the Wiimote or nunchuck upwards. This will be different based on whether you are right or left handed. Every time the ball reaches your hand strike upwards to keep the ball juggling. But it doesn't stop there, now another ball is added increasing the difficulty, having to concentrate on 2 balls at once, while still keeping your balance. Just to make things even harder for you, more balls are added and occasionally one of the troublesome toons will throw a bomb at you. You will have to shift your weight on the board in order to avoid it, but be careful not to over balance or you will fall off. This make take some practice, but when you've got it down it gives you a great work out for body and mind!

Birds-eye Bullseye

■ Gameplay Tips:

Take control of a chicken version of your Mii in this wacky exercise. You only need to use the Wii Balance Board in this game even though you are going to be flapping your arms. To move your Mii, lean forward on the board and flap those arms to get some forward motion, by leaning left or right you will turn in the corresponding direction. Head for the giant platform with a light beam surging out of it. Here you will need to land to gain some extra time. Stand central on your board and slow your arm flapping down to gradually glide down. Once you have landed get flapping again and lean forward to get some speed going, once again head towards the platform for some more added time. Some of the platforms will have bullseye circles in them, so the closer to the centre you can get the more time and points you will accrue. It is going to take some practice getting those landings right but will give those arms of yours a great workout. Not to mention make you look silly too!

map in the bottom right, look for the red flag, this is your next target. The checkpoints are in a pre-determined order so short cutting is going to be minimal, but possible. Try to avoid steep hills, it is sometimes faster to go around rather than over. There are a certain amount of checkpoints to reach based upon the difficulty, once you have passed through all of them you need to head back to the start point, which doubles as the finish line.

Perfect 10
■ Gameplay Tips:

It's time to work those hips in this game. You will be presented with a various selection of buttons surrounding your Mii, each of them will have a number on them. The objective here is to swing your hips in the direction of the button you wish to use, making sure all the selected buttons add up to 10. If you make a

Golf Range

■ Gameplay Tips:

Take to the tee in this cool exercise designed to help your golf swing. Turn your Wii Balance Board to the side, so your are standing side on to your television, now place the Wiimote in your hand like you would hold a real golf club, clutching it with both hands. Take some practice swings if necessary, but when you are ready press and hold the A button to step forward to the tee and take a swing. You will see on the screen an actuation graph of your accuracy, represented by a red dot. The closer you keep this to the vertical central line during your swing the more accurate your drive will be. As you get better you will want to increase the strength to hit the ball further, but with this will come inaccuracy again. So practice, practice, practice and that swing will soon be as good as the pros. Not a very intensive workout, but if you play for long enough you will begin to feel it in your arms.

Cycling

■ Gameplay Tips:

Time to burn some calories in this great cardiovascular workout. Hold your Wiimote in your hands much like a handle bar and step onto the Balance board. Lift your feet up and down in a walking motion to start peddling and

use the Wiimote to steer. The objective is to pass through all the check points in as little distance as possible, so don't miss one. But just to make it a little more tricky for you, the checkpoints are not on a simple pathed course, you are going to need to go off-road and up hills, which is going to require some extra footwork. If you are lost you can press and hold the minus button to zoom-out your mini

Obstacle Course

■ Gameplay Tips:

Not quite the type you would expect to find at an Army base, but still a good work out. Using the Balance

board adopt a walking type motion with your knees slightly bent to move your Mii forward, the faster you do it the faster your Mii will go. Many obstacles block your way, from swinging giant balls to rolling logs to even big holes and moving platforms.

To help you get passed these, you are able to jump, to do this quickly straighten your legs almost as though you were going to jump but never create enough force to actually leave the ground. Beware additional hazards like the icy floor, even if you slow your pace down you will still slide for a short time, so make sure if you are trying to wait for the right timing to surge forward as you will need to slow down much sooner. You will also have to contend with conveyor belts. Some are going in the direction you are running so will almost act like ice, requiring an early slowing point. Whereas the ones working against you will require you to pick the pace up to overcome the negative motion. As for the sideways ones you are going to need to get across them as quick as possible before you slide off the edge.

wrong move and select a button that won't help make 10 you can always hit it again to deselect it, of course this is going to waste valuable time. As each game based upon the difficulty only have a specific time limit, the more correct combinations you make the higher your score and rank will be at the end. This game is going to give the hips and Gluteus Maximus a great workout, as well as test you at doing quick equations, even though the answer is always 10 making the number available to you add up as quickly as possible can sometimes become quite a challenge.

Rhythm Kung Fu
■ Gameplay Tips:

The basic concept behind this exercise is to mimic the other Mii's in the Dojo, they are stood in tiers; 2 at the back 2 in the middle and you at the front, so you will see the moves done twice before it is your turn. You will need to stand on your Wii Balance Board while holding the Wiimote and Nunchuck to successfully accomplish this. Timing is of the essence as the name of the game would suggest. So you will need to play close attention to the speed at which the other Mii's perform each move. Moves will vary from a simple forward punch to tricky 1 legged stances. As the game progresses the combination of different moves increases during each set. Also, occasionally a wind up move will be thrown in just to send you off the stride a little, what we mean by a wind up move is all the Mii's on the screen prepare for a move simultaneously but the release is staggered, with you being the final one to make the move, almost like a quick-fire round. The more correct moves you manage to mimic the

Segway Circuit

■ Gameplay Tips:

Very similar to the cycling but with a little twist. As with the cycling hold your Wiimote length ways like you would handlebars and step onto the Wii Balance Board. To move forward all you need to do is lean forward, leaning backwards will make you reverse. Steer by turning your Wiimote left or right. Your objective; to pop all the balloons that appear out of the many mole hills scattered

higher your score is going to be. With such a great variety of moves and stances this game is going to test your observational skills as well as an array of muscle groups.

Rhythm Parade
■ Gameplay Tips:

Time to test that rhythm and coordination of yours in this tricky and exhausting game. You are a member of a marching band performing at a parade in the centre of a busy square. Step onto your Wii Balance board and have your Wiimote and Nunchuck in the correct

around the surrounding area. Consider these checkpoints, but with an attitude. As you will quickly discover, when approaching some of these pesky balloons they will deflate into the hole. You can stop and wait for it to inflate again or move onto the next one and come back in a bit. Use the minus button to zoom your mini map (bottom right of the screen) out to find the different balloons. Once you only have one left be ready for a chase. The sneaky mole has stolen it and runs off on his Segway, make chase to catch him. Don't be fooled by popping the last balloon, no, it was just a decoy, he's off again with the real one this time. This mole can be quite a nuisance stopping and making sharp turns so be at the ready to do many U-turns!

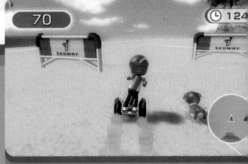

hand. The game begins with a simple march, requiring you to step in time with the whistles. If your steps are of the perfect rhythm, blue flashes appear from your Mii's feet telling you, you are doing it right. Almost as soon as you get used to doing that it starts the next stage, this requires perfect timing with your Wiimote and Nunchuck. 2 circles appear on the screen, one on the right and one on the left. What's going to happen now is buttons will begin to rain down your screen, depending if you are left or right handed will determine which side the specific symbols appear. If you are right handed a symbol of a Wiimote will appear on the right and a Nunchuck on the left, vise versa for left handed people. As the button makes its way over the previously mentioned circle on the screen, you must raise the corresponding controller. Sometimes it will be at the same time so be prepared. All the while still keeping that marching rhythm going. This is tricky to get right at first, but when you have mastered it you can burn some calories, as this game lasts a while.

Table Tilt Plus
■ Gameplay Tips:

Extreme balancing skills and precision will be needed to complete this cool mini game. Your movement on the Wii Balance Board controls the platform on the screen, on this platform are balls which you need to maneuver into the correct holes shown by a beam of light. Different obstacles are in your way though, ranging from spinning doorways to slopes and of course the edge of the platform itself is the most important thing you are going to need to avoid, as when a ball disappears into the void the platform will spine violently making all other balls go out of control and possibly going off the edge themselves. You will then have to start all over again. All of this will require you to be extremely careful and precise with every movement, especially with multiple balls on the platform. The trick is practice and knowing how to accomplish the goal on each round. With a clock working against you it's easy to get panicked, but keep trying as this is such a great game to play.

Tilt City
■ Gameplay Tips:

In the Tilt City exercise you use your Wiimote to tilt the upper paddle and your Wii Balance Board to tilt the lower two by leaning to the left or right. The objective of this game is to get the coloured balls that drop from top right to the pipes of their respective colour. There are two kinds of balls; firstly solid balls, that give you just one point and balls with Mii faces on them, these will give you two points. If and when you get consecutive balls into their correct pipes the score given by each ball is multiplied by the number of balls you have managed to place correctly before it, up to a multiplier of 10. At this point each solid ball will give you ten points and Mii balls will give 20. The game ends when the set number of balls are dropped and your final score will be shown. This mini-game can be very challenging to master because of the feet-eye coordination required to get high points, although in order to get the best out of the game and to make those top scores, you really need to keep practicing. ■

Skateboard Arena
■ Gameplay Tips:

Pick up that board and head to the arena is this very realistic game of Skateboarding. For this game you are going to need to turn your Wii Balance Board head on to the television. No Nunchuck is required so you can disconnect that. To control your skater stand on the Balance Board with your side towards the TV, step onto the floor to make your Mii push off, this can also be used to make yourself go faster if you do it over and over. Be careful though as it is quite tricky to steer and push off at the same time. To steer you simply need to lean back for left or forward to go right, this will be the other way round if you are left footed. There are 6 stages to this game, 5 of which teach you some different controls or tricks. The final stage is where you combine all you have learned to get the highest score you can. Each stage requires you to maneuver over a certain number of blue light strips to complete the task using the skill that stage is teaching you. The final stage will require you to pass over 40 of these light strips in all manor of fashions. Doing it as quickly as possible will add more points to your final score.

Snowball Fight
■ Gameplay Tips:

Put those warm gloves on and start rolling some snowballs in this fun game to test your accuracy. Your Mii will be stood behind a protective screen and by

leaning left or right on your Wii Balance Board your Mii will pop out in the retrospective direction. Point your Wiimote at the screen to aim your snowballs and press A to throw a ball.

You only have a set time limit to this game and the objective is to hit as many of the other Mii's on the play field. They do move about running between the various barriers, so some prediction throwing will be required. You have 3 hearts that represent your lives and the game is over if you lose them all. Don't panic too much if you lose a heart as it will slowly regenerate. When you get hit by a snowball your screen will become smeared with snow making it very difficult to see, so it would be advisable to wait for it to clear as you won't be able to see any more incoming snowballs. This of course will waste some of your valuable time, but will reduce the risk of losing all your hearts. The more Mii's you hit in the time limit the higher your final score will be. This isn't the best of workouts with only having to do a bit of leaning, but it is still great fun!

making the most from your balance board

there are many more ways to enjoy your Wii Fit Balance Board once you have finished your fitness training for the day. From walking the fashion catwalks to stepping into the boxing ring. What follows is our break down of the best balance board compatible games around.

ALL STAR CHEERLEADER

Publisher: THQ
Genre: Party Game

■ ABOUT THE GAME... All Star Cheer Squad allows you to participate in the competitive sport of Cheer, combining traditional cheerleading, dance, gymnastics and squad based teamwork. Create your own avatar, learn cheer and dance moves.

Includes such features as: Using the Wii Remote, Nunchuck and Wii Balance Board to perform dozens of real-world cheer/dance moves, designed by Tony G, world renowned cheer choreographer, best known for his work on the "Bring It On" movies.

Learn new moves and choreograph your own cheer routines to music. Take part in squad competitions and one-on-one cheer-offs. Customise your cheer squads by choosing the look of your team including facial

features, hair and outfits. Then follow a year in the life of a cheerleader, starting with try-outs and grow your all-star squad to be the best as you lead them to the championship as Cheer Captain.

■ IN SUMMARY... Although the appeal of this title will be somewhat limited to female gamers there is still much fun to be had by the rest of the family. The dance routines almost doubling for a fast paced and fun fitness workout and the catchy music will have most toes tapping.

BABYSITTING PARTY >>>

Publisher: Ubisoft
Genre: Party Game
■ ABOUT THE GAME...
BABYSITTING PARTY is the second game of the UBISOFT Party Game range, named "PLAY ZONE". The game will provide immediate fun to all family members, thanks to short gameplay sessions. Featuring a variety of 30 mini-games that can be played head-to-head or cooperatively among your family or with

your friends. Live a great adventure if you play alone or have fun with your friends, up to 4 players.

Wii Remote gestures are intuitive, making the game easy to pick up and play, and some games can be played with the Balance Board. You can play indoor & outdoor mini-games following the typical day of a baby and his/her babysitter, and prove that you are the best babysitter, alone or with your friends.

Thanks to intuitive motions the game is easy to pick-up and play and the use of the Wii Balance Board makes the Party Games experience brand new. To start, choose the families you want to baby sit for. As a member of a babysitting academy, you will have to do your best to graduate and become the best Babysitter. Then unlock a huge range of more than 50 cute and funny outfits and customise all the babies you take care of.

FAMILY SKI

Publisher: Nintendo
Genre: Sports

■ ABOUT THE GAME...
Hit the slopes with your friends in Family Ski
...Welcome to the Happy Ski Resort, where fresh powder, groomed runs, multiple trails, and state of the art facilities await! Family Ski takes you down the slopes in the most exciting skiing game to hit the Wii! Grab your Wii Remote and Nunchuck or step onto your Wii Balance Board to execute perfect wedge stops, shred the slaloms, and negotiate moguls with ease. With an in-depth Ski School and over a dozen lengthy runs packed with jumps, races, and more, you and your friends won't want to leave the slopes again!

■ IN SUMMARY...
There are moments during the mini games where the majority of gamers will find entertainment, the style and the presentation of Babysitting Party will limit its long term appeal to younger female gamers, which is clearly the intended audience for the game. A recommended purchase for pre-teen female family members or friends.

DON KING BOXING >>>

Publisher: Take 2
Genre: Sports

■ ABOUT THE GAME...
Step into the ring with the Wii Balance Board! Throw jabs, hooks, uppercuts and KO punches with both hands - all the while ducking and dodging blows on the Wii Balance Board. Featuring over 20 licensed boxers in real life venues like Madison Square Garden, Boardwalk Hall, and Trump Taj Mahal. Experience epic 3D boxing action on the Wii as every head and body shot delivered draws you further into each match through an immersive, in-your-face first person camera system. Play fun mini-

friends or foes can box against each other with the same menacing proximity found in the actual ring. Utilise a unique tutorial mode that employs many of the training exercises and techniques used by boxing's best to develop the true skills necessary to dominate the ring. Face true legends of boxing in 10 fantasy match-ups. Do you have what it takes to send the likes of Rocky Marciano, Joe Luis, or Larry Holmes to the mat?

The Boxing AIs have been finely tuned to represent many of the different types of boxers seen in the sport. Players must use genuine boxing tactics and skills to defeat these opponents. Several difficulty settings are available so all levels of players can enjoy a fun and challenging boxing experience.

games to earn fitness points and track your progress with a Fitness Chart and in-game calendar. Live out the rags-to-riches underdog story of "The Kid" in the deep career mode. From his start at a local boxing gym to his rise as an international star, you experience both the splendors and hard knocks of professional boxing. Using a first person split screen display,

■ IN SUMMARY...
Whilst offering depth for the single player fight fan, with the great bonus of the innovative use of the Balance Board during both fighting and training, Don King Boxing steps up the heavy weight ranks during the two player multiplayer mode, which might not be suitable for all ages but is certainly perfect for teen boxing fans and beyond.

Family Ski is the latest release from Nintendo that makes full use of the Wii Board peripheral. Take the nunchuck and remote in your hands and step on the Wii Board to really take advantage. Family Ski is a relaxed winter sports game and uses the motion controllers to let players Ski. The Wii remote and Nunchuck simulate the Ski Poles, used to accelerate and move off from a stationary point and turn in a specific direction. When these are used in collaboration with the Wii Fit peripheral, the Wii board, players can be further immersed into a unique experience of skiing. The Wii Board takes over to allow the player to turn whilst skiing by measuring the swaying and leaning of the body.

With such key features as: You and up to four others can whistle your way down the slopes using the motion sensing controls and pressure-sensitive pad. We Ski lets you whisk up a character from scratch and customise with lots of purchasable equipment, or you can import your Mii for realism. You can ski in a fantasy ski resort inhabited by a community of NPC, and have the chance to participate in events or just relax. You can also take photographs on the slopes with up to 4 other skiers and share their skiing experience with others using Wii message board & Wii connect24.

■ IN SUMMARY...
Shy of playing directly in front of an open freezer whilst family members throw flakes of ice in your face, Family Ski is about as close as you can get to the piste from the comfort of your lovely warm home! Brilliant fun for all comers, renders this a game that has to be owned by all sports fans and all Balance Board owners looking for new thrills.

FAMILY SKI & SNOWBOARD

Publisher: Namco Bandai
Genre: Sports

■ ABOUT THE GAME...
Fresh powder, miles of pristine slopes and unstoppable winter fun drift onto the Wii in this exciting, fun and feature-packed snowboarding and skiing sequel to the critically acclaimed Family Ski. Featuring advanced snowboarding and skiing, perfect for beginners or experts! With a game map of 7,000 vertical meters across two huge mountains. Using your Wii Balance Board provides an even more authentic experience. Enjoy the open environment that's fully interactive with incredible scenery.

Learn Enhanced Maneuvering – Trick skiing, including backwards-riding, flips, daffy ducks and helicopters are now possible! Snowboard goofy or regular and twist, turn and flip as much as your body can bear. Jump anywhere, anytime! And put your improved skill set to the test in the brand new Family Ski & Snowboard Fun Park, complete with huge half-pipe, rails and fun boxes. *Explore the Interactive,*

Dynamic Environment – Perform jumps wherever you want to on skis or snowboards in a fully-explorable environment. Relive the action with the replay feature, that you can access in any game mode at any time, and from multiple camera angles, just like on TV! With all new Interactive Additions – Non Playable Character's (NPC's) can be recruited in game play as tour guides around the mountain, and NPC's and Mii's are there to keep you company, skiing or snowboarding with you, ahead of you or behind you.

■ IN SUMMARY...
With a large variety of gameplay options and an even wider array of easily accessible tricks and special moves, no matter the age range or experience of the player, you will find much to enjoy. Family Ski & Snowboard is a great deal of fun for the entire family and a definite step up from the fab original.

IMAGINE FASHION IDOL

Publisher: Ubisoft
Genre: Lifestyle

■ ABOUT THE GAME...
Participate in a TV show and get discovered as the best young fashion designer through a series of challenges! Express your creativity in numerous & expanded backstage workshops & go on stage to present your designs &

convince the jury that you are the best fashion designer of the show! Choose clothes, accessories, patterns, colours. Do your make up (choose the foundation, eye shadow, blusher, mascara, lipstick) and do the model's hair (22 hair cuts & 6 hair colours available)

Discover 8 chapters with about 40 missions to achieve (in the Fashion TV Show mode). Go on stage to present your designs in front of a fierce jury. Show your designs during the catwalks. Make the right movements with the controllers to have your model pose correctly. During the catwalk session, some unexpected events could happen & you will have to do some retakes as fast as possible. Participate in photo shoot sessions & collect the pictures you took in your portfolio.
Tools of the profession: use the Wiimote & Nunchuck as scissors, brushes, lipstick

Multiplayer up to 2 players: discover around 40 fun and fast mini games full of challenges.

■ IN SUMMARY...
Its hard to picture dads and older brothers really sinking their teeth and their time into this game, but for pre and early teen girls this game is close to perfection. Walk the catwalk in clothes you have designed and share your fashion sense with the world. A little limited in scope, but certainly well tailored to its audience.

JILLIAN MICHAELS' FITNESS ULTIMATUM 2009

Publisher: Deep Silver
Genre: Lifestyle

■ ABOUT THE GAME...

Guiding the fitness student through all exercises is celebrity fitness trainer Jillian Michaels, the strength trainer and life coach on the popular American television series "The Biggest Loser". Integrating a tiered fitness regime,

expert advice and exercise techniques from the charismatic Jillian Michaels, the game delivers a focused workout that will help players reach their own personal fitness goals.

In Jillian Michaels' Fitness Ultimatum 2009, players become new recruits in Jillian's boot camp where they enroll in a unique training program composed of challenging fitness tests and an ever-changing series of workouts.

Players choose their workout from four types— (Weight Loss, Strength Training, Intervals and Hill Climb-) and set the intensity to light, medium or hard for a duration between 10 and 60 minutes. By completing exciting Wii Remote and Wii Balance Board motion-based challenges that range from crossing monkey bars to climbing ladders and rowing, players can also unlock lifestyle and fitness video tips

from Jillian. Players can even track their progress based on calories burned and workout intensity. In addition, a Competitive Party Mode lets two players race against each other through entertaining individual challenges or through the entire Physical Training course to earn the winning time.

■ IN SUMMARY...
If you are a fan of Jillian Michaels you will already be sold on this title, for the rest of us who aren't so familiar with the star of "The Biggest Loser" you may want to try before you buy. There is a decent enough array of training tasks to perform and a few neat touches, but even the less demanding gamer will be put off by the poor visuals and presentation.

MARBLES! BALANCE CHALLENGE >>>

Publisher: Konami
Genre: Action Puzzle

■ ABOUT THE GAME...
Marbles! Balance Challenge is a skill-based action title where the player helps an Ant called Anthony save his colony via a series of physical tests. Wii Balance Board users can access Marbles! Balance Challenge's 100 specially-created stages where the players steer a ball using the shifting weight of their physical movements. This unique way to control the game offers a new experience and combines fun and physical exercise. Players can also use gentle

deserts, watery settings and even a space station. In addition to rolling through the colourful stages, the player must also collate parts needed to extend and repair the roads they traverse, which – when assembled – give access to the game's final stage. Similarly, other items of ephemera can be collected and used to add new elements within the extensive edit mode.

Marbles! Balance Challenge includes tough multi-player modes where up to four players battle it out in a race to the finish, and an edit mode that allows users to create their own stages and share them among friends via the Nintendo Wii Connect24 service. The competitive element of the game can also be explored globally, with online leaderboards detailing the best scores for all to see.

■ IN SUMMARY...
Like all the best puzzle games the task at hand is deceptively simple and massively challenging. The use of the Balance Board turns the player into the controller and stands as one of the most original uses of the addon since its launch. For this reason alone Marbles! Balance Challenge comes highly recommended.

movements of the Wii Remote, with steering the ball through 200 different stages in a quest to locate the mythical 'Golden Sunflower Seed.'

As the player progresses, the level designs grow ever more complex as they introduce houses, snow-capped mountains,

MY FITNESS COACH >>>

Publisher: Ubisoft
Genre: Lifestyle

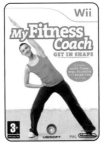

■ ABOUT THE GAME...
First, Maya (Your own personnal trainer) tests your fitness level in order to establish your goals and set you up a commitment calendar. Maya will guide you through dynamic workouts featuring over 500 unique exercises – which ensures no two workouts are ever the same. Choose your music, your mood, your focus and Maya will take care of the rest.

Maya provides you with fitness advice and motivational pep talks during workouts that help keep you moving and on the way to your fitness goals. Evaluate your current fitness level in order to determine your baseline fitness. *Fitness goals and workout calendar:* decide if your fitness goal is weight loss, upper body strength, lower body strength, core body strength, cardiovascular fitness, or flexibility. Then choose the length of your program and establish how often you plan to workout.

Training sessions with over 500 unique exercises featuring Yoga, Pilates, Cardiovascular fitness, Strength Training, Flexibility, and Weight Loss Routine.

Follow the tutorials! During the workout you can pause the action and watch a model demonstrate exactly how a move is done correctly. Each tutorial includes a choice of

view speeds and camera angles to give you the best instructional view.

Charting your progress! See your success tracked and displayed graphically as you work out. Maya will take you through a similar evaluation after every 10th workout to measure your progress (e.g. push-ups, squats, crunches, etc.) Or enter the Meditation garden to find the perfect place to practice stretching, Yoga and complete relaxation.

■ IN SUMMARY...
Thinking of this game as an add-on to Wii Fit will serve you well, but those looking for an alternative to Nintendo's senimal release will find yourself a little underwhelmed. Some novel touches and gameplay tweaks intrigue, but minor flaws soon begin to annoy.

PUNCH-OUT!! > > >

Publisher: Nintendo
Genre: Sports/Action

■ ABOUT THE GAME... One of the biggest names in boxing returns after a 15-year hiatus. Grab a Wii Remote controller in one hand and a Nunchuck controller in the other and step back into the ring with a modern update of the classic Punch-Out!!

Little Mac is back! Everyone's favourite underdog from the 1980s joins the best of the original Punch-Out!! cast in a modern re-imagination of the series. Players will find familiar names like Glass Joe, King Hippo and trainer Doc Louis. These boxers come to life again in cell-shaded 3-D, complete with hilarious fighting animations and back stories that

RAYMAN RAVING RABBIDS TV PARTY >>>

Publisher: Nintendo
Genre: Party Game

■ ABOUT THE GAME...
In Story Mode, play through a week of television, with each day bringing new wacky challenges of skill and insane movements in a compilation of mini-games.

With up to eight players in turn-based mode and four players simultaneously, get ready for you and all your friends to go insane! *Key features include:* A unique use of the Wii Balance Board. Play loads of exciting new games with the new

Wii Balance Board and experience the first game in the world that you can play with your rear end! 65+ brand-new games that spoof popular culture, from TV series to TV classics, not to mention insane ads! Play co-op or battle your friends simultaneously with up to four players, or go crazy with up

to eight players in party mode! You can even sabotage your friends while they are playing! Discover new and innovative ways to play with eight types of gameplay, including shaking, precision, dexterity and balance. Use the Wii Remote and Wii Balance Board to dance and wiggle your booty. Then pimp your bunny out, take his photo and send it to your friends online!

■ IN SUMMARY...
Utterly insane, very funny and completely addictive, Ubisoft once again get the balance between gameplay and personality just right. One of the best party games ever gets even better when you bring your Balance Board along for the ride. A classic game and a fantastic show case for the Balance Board.

capture all the fun and flair of the original Punch-Out!! games.

The motion-sensitive controls of the Wii console mean that when players throw punches, Little Mac throws punches as well. Additionally, you can control hooks and jabs by combining motion control with control-stick movement. The motion-sensing Wii Remote and Nunchuck controllers turn real-life swings into on-screen punches, so anyone can play. The game can also be played with classic NES-style controls by turning the Wii Remote sideways.

Including such characters as: Little Mac, Glass Joe, King Hippo, Doc Louis, Von Kaiser and other favourites. Once they have selected their character, players can obtain special "Star

Punches," which allow Little Mac to take more Health from his rival in a single punch.

■ IN SUMMARY...
Takes every element of the classic original and updates it perfectly for the Wii, making extremely inventive use of the Balance Board to boot. The cartoon visuals and overblown gameplay enable play from gamers of all ages and the multiplayer mode will have you stepping into the ring as often as possible!

SHAUN WHITE SNOWBOARDING: ROAD TRIP

Publisher: Ubisoft
Genre: Extreme Sports

■ ABOUT THE GAME... Shaun White Snowboarding: Road Trip takes the action-sports genre to a whole new level. For the first-time ever, feel the rocky weight of the mountain push up against your toes in your very own living room, with the revolutionary Wii Balance Board. Whether you're coasting down bunny slopes or carving through black diamonds, don't expect to survive this wild ride alone – you will need the support of an entourage and friends to make it down this mountain. Developed in close collaboration with Olympic Gold Medalist Shaun White – the most successful snowboarder in the history of the sport – Shaun White Snowboarding is set to redefine the action-sports genre.

So get yourself into the game like never before by using the Balance Board to control your rider. Control your jumps and tricks with the intuitiveness and fun of having a snowboard in your own living room.

Everybody loves a road trip! As you and your crew travel the world to participate in a variety of the fun and exciting events to become a world-renowned athlete. Hit the half-pipe competitions, race down the mountains, or just do some freeriding – there's plenty of boarding action to satisfy all your needs.

Ubisoft worked in close contact with Shaun White in order to infuse the experience with the most authentic elements of his riding style, personality and sense of humour. Shaun will act as a good-natured friend and mentor to the player, hooking him up with the right friends to conquer challenges together, introduce him to new locales, or simply be around to share in a laugh.

Engage in a seamlessly integrated multiplayer experience for two to four players in both cooperative and competitive gameplay. In the world of snowboarding, it pays to have friends on your side. Your crew of friends will always be there to help you by offering you unique abilities to improve both your riding and keeping you grounded with friendly pranks; filming all the antics along the way. Undertaking Dares from your friends will lead you to snowboard in a variety of events such as Slopestyles, Big Airs, Half Pipes, Rail Jams, Slaloms, Bordercross and Downhill events. You can even chill in the backcountry with your friends and enjoy riding at your own pace.

■ IN SUMMARY... With amazing graphics, intriguing gameplay and a rocking soundtrack this game is the perfect choice for fans of Shaun White or for those that want a little extra realism in the extreme sports games. Younger players would be better advised to seek out Family Ski as the challenge here is as deep as a monster snow storm!

SKATE CITY HEROES >>>

Publisher: Zushi
Genre: Extreme Sports

■ ABOUT THE GAME... Virus, your arch-nemesis, has just kidnapped your skating buddy and it's up to you to save him! And best of all, its totally Balance Board compatible.

Become a skateboard master as you zip between hover cars, grind on rails, and pull sick tricks and combos throughout a futuristic metropolis. Hidden bonuses and items will help you impress the evil captor in order to free your friend.

Your grappling laser and trusty skateboard are all you need to smack down your nemesis and restore peace to the city!

Choose from six playable characters - each with their own unique skills and skating strengths. Ride in futuristic environments around the city - grinding high on top of skyscrapers, flipping through ultramodern

factories, racing between aerial trains and hover cars is just the beginning.

Use different combinations and attack moves to get rid of aggressive opponents. Unique missions and side-games will keep the players progressing through the story and up to four players can battle it out in a variety of multiplayer modes.

■ IN SUMMARY... A wise investment for the younger male Wii gamer, with the blend of extreme skateboarding and wild cartoon inspired visuals and a well implemented use of the Balance Board. The lack of depth may be off putting to more mature and experienced gamers, yet there is still much to enjoy here.

Wii MUSIC >>>

Publisher: Nintendo
Genre: Music Creator

■ ABOUT THE GAME...
Create a musical masterpiece with up to four players. Anyone can play the huge selection of instruments in Wii Music with simple motions—like strumming and drumming.

It's easy to play improvised jams. Musicians in your band jam by simply playing their instruments to the beat of a song or by improvising to their heart's content. Play faster. Play slower. Skip a beat, or throw in 10 more. No matter what you do, Wii Music automatically transforms your improvised styles, into great music. There are no mistakes—just playing for the pure joy of playing. *Wii controls immerse you in the music.* You can play most of the 60-plus instruments in Wii Music using simple motions with the Wii Remote and Nunchuck controllers. Strum to play guitar, banjo and sitar. Drum to play jazz drums, congas and marching drums. Hammer away to play piano, vibraphone and marimba. Unlike most music games, Wii Music doesn't make you use complex buttons. You only need to imitate playing the instrument.

Wii Music offers virtually endless ways to make music. You choose the song and instruments and decide whether to blaze through a rock song or take on classical songs, put a jazzy spin on folk tunes or transform Nintendo classics like the Super Mario Bros.® theme into Latin-flavoured numbers.

The song list is only a take-off point—it's how you improvise with the songs that matters.

Send your band-jam recordings to Wii Friends who have Wii Music. They'll see your Mii band members, your players' improvised styles and your instrument selections. They can watch your recordings, or play over parts of your song, then send their modified recording back to you. Improvised jams can be sent back and forth over WiiConnect24 and changed again and again.

Wii Music includes many other modes besides the main band jams, including several musical games and an enhanced video playback mode for recorded jams. *Play it again:* Use the playback mode to see your jam recordings brought to life with dramatic camera angles.

Pick up the baton: Command an orchestra in the conducting game where you'll wave the Wii Remote controller like a conductor's baton to lead a Mii orchestra through orchestrated music. Make them play quickly, slowly, strongly or gently.

Ring a bell? Play a handbells game where you'll swing your Wii Remote and Nunchuck controllers to play your two handbells as part of a larger ensemble. *Everyone on the team has a job to do:* Play one of your notes only when the tune demands it.

An ear for music: Take a tone quiz that tests your musical ear by giving you challenges, like putting note-playing Miis in order from lowest to highest pitch.

Bang the drum: Play a virtual drum set in the drumming mode, the one mode in Wii Music that also uses the Wii Balance Board accessory (sold with Wii Fit™). You'll use the Wii Remote and Nunchuck controllers as drumsticks, and place both feet on the Wii Balance Board—which work as virtual pedals for the bass drum and hi-hat cymbal.

> ■ IN SUMMARY...
> The use of the Balance Board makes one of the Wii's best games that much better and somehow makes the amazing gameplay even more amazing! We aren't sure how this is possible as we adore Wii Music, but Nintendo have managed it! If you own a Balance Board you need to own this game too!

SKATE IT >>>

Publisher: EA
Genre: Extreme Sports

■ ABOUT THE GAME...
EA Montreal and Black Box, studios of Electronic Arts Inc's award-winning Skate It brings extreme sports to the your living room in style! With intuitive Wii and the Wii Balance Board, Skate It delivers a fun and unique skateboarding experience for skate fans and gamers of all ages.

worked in Hall of Meat, and earning the opportunity to travel the world, all on their path to becoming Thrasher Magazine's Skater of the Year. In Skate It, gamers will be able to make skate spots their own by moving objects like ramps, rails, and benches to fit their individual skating styles. The game also boasts a variety of multiplayer challenges, including Best Trick and Best Line, which will have players ripping it up with their friends as they prove their skateboarding prowess.

> ■ IN SUMMARY...
> Although an exciting leap into the world of extreme sports when played with the Wii-mote and Nunchuck, Skate It jumps to a whole new level when played with the Balance Board. Offering a skating experience so real you will need knee pads and one that can be embraced by all players.

Skate It brings gamers back to San Vanelona, a city that's been safely evacuated, but left in ruins after being hit by a series of crazy events. Here, players are rediscovering their favourite spots, getting

nintendo Wii active games
a-z of cheats, codes and tips!

there are so many Wii games that are so good that you can't help jumping to your feet and leaping around the room with your Wii-mote spinning cartwheels and as you know any exercise is good exercise! With this in mind we have put together our exclusive A-Z of cheats for those addictive active games, so there is nothing stopping you!

BOOGIE

■ UNLOCKABLES

Unlocking the Bonus Songs
To unlock this bonus song, Boogie Oogie Oogie, you must complete Bubba's story.
To unlock this bonus song, Dancing in the Street, you must complete Julius' story.
To unlock this bonus song, Love Shack, you must complete Lea's story.
To unlock this bonus song, SOS, you must complete Jet's story.
To unlock this bonus song, Tu y Yo, you must complete Kato's story.

BOOGIE SUPERSTAR

■ CHEAT CODE

To Unlock the Bonus "Dance Dance" song You must enter the following cheat code on the "Select An Icon" screen; Diamond, Heart, Broken Heart, Cherries.

CARNIVAL GAMES

■ UNLOCKABLE

Unlock The End Credits
To unlock the End Credits without having to complete the game, you must highlight the word "Games" on the Main Menu screen and press A.

EXCITE TRUCK

■ UNLOCKABLES

Unlocking the Silver Cup
To successfully unlock the Silver Cup

in Excite Race, you must complete the Bronze Cup having claimed a Bronze rank on all tracks.
Unlocking the Gold Cup
To successfully unlock the Gold Cup in Excite Race, you must complete the Silver Cup having claimed a Bronze rank on all tracks.
Unlocking the Platinum Cup
To successfully unlock the Platinum Cup in Excite Race, you must complete the Bronze Cup, Silver Cup and Gold Cup having claimed a S rank on all tracks.
Unlocking Super Excite Mode
To successfully unlock the Super Excite Race, you must complete the Bronze Cup, Silver Cup, Gold Cup and Platinum Cup having claimed a S rank on all tracks in Excite Mode.
Unlocking the Diamond Cup
To successfully unlock the Diamond Cup in Super Excite Race, you must complete the Bronze Cup, Silver Cup, Gold Cup and Platinum Cup having claimed a S rank on all tracks.
Unlocking Mirror Mode Race
To successfully unlock the Mirror Mode races, you must claim an S rank on each track on Super Excite Mode.
Unlocking Alternative Paint Jobs
To unlock the Alternative Paint Jobs

you must successfully complete a total of three races with a S rank using the same truck.
Unlocking the Monster Truck
To unlock the Monster Truck you must successfully unlock the Alternative Paint Jobs for all trucks.
Unlock the Crazy Monster Truck.
To unlock the Crazy Monster Truck you must successfully claim an S rank on every track whilst playing on Mirror Mode.
Unlocking the Crystal Road
To successfully unlock the Crystal Road race in Super Excite Race, you must complete the Bronze Cup, Silver Cup, Gold Cup and Platinum Cup having claimed a S rank on all tracks.

GUITAR HERO WORLD TOUR

■ CHEAT CODES

Enter the following cheat code on the "Enter New Cheat" screen from the main Cheats menu: Red, Red, Blue, Yellow, Green, Green, Green, Yellow to **unlock the Air**

Instruments cheat.
Enter the following cheat code on the "Enter New Cheat" screen from the main Cheats menu:
Green, Green, Red, Red, Yellow, Red, Yellow, Blue to **unlock the Always slide cheat.**
Enter the following cheat code on the "Enter New Cheat" screen from the main Cheats menu: Yellow, Green, Red, Blue, Blue, Blue, Blue, Red to **unlock the Auto Kick cheat.**
Enter the following cheat code on the "Enter New Cheat" screen from the main Cheats menu:
GREEN, RED, GREEN, BLUE, RED, RED, YELLOW, B to **unlock the Change Flame Colour cheat.**
Enter the following cheat code on the "Enter New Cheat" screen from the main Cheats menu:
BLUE, RED, RED, GREEN, RED, GREEN, RED, Y to **unlock the Change Gem Colour cheat.**
Enter the following cheat code on the "Enter New Cheat" screen from the main Cheats menu:
Green, Blue, Red, Yellow, Yellow, Red, Green, Green to **unlock the Hyperspeed cheat.**
Enter the following cheat code on the "Enter New Cheat" screen from the main Cheats menu:
Green, Red, Yellow, Yellow, Yellow, Blue, Blue, Green to **unlock the Invisible Rocker cheat.**
Enter the following cheat code on the "Enter New Cheat" screen from the main Cheats menu:
Blue, Red, Blue, Blue, Yellow, Yellow, Yellow, Green to **unlock Johnny Viper cheat.**
Enter the following cheat code on the "Enter New Cheat" screen from the main Cheats menu:
Green, Red, Blue, Green, Red, Blue, Blue, Green to **unlock Nick cheat.**
Enter the following cheat code on

the "Enter New Cheat" screen from the main Cheats menu:
Yellow, Yellow, Blue, Red, Blue, Green, Red, Red to **unlock the Performance mode cheat.**
Enter the following cheat code on the "Enter New Cheat" screen from the main Cheats menu: Blue, Red, Green, Green, Yellow, Yellow, Yellow, Green to **unlock Rina cheat.**
Enter the following cheat code on the "Enter New Cheat" screen from the main Cheats menu: RED, RED, YELLOW, RED, BLUE, RED, RED, B to **unlock the Star Colour cheat.**
Enter the following cheat code on the "Enter New Cheat" screen from the main Cheats menu:
YELLOW, GREEN, RED, RED, GREEN, BLUE, RED, Y **Unlock AT&T Ballpark cheat.**
Enter the following cheat code on the "Enter New Cheat" screen from the main Cheats menu: Blue, Blue, Red, Green, Green, Blue, Blue, Yellow to **unlock the All Songs cheat.**
Enter the following cheat code on the "Enter New Cheat" screen from the main Cheats menu: RED, GREEN, GREEN, YELLOW, BLUE, GREEN, YELLOW, Green to unlock the Vocal Fireball cheat.

GUITAR HERO III: LEGENDS OF ROCK

■ CHEAT CODES
Unlock The All Items Cheat
Enter the following cheat combination on the Cheats Menu screen to unlock all items in the Shop: Green/Red/Blue/Orange, Green/Red/Yellow/Blue, Green/Red/Yellow/Orange, Green/Blue/Yellow/Orange, Green/Red/Yellow/Blue, Red/Yellow/Blue/Orange, Green/Red/Yellow/Blue,

Green/Yellow/Blue/Orange, Green/Red/Yellow/Blue, Green/Red/Yellow/Orange, Green/Red/Yellow/Orange, Green/Red/Yellow/Blue, Green/Red/Yellow/Orange.
Unlock The No Failure Cheat
Enter the following cheat combination on the Cheats Menu screen: Green & Red, Blue, Green & Red, Green & Yellow, Blue, Green & Yellow, Red & Yellow, Orange, Red & Yellow, Green & Yellow, Yellow, Green & Yellow, Green & Red.
NOTE: This cheat doesn't work when playing on Career Mode.
Unlock The Hyperspeed Cheat
Enter the following cheat combination on the Cheats Menu screen: Orange, Blue, Orange, Yellow, Orange, Blue, Orange, Yellow.
Unlock The Air Guitar Cheat
Enter the following cheat combination on the Options Menu screen: Blue & Yellow, Green & Yellow, Green & Yellow, Red & Blue, Red & Blue, Red & Yellow, Red & Yellow, Blue & Yellow, Green & Yellow, Green & Yellow, Red & Blue, Red & Blue, Red & Yellow, Red & Yellow, Green & Yellow, Green & Yellow, Red & Yellow, Red & Yellow.
Unlocking All Songs
Enter the following cheat combination on the Options Menu screen: Yellow & Orange, Red & Blue, Red & Orange, Green & Blue, Red & Yellow, Yellow & Orange, Red & Yellow, Red & Blue, Green & Yellow, Green & Yellow, Yellow & Blue,

MARIO POWER TENNIS

■ UNLOCKABLES
Unlocking The Star Cup Mode
To successfully unlock this bonus you must complete the three tournaments that make up the Normal Cup.
Unlocking The Hard Difficulty Setting
To successfully unlock this bonus you must complete the three tournaments that make the Star Cup.
■ UNLOCKABLE CHARACTERS
Unlocking Piranha Plant As A Playable Character
To successfully unlock this bonus you must complete both Special tournaments, Fire and Thunder whilst playing in doubles matches.
Unlocking Paratroopa As A Playable Character

To successfully unlock this bonus you must complete all 3 normal tournament cups.
Unlocking Wiggler As A Playable Character
To successfully unlock this bonus you must complete normal Flower Cup whilst playing in doubles matches.
Unlocking Shy Guy As A Playable Character
To successfully unlock this bonus you must complete the normal tournament having played on all three courts.

Yellow & Blue, Yellow & Orange, Yellow & Orange, Yellow & Blue, Yellow, Red, Red & Yellow, Red, Yellow, Orange. NOTE: This cheat only works when playing on Quick Play Mode

MARIO & SONIC AT THE OLYMPIC GAMES

■ UNLOCKABLES
To unlock the Olympic Record Emblem you must break an Olympic Record
To unlock the World Record Emblem you must break a World Record
To unlock the Knight's Emblem you must win a total of 15-0 in Individual epee
To unlock the Network Emblem you must connect to Nintendo WFC Rankings
To unlock the Rocket Emblem you must perform a perfect start

dash in 100m
To unlock the Friendly Emblem you must lay an Event with 2 to 4 Players
To unlock the Track Champ Emblem you must win a Gold Medals in All Track Events in Single Match
To unlock the Field Champ Emblem you must win a Gold Medals in All Field Events in Single Match
To unlock the Bouncing Emblem you must obtain a 10 rating on the Trampoline
To unlock the Gallery Owner Emblem you must unlock everything in the Gallery
To unlock the Penalty Emblem you must commit a Foul in the 100m
To unlock the Collaborative Emblem you must play the game as

all the characters
To unlock the Knuckles Emblem you must complete Mission mode with Knuckles
To unlock the Bowser Emblem you must complete Mission mode with Bowser
To unlock the Vector Emblem you must complete Mission mode with Vector
To unlock the Wario Emblem you must complete Mission mode with Wario
To unlock the Mario Emblem you must complete Mission mode with Mario
To unlock the Amy Emblem you

must complete Mission mode with Amy
To unlock the Luigi Emblem you must complete Mission mode with Luigi
To unlock the Blaze Emblem you must complete Mission mode with Blaze
To unlock the Sonic Emblem you must complete Mission mode with Sonic
To unlock the Daisy Emblem you must complete Mission mode with Daisy
To unlock the Shadow Emblem you must complete Mission mode

with Shadow
To unlock the Yoshi Emblem you must complete Mission mode with Yoshi
To unlock the Peach Emblem you must complete Mission mode with Peach
To unlock the Tails Emblem you must complete Mission mode with Tails
To unlock the Waluigi Emblem you must complete Mission mode with Waluigi

MARIO KART Wii

■ **UNLOCKABLES**
UNLOCKING NEW COURSES
Unlocking the Star Cup
To unlock the Star Cup, you must place at least 3rd when racing on the Flower Cup on any "CC".
Unlocking the Special Cup
To unlock the Special Cup, you must place at least 3rd when racing on the Star Cup on any "CC".
Unlocking the Leaf Cup
To unlock the Leaf Cup, you must place at least 3rd when racing on the Banana Cup on any "CC".
Unlocking the Lightening Cup
To unlock the Lightning Cup, you must place at least 3rd when racing on the Leaf Cup on any "CC".
Unlocking Mirror mode
To successfully unlock the Mirror mode for all Cups and Course you must firstly place 1st on all Cups when reaching on the 150cc class.
■ **UNLOCKING THE HIDDEN CHARACTERS**
Unlocking King Boo
To unlock the following racer, King Boo you must firstly place 1st on the 50cc Star Cup
Unlocking Diddy Kong
To unlock the following racer, Diddy Kong you must firstly place 1st on the retro 50cc Cups
Unlocking Baby Daisy
To unlock the following racer, Baby Daisy you must obtain a total of 1 Star in all 50cc Wii-Cups
Unlocking Dry Bones
To unlock the following racer, Dry Bones you must firstly place 1st on the 100cc Leaf Cup
Unlocking Bowser Jr
To unlock the following racer, Bowser Jr. you must obtain a total of 1 Star in all 100cc Retro-Cups
Unlocking Daisy
To unlock the following racer,

Daisy you must firstly place 1st on the 150cc Special Cup
Unlocking Dry Bowser
To unlock the following racer, Dry Bowser you must obtain a total of 1 Star in all 150cc Wii-Cups
Unlocking Rosalina
To unlock the following racer, Rosalina you must obtain a total of 1 star in all Mirror Mode Retro-Cups
Unlocking Funky Kong
To unlock the following racer, Funky Kong you must successfully unlock at least four Expert Staff Ghost Data in Time Trials

Unlocking Baby Luigi
To unlock the following racer, Baby Luigi you must successfully unlock at least eight Expert Staff Ghost Data in Time Trials
Unlocking Birdo
To unlock the following racer, Birdo you must play on Time Trial mode for at least 16 different courses.
Unlocking Toadette
To unlock the following racer, Toadette you must play on Time Trial mode on all 32 courses.
■ **UNLOCKABLE KARTS**
To unlock the following kart, Aero Glider you must obtain at least 1 Star on all 150cc Retro Cups.
To unlock the following kart, B Dasher Mk 2 you must unlock a minimum of 24 Expert Staff Ghosts.
To unlock the following kart, Blue Falcon you must successfully place 1st on the Mirror Lightning Cup.
To unlock the following kart, Cheep Charger you must obtain at least 1 Star on 50cc Retro Grand Prix Cups.

To unlock the following kart, Dragonetti you must successfully place 1st on the 150cc Lightning Cup.
To unlock the following kart, Piranha Prowler you must successfully place 1st on the 50cc Special Cup.
To unlock the following kart, Rally Romper you must unlock a minimum of one Expert Staff Ghosts.
To unlock the following kart, Royal Racer you must successfully place 1st on the 150cc Leaf Cup.
To unlock the following kart, Turbo Blooper you must successfully place 1st on the 50cc Leaf Cup.

■ **UNLOCKABLE BIKES**
To unlock the following bike, Quacker you must successfully place 1st on the 150cc Star Cup.
To unlock the following bike, Bubble Bike you must successfully place 1st on the Mirror Leaf Cup.
To unlock the following bike, Magikruiser you must play on Time Trials on a minimum of eight courses.
To unlock the following bike, Rapide you must successfully place 1st on the 100cc Lightning Cup.
To unlock the following bike, Nitrocycle you must obtain at least 1 Star on all 100cc Wii Grand Prix Cups.
To unlock the following bike, Dolphin Dasher you must successfully place 1st on the Mirror Star Cup.
To unlock the following bike, Twinkle Star you must successfully place 1st on the 100cc Star Cup.
To unlock the following bike, Phantom you must successfully place 1st on the Mirror Special Cup.
To unlock the following bike, Torpedo you must unlock a minimum of 12 Expert Staff Ghosts.

To unlock the **Dr. Eggman Emblem** you must complete Mission mode with Dr. Eggman

To unlock the Dream Champ Emblem you must win the 1st Medal in all Dream Events

To unlock the Full Play Emblem you must play All Events

To unlock the Complete Game Emblem you must unlock All Events

To unlock the Planet Circuit you must win a Medal (Gold, Silver or Bronze) in Stardust Circuit

To unlock the Aquatics Champs Emblem you must win a Gold Medals in All Aqautics Events

To unlock the Gymnastics Champ Emblem you must a Gold Medals in All Gymnastics Events

To unlock the Ping Pong Emblem (Table Tennis) you must win a 11-0 in Singles Table Tennis

To unlock the Shooting Emblem (Shooting) you must win by 40 Points in Skeet

To unlock the Somersault Emblem (Vault) you must obtain a 10 rating on the Vault

To unlock the Thanks for Playing Emblem you must play the game 50 times

To unlock the Hunter Emblem you must gain 120 points in archery

RAYMAN RAVING RABBIDS

■ UNLOCKABLES

UNLOCKING BONUS ITEMS
You successfully unlock the bonus: Artwork 1 you must obtain a minimum score of 5000 Points whilst playing in Score Mode.

You successfully unlock the bonus: Bunnies Don't Like Taking a Bath you must obtain a minimum score of 9000 Points whilst playing in Score Mode.

You successfully unlock the bonus: Bunnies Don't Do Vacuum Cleaning you must obtain a minimum score of 21000 Points whilst playing in Score Mode.

You successfully unlock the bonus: Bunnies Can't Infiltrate Games Convention you must obtain

ROCK BAND 2

■ CHEAT CODES

Enter the following cheat code on the Modify Game menu screen; Yellow, Blue, Orange, Yellow, Blue, Orange, Yellow, Blue, Orange to successfully **unlock the Better Note Detection cheat.**

Enter the following cheat code on the Modify Game menu screen; Red, Red, Red, Red, Yellow, Yellow, Yellow, Yellow to successfully **unlock the New Venues only cheat.**

Enter the following cheat code on the Modify Game menu screen; Blue, Blue, Red, Red, Yellow, Yellow, Blue, Blue to successfully **unlock the Remove the Note Display cheat.**

Enter the following cheat code on the Modify Game menu screen; Blue, Yellow, Red, Blue, Yellow,

Red, Blue, Yellow, Red to successfully **unlock the Stage Mode cheat.**

Enter the following cheat code on the Modify Game menu screen; Red, Yellow, Blue, Red, Red, Blue, Blue, Red, Yellow, Blue to successfully **unlock the Unlock All Songs cheat.**

Enter the following cheat code on the Modify Game menu screen; Blue, Orange, Orange, Blue, Yellow, Blue, Orange, Orange, Blue, Yellow to successfully **unlock the Unlock All Venues cheat.**

PRO EVOLUTION SOCCER 08

■ UNLOCKABLES

Unlocking Mii Match Mode
To successfully unlock this Wii exclusive mode you must place on top of the practice league whilst playing on the Champions Road mode.

■ UNLOCKING THE CLASSIC TEAMS

To successfully unlock the Classic Brazil team you must win the World Cup with Brazil.

To successfully unlock the Classic Argentina team you must

win the World Cup with Argentina.

To successfully unlock the Classic Netherlands team you must win the World Cup with Netherlands.

To successfully unlock the Classic Italy team you must win the World Cup with Italy

To successfully unlock the Classic Germany team you must win the World Cup with Germany.

To successfully unlock the Classic France team you must win the World Cup with France.

To successfully unlock the Classic England team you must win the World Cup with England.

a minimum score of 48000 Points whilst playing in Score Mode.

You successfully unlock the bonus: French Bastille Day you must obtain a minimum score of 57000 Points whilst playing in Score Mode.

You successfully unlock the bonus: Bunnies Can't Cook Eggs you must obtain a minimum score of 84000 Points whilst playing in Score Mode.

You successfully unlock the bonus: Artwork 2 you must obtain a minimum score of 93000 Points whilst playing in Score Mode.

You successfully unlock the bonus: Bunnies Never Close Doors you must obtain a minimum score of 111000 Points whilst playing in Score Mode.

You successfully unlock the bonus: Bunnies Can't Play Soccer you must obtain a minimum score of 138000 Points whilst playing in Score Mode.

You successfully unlock the bonus: US Independence Day you must obtain a minimum score of 165000 Points whilst playing in Score Mode.

RAYMAN RAVING RABBIDS 2

■ UNLOCKABLES

UNLOCKING THE BONUS COSTUMES
Unlock the Altair - Assassin's

Creed outfit by obtaining the high score whilst playing on Wiimote Only mode on the USA stage.

Unlock the HAZE Armor by successfully shooting the HAZE Rabbid whilst playing on Big City Fights.

Unlock the Indiana Jones outfit by successfully obtaining a total of 12,000 Points whilst playing on Rolling Stone.

Unlock the Jason – Friday the 13th outfit by successfully obtaining a total of 12000 whilst playing on Dial R for Rabbid.

Unlock the Spider-Rabbid outfit by successfully obtaining Spider Rabbid Game award.

Unlock the TMNT outfit by successfully obtaining a total of 12,000 Points whilst playing on Usual Rabbids.

RAYMAN RAVING RABBIDS TV PARTY

■ UNLOCKABLES

Unlock the Pimp My Rabbid Costumes
To successfully unlock these bonus outfits, you must complete the Pimp My Rabbid minigame having obtained a total score of 15,000.

Unlocking the Minigames in Training Mode To unlocking these minigames in Training mode you must obtain a total of 10,000 points on each minigame whilst playing on Solo mode.

SEGA SUPERSTARS TENNIS

■ UNLOCKABLES
UNLOCKING THE HIDDEN CHARACTERS
Unlocking Alex Kidd
To successfully unlock Alex Kidd as a playable character you must complete Mission #1 when playing in Alex Kidd's World.
Unlocking Amy Rose
To successfully unlock Amy Rose as a playable character you must complete Mission #2 when playing in Sonic The Hedgehog's World.
Unlocking Gilius
To successfully unlock Gilius as a playable character you must complete Mission #1 when playing in Golden Axe's World.
Unlocking Gum
To successfully unlock Gum as a playable character you must complete Mission #12 when playing in Jet Grind Radio's World.
Unlocking Meemee
To successfully unlock Meemee as a playable character you must complete Mission #8 when playing in Super Monkey Ball's World.
Unlocking Pudding
To successfully unlock Pudding as a playable character you must complete Mission #1 when

SUPER MARIO GALAXY

■ UNLOCKABLES
Unlocking Luigi
To successfully unlock Luigi as a playable character you will must collect all 120 Stars and then return to the Comet Observatory and successfully replay the final battle with Bowser. Now watch the end credits and you will now be rewarded with Luigi as a playable character.

Unlocking the Bonus Galaxy.
To unlock the Bonus galaxy, you must replay the game and collect all 120 stars using Luigi and beat Bowser, this will unlock the Grand Finale Galaxy. Now simply collect a total of 100 purple coins to gain the final star, bringing your total to 121.

playing in Space Channel 5's World.
Unlocking Reala
To successfully unlock Reala as a playable character you must complete Mission #2 when playing in NiGHTs' World.
Unlocking Shadow The Hedgehog
To successfully unlock Shadow The Hedgehog as a playable character you must complete Mission #14 when playing in Sonic The Hedgehog's World.

SHAUN WHITE SNOWBOARDING: ROAD TRIP

■ UNLOCKABLE
To unlock Shaun White as a playable character you must successfully complete the Reunion stage and the immediantly replay it.

SKATE IT

■ UNLOCKABLES
UNLOCKING NEW PRO SKATERS
To unlock Chris Haslam As a player skater you must successfully complete the

Almost sponsorship challenge whilst playing on career mode
To unlock Danny Way As a player skater you must successfully complete the Plan B sponsorship challenge whilst playing on career mode
To unlock Eric Koston As a player skater you must successfully complete the Lakai sponsorship challenge whilst playing on career mode
To unlock Jake Brown As a player skater you must successfully complete the Blind sponsorship challenge whilst playing on career mode
To unlock Lucas Puig As a player skater you must successfully complete the Cliche sponsorship challenge whilst playing on career mode
To unlock Mike Carroll As a player skater you must successfully complete the Girl sponsorship challenge whilst playing on career mode
To unlock Rob Dyrdek As a player skater you must successfully complete the Alien Workshop sponsorship challenge whilst playing on career mode
To unlock Terry Kennedy As a player skater you must successfully complete the Baker sponsorship challenge whilst playing on career mode

SSX BLUR

■ CHEAT CODES
Unlocking the All Characters Cheat
To successfully unlock the following cheat code you must enter it on the Cheat Menu screen: NoHolds
Unlocking the All Clothes Cheat
To successfully unlock the following cheat code you must enter it on the Cheat Menu screen: ClothShop

SUPER SMASH BROS. BRAWL

■ UNLOCKABLES
Unlocking The Bonus Stage Builder Parts
To unlock the Edit Parts A, you must play on the custom stages you have built at least ten times.
To unlock the Edit Parts B, you must successfully build at least five stages.

To unlock the Edit Parts C, you must successfully build at least 15 stages.
Unlocking All-Star Mode
To successfully unlock the bonus All-Star Mode, you must have unlocked all thirty-five characters.
Unlocking Boss Battle Mode
To successfully unlock the bonus Boss Battle Mode, you must firstly complete the Subspace Emissary mode.

■ UNLOCKING THE BONUS STAGES
To successfully unlock the 75m Bonus Stage you must play as DK 20 times
To successfully unlock the Big Blue Bonus Stage you must play as Falcon 10 times
To successfully unlock the Electroplankton Bonus Stage you must complete Event Match #28
To successfully unlock the Flat Zone 2 Bonus Stage you must unlock Mr. Game & Watch
To successfully unlock the Great Sea Bonus Stage you must unlock Toon Link
To successfully unlock the Green Greens Bonus Stage you must play Kirby 20 times
To successfully unlock the Green Hill Zone Bonus Stage you must unlock Sonic
To successfully unlock the Jungle Japes Bonus Stage you must play VS. Mode at least ten times
To successfully unlock the Luigi's Mansion Bonus Stage you must brawl with Luigi in VS. Mode at least three times
To successfully unlock the Mario Bros. Bonus Stage you must complete Event Match #19

SUPER MONKEY BALL: BANANA BLITZ

■ UNLOCKABLES
Unlocking Bonus World Nine

To successfully unlock this bonus World, you must complete Worlds One to Eight without using a single continue.

Unlocking Bonus World Ten
To successfully unlock this bonus World, you must complete World Nine without using a single continue.

TIGER WOODS PGA TOUR 08

■ CHEAT CODES
Enter the following code into the password screen,
CLEVELAND to successfully unlock the Cleveland Golf-items
Enter the following code into the password screen,
GUYSAREGOOD to successfully unlock the Precept-items
Enter the following code into the password screen, **INTHEGAME to successfully unlock the EA-items**
Enter the following code into the password screen,
JANNARD to successfully unlock the Oakley-items
Enter the following code into the pass-word screen,
JLINDBERG to successfully unlock the J. Lindberg-items
Enter the following code into the password screen, **JUSTDOIT to successfully unlock the Nike-items**
Enter the following code into the password screen,
JUSTSHAFTS to successfully unlock the Grafalloy-items
Enter the following code into the password screen,
LIGHTNING to successfully unlock the PGA Tour-items
Enter the following code into the password screen, **MACTEC to successfully unlock the MacGergor-items**
Enter the following code into the password screen, **MRADAMS to successfully unlock the Taylormade-items**

TIGER WOODS PGA TOUR 09

■ CHEAT CODES
By entering the following code on the Password screen, **CEPHALUS you will unlock the Big Head Spectator Mode cheat.**
By entering the following code on the Password screen, **SWOOSH you will unlock the Nike Shop Items Unlocked cheat.**

WARIOWARE: SMOOTH MOVES

■ UNLOCKABLES
Unlocking the Movie Theatre mode To successfully unlock this mini-game you must firstly complete the Wario stage.
Unlocking the Multiplayer Mode To successfully unlock this mini-game you must firstly complete the single-player game.

Gimme five!

■ UNLOCKABLE MINI-GAMES
Unlock the Balloon Trip Mini-game. To successfully unlock this mini-game you must firstly complete Dr Crygor's Workout stage.
Unlock the Block Star Mini-game. To successfully unlock this mini-game you must firstly complete the Young Cricket stage.
Unlock the Can Shooter Mini-game. To successfully unlock this mini-game you must firstly complete the Ashley stage.
Unlock the Tortoise and Hare Mini-game. To successfully unlock this mini-game you must firstly complete the Orbulon stage.
Unlock the Tower Mini-game. To successfully unlock this mini-game you must firstly complete the Kat and Ana stage.
Unlock the Pyoro S Mini-game. To successfully unlock this mini-game you must firstly complete every mini-game in the entire game.

Wii MUSIC

■ UNLOCKABLES
UNLOCKING BONUS VENUES
Unlock the Truck by successfully completing every Rock Lesson and All Minigames!
Unlock the Space by successfully completing every Rock Lesson and All Minigames!

TIGER WOODS PGA TOUR 07

■ CHEAT CODE
Unlockin the Cobra Gear
To successfully unlock the Cobra Gear, you must enter the following cheat code on the "Password" menu screen: SnakeKing

MINI GUIDE – TIGER'S PERFECT SWING TIPS!
During this mini-guide we will break down how you perform the perfect swing, the easy way!
Unlike Wii Sports Golf, mimicking the golf swing of the onscreen character will not provide you with the best possible results here. Understanding the swing dynamics of this game is the most essential element of the gameplay, so what follows is our break down of the key factors that you must get to grips with both entering any of the game's later stages.

STEP ONE: CONTROLLING THE BACK SWING
During a long distance drive, your initial thoughts regarding your back swing would be to grasp the Wii-mote with both hands and swing backwards to the highest possible position – ending the arc with your hands directly in line with the top of your head – and then swing forward to the same position in one continuous movement. Whilst mimicking the real life movements of Tiger and his fellow golfing Pros, lends a sense of realism to the proceedings. We have found that you can achieve a 100% rating from each of your clubs using the below technique.

NOTE: Carefully watch your on screen character and notice how they're movements do not mimic yours but instead exaggerate them!

First Step: Draw your Wii-mote back at a 45-degree angle from your back. Pause for a second at this point to add an extra 10% to your swing power.
Second Step: From the first step position quickly but smoothly move it forward to a 90-degree angle from your chest.
STEP TWO: JUDGING THE DISTANCE OF YOUR SWING.
Certain shots will call for you to control the speed and resulting distance of your shot, the easiest way to limit your shots is as follows. Using the onscreen map you will notice that the full distance of your club is displayed as a straight line, with the optimum distance achievable at the far end of this line. For example if the green is 50 feet from your position and you don't have a club suitable for that distance, cycle through your clubs to find one that can hit almost double the distance you require – 100 feet. Now perform a test swing to see the height of the highest arc of your on screen character's swing animation, if you strike the ball at this position you will hit it over the 100 feet mark. Instead watch the swing animation until you are approximately half way through the swing and then swing the Wii-mote forward to the 90-degree angle and your shot should hit the target, discounting any environmental changes etc.

Unlock the Music Room by successfully completing every Rock Lesson and All Minigames!
Unlock the Apartment levels by successfully completing every Rock Lesson and All Minigames!

■ UNLOCKING THE BONUS JAM SESSION COSTUMES
Enter the following cheat combination using the Wii-mote on the Start screen:
Press and hold Right and press Start to successfully unlock the Wii Music T-shirt outfit.
Enter the following cheat combination using the Wii-mote on the Start screen:
Press and hold B + Down and press Start to successfully unlock the Karate outfit.
Enter the following cheat combination using the Wii-mote on the Start screen: **Press and hold Left and press Start to successfully unlock the Cat outfit.**
Enter the following cheat combination using the Wii-mote on the Start screen: **Press and hold B + Left and press Start to successfully**

Wii FIT PLUS
■ UNLOCKABLE
Unlocking the Ultimate Balance Test and the Scale Challenge
To unlock both of these bonuses, head to the statistics screen and now click on the Mii running on the treadmill in the background. You will now be able to access both the Ultimate Balance Test and the Scale Challenge.

unlock the Cheerleader outfit. Enter the following cheat combination using the Wii-mote on the Start screen: **Press and hold B + Right and press Start to successfully unlock the DJ outfit.**
Enter the following cheat combination using the Wii-mote on the Start screen: **Press and hold Down and press Start to successfully unlock the Dog outfit.**
Enter the following cheat combination using the Wii-mote on the Start screen: **Press and hold B + Up and press Start to successfully unlock the Hip hop outfit.**
Enter the following cheat combination using the Wii-mote on the Start screen: **Press and hold Up and press Start to successfully unlock the Tuxedo outift.**

Wii PLAY
■ CHEAT CODE
Unlock The Bonus Laser Hockey Paddle To successfully unlock this cheat you must press and hold the A-Button and B-Button before the start of your bout.

Wii SPORTS
■ CHEAT CODES AND UNLOCKABLES
Wii Sports Bowling Cheats
MULTICOLOURED BOWLING BALL CHEAT
Unlock the Blue Bowling Ball Cheat To successfully unlock this cheat you must press and hold Up on the D-Pad having selected your Mii character.
Unlock the Green Bowling Ball Cheat To successfully unlock this cheat you must press and hold Down on the D-Pad having selected your Mii character.
Unlock the Gold Bowling Ball Cheat To successfully unlock this cheat you must press and hold Right on the D-Pad having selected your Mii character.
Unlock the Red Bowling Ball Cheat To successfully unlock this cheat you must press and hold Left on the D-Pad having selected your Mii character.
Unlocking the Pro Bowling Ball
To successfully unlock this bonus Pro Ball, you must raise and maintain a Pro score of over 1,000 points.

NOTE: If you loose a game you will also loose points so be aware that you can also loose your Pro Status and Ball.

Wii SPORTS TENNIS CHEAT
Unlocking the Bonus Tennis Court
To successfully unlock this cheat you must press and hold the 2-Button on the D-Pad having selected your Mii character.
Wii SPORTS BOXING CHEAT
Unlock the Silver Gloves
To successfully unlock this cheat you must firstly have defeated the final Boxer in this mode, and then restart your game and press and hold the 1-Button on the D-Pad having selected your Mii character.

WINTER SPORTS 2009: THE NEXT CHALLENGE
■ CHEAT CODES
Enter the following cheat combination on the Challenges menu

TONY HAWK'S PROVING GROUND
■ CHEAT CODES
Enter the cheat code on the Options menu screen; **STILLAINTFALLIN** to unlock Perfect Manual cheat.
Enter the cheat code on the Options menu screen; **AINTFALLIN** to unlock Perfect Rail cheat.
Enter the cheat code on the Options menu screen; **BOOYAH** to unlock Super Check cheat.
Enter the cheat code on the Options menu screen; **MYOPIC** to unlock Unlimited Focus cheat.
Enter the cheat code on the Options menu screen; **SUPERSLASHIN** to unlock Unlimited Slash Grind cheat.
Enter the cheat code on the Options menu screen; **FOREVERNAILED** to unlock 100% Branch Completion cheat.
Enter the cheat code on the Options menu screen; **ANDAINTFALLIN** to unlock No Bails cheat.
Enter the cheat code on the Options menu screen; **THEMISSING** to unlock Invisible Man cheat.

Enter the cheat code on the Options menu screen; **TINYTATER** to unlock Mini Skater cheat.
Enter the cheat code on the Options menu screen; **MAGICMAN** to unlock No Board cheat.
Enter the cheat code on the Options menu screen; **LOVEROCKNROLL** to unlock Judy Nails cheat.

Enter the cheat code on the Options menu screen; **CRAZYBONEMAN** to unlock the Boneman skater.
Enter the cheat code on the Options menu screen; **MOREMILK** to unlock the Bosco skater.
Enter the cheat code on the Options menu screen; **NOTACAMERA** to unlock the Cam skater.

screen; **Right, Left, Down, Up, Up, Down, Left, Right to unlock the All Challenges Open cheat.**
Enter the following cheat combination on the Challenges menu screen; **Up, Down, Left, Right, Right, Left, Down, Up to unlock the All Venues Available cheat.**